D0234576

GEOGRAPHIES: AN INTERMEDIATE SERIES
EDITED BY PROFESSOR R. W. STEEL MA, BSc

PHYSICAL GEOGRAPHY

A

GEOGRAPHIES: AN INTERMEDIATE SERIES
Edited by Professor R. W. Steel

LATIN AMERICA
By G. J. Butland

AFRICA AND THE ISLANDS
By R. J. Harrison Church, J. I. Clarke, P. J. H. Clarke
and H. J. R. Henderson

THE COUNTRIES OF NORTH WESTERN EUROPE
By F. J. Monkhouse

Physical Geography

R. Kay Gresswell M.A., Ph.D., FGS
Senior Lecturer in Geography, University of Liverpool

LONGMAN

LONGMAN GROUP LIMITED
London

*Associated companies, branches and representatives
throughout the world*

First published 1967
Fourth impression 1972

ISBN 0 582 31066 0

*Printed in Hong Kong by
Peninsula Press Ltd*

Preface

IF there is one conviction which I have tried to keep before me more than any other whilst writing this book, it is that a mere descriptive catalogue of physical features is of but little use unless it is accompanied by as full an explanation as possible of the reasons for their existence and the *modus operandi* of their development. In other words, this book does not seek merely to answer the question 'What?' with regard to each facet of physical geography, it especially also tries to answer the two much more exciting questions of 'How?' and 'Why?' That way, the catalogue ceases to be merely descriptive but becomes sense; knowledge is supplemented by understanding. With understanding comes a vastly increased ease of remembrance, for it is certainly true that an appreciation of the sequence of events which lead to a result, besides giving intellectual satisfaction, provides also the inability to forget. I do not pretend that complete explanations of all processes have been given in the pages that follow – occasionally this would have made the book far too lengthy, and so a somewhat abbreviated version has had to suffice. Surprisingly often too we have reached the limits of knowledge and all we can say is that so far no one knows. Occasional controversial suggestions have been put forward, but always with their uncertainty clearly emphasised.

Believing that it is foolish not to make use of as many of our senses as is possible, the book contains a particularly large number of illustrations, both photographic and diagrammatic. Not a single photograph has been included without its showing some very special and essential feature of the subject that is being discussed and every one is completely integrated into the text, each for a particular purpose.

I hope therefore that this will be found to be a book which makes pleasant reading and good sense, so that what it says will be easy to retain in one's memory. I have been blessed by a genial and encouraging editor, agreeable and helpful publishers, and a draughtsman with whom I have been in almost daily contact, and who has long known my ways and the kind of diagram that I seek. So I thank Professor R. W. Steel, the General Editor of this Intermediate Series; Mr J. R. C. Yglesias, Mr Roger Watson and Miss Mary

Evans who have been particularly and painstakingly concerned with seeing this book from its manuscript to its final stages; and to Mr A. G. Hodgkiss, cartographer in the Department of Geography of the University of Liverpool, for drawing all the maps and diagrams. One of my ideas was that oblique air photographs very greatly aid the general appreciation of many landforms, and thus a large number of the photographic illustrations come from the vast collection of Messrs Aerofilms Limited, in whose library of photographs I spent five mentally energetic days before ever a word was written. Formal acknowledgment to them and to others who have contributed photographs is made below.

So here is my book, the result of several year's enjoyable 'spare' time work, often during hours when my wife and family should have seen more of me than they did. I thank them too for their patient understanding and very real encouragement. And I hope that you, as Reader, find it useful and enjoyable.

University of Liverpool
November 1966   R. KAY GRESSWELL

Acknowledgements

We are grateful to the following for permission to reproduce photographs: Aerofilms Ltd.: Figs. 86, 101, 103 and Jacket, 109, 130–133, 143, 166, 167, 182, 203, 245, 247, 254–257, 262, 284, 286, 297, 304, 307, 308, 311, 312, 318, 320, 326–328, 353, 370, 379, 380, 383; The Aircraft Operating Co. of Africa Ltd.; Fig. 156; The Australian News and Information Bureau: Fig. 377; Barnaby's Picture Library: Fig. 368; R. R. Bolland: Fig. 124; Anne Bolt: Fig. 299; J. Allan Cash: Figs. 359, 372, 373, 376; East African Railways and Harbours, Nairobi, Kenya: Fig. 73; The Fairchild Aerial Surveys, Inc.: Figs. 292, 352; French Government Tourist Office (photo Denise Bellon): Fig. 3?5; Ewing Galloway: Figs. 72, 93 and Jacket; The Lockwood Survey Corporation: Fig. 127; Professor Dr. Carl M.son Mannerfelt: Figs. 212, 218; Negretti and Zambra Ltd.: Figs. 3, 5, 25, 26; Professor Nicholas Polunin: Fig. 374 from *Introduction to Plant Geography* (Longmans); Paul Popper Ltd.: Figs 350, 351, 354, 356, 362; Royal Meteorological Society, Clarke Collection: Fig. 19; Swissair: Figs. 190, 191, 193; Inst. Cdr. E. R. Trendell, R.N. (Rtd.): Fig. 17; Widerøe's Flyveselskap A/S: Fig. 155; White's Aviation Ltd., Auckland: Figs. 172, 187. Fig. 121 is a PMR photograph by Jack Urwiller. The remaining 98 photographs are by the author.

Figures 345, 346 and 347 are modified from a figure in *Lake, Physical Geography*, Cambridge University Press, and are based upon British Admiralty Chart No. 5058 with the permission of the Controller of H.M. Stationery Office and of the Hydrographer of the Navy.

Contents

PREFACE   V

CHAPTER

  1 Introduction to physical geography   1

PART ONE: THE ELEMENTS OF METEOROLOGY

  2 Gas, evaporation and water vapour   5
  3 Temperature and stability   13
  4 Clouds and precipitation   25
  5 Air currents and air masses   34

PART TWO: THE ELEMENTS OF CLIMATOLOGY

  6 The world's climates   47
  7 Equatorial climates   53
  8 Tropical climates   64
  9 Temperate climates   72
10 Arctic climates   89
11 Changing climates   93

PART THREE; WEATHERING AND RIVERS

12 Weathering   99
13 Mass movement   112
14 Slope development   122
15 Underground water and karst topography   131
16 Channelled fluvial flow   146
17 The development of single-cycle river systems   174
18 Composite and polycyclic fluvial topography   205

PART FOUR: ICE AND GLACIATION

19 Glaciation and glaciers   219
20 Glacial deposition   241
21 Deglaciation   261
22 Glacial chronology   275
23 Glaciated landscapes   297
24 Lakes   320

PART FIVE: COASTS AND THE SEA

25 Waves and currents   327
26 Beaches   340
27 Coastlines   354
28 Relative changes of land and sea level   376
29 Aeolian erosion and deposition   389
30 Oceans and ocean floors   400
31 Sea water   411

PART SIX: VOLCANOES AND VULCANISM

32 Vulcanic landforms   429

PART SEVEN: SOILS AND NATURAL VEGETATION

33 Soil and soils   447
34 World vegetation   459
35 Tropical vegetation   462
36 Temperate vegetation   475
37 Arctic and mountain vegetation   486

INDEX   491

MEASUREMENTS

ALL dimensions are given in both the British and metric systems. An attempt has been made to give as the equivalents, figures which indicate the kind of accuracy intended by the author, and which some one who normally used the metric system would be likely to give in a similar context.

Precise measurements have the exact equivalent. For example, 89 feet is 'translated' as 27 metres. Often, however, figures are intended only to indicate the order of size. For example, when one says that two places are 100 miles apart, the indication generally is that the actual distance may be between 95 and 105 miles. In such circumstances, it is very misleading to quote 100 miles as equivalent to 161, or even 160, kilometres. A geographer who always used the metric system would certainly have put 150 kilometres, and dimensions of *equivalent meaning* in this way have been used throughout this book.

CHAPTER ONE

Introduction

ASTRONOMY concerns itself with universes, solar systems and the Earth. Once its origin and our planet's place in the rest of existence is studied, the geologist enters and busies himself with the making, alteration and re-making of rocks, with mountain-building and the formation of depressions such as rift valleys and the ocean basins themselves. At this stage, the geomorphologist takes over, and he in his turn seeks to understand the ways in which land and oceanic relief have been formed and are constantly being modified, chiefly by means of energy supplied by the Sun in its influence upon the liquid and gaseous parts of the Earth's envelope. Here it is that the meteorologist and climatologist both join as partners with the geomorphologist, and together promote the study which is known as *physical geography*.

The first five parts of this book take the different aspects of physical geography in due sequence. The elements of meteorology lead directly to climatology, and a realisation of the varied nature of climate in different parts of the world prepares the way for a study of weathering, mass movement and fluvial action, the characteristics of underground water and the production of topography in regions where these processes acted alone or have dominated. Cooler climatic areas have experienced or still experience the presence of ice and glaciation, whilst the boundary between land and ocean, a narrow belt of land of very special importance to man, is considered in the last of these five parts.

After a brief digression into the topographic effects of some landforms resulting from igneous action, the seventh part goes a little way beyond strict physical geography into the realm of biogeography, and touches upon the effects of what has already been considered upon the natural vegetation which clothes so much of the Earth's land-surface. By finishing in this manner, one is made ready for the diverse branches of human geography – one understands a little more the possibilities available to man and the influence which he can have upon his environment.

A2

Described this way, physical geography appears to be the penultimate in a sequence of learnings which culminate in the study of man. It is the essential foundation upon which these final considerations must inevitably be based, and as such it is of fundamental and primary importance. All studies are inter-related. None can be alone. Nevertheless to comprehend, if only a little, the ways in which the countryside came into its present expression leads to appreciation and pleasure. Without understanding there is little enjoyment.

Part One

The Elements of Meteorology

CHAPTER TWO

Gases, Evaporation and Water Vapour

BOTH the geomorphological processes which occur on the surface of the land and the vegetation which grows thereon are very largely controlled by the conditions that prevail in the atmosphere above them, for temperature, humidity, rainfall, wind and each of the other meteorological elements have their individual effects on the land surface and the plants, and thus indirectly, as well as directly, on the animals. In making a study of physical geography, it is first necessary to understand at least the elementary facts about weather and climate in various parts of the world, and the following chapters thus give a brief outline of the chief meteorological factors which together make weather and climate.

The outer shell of the Earth consists of three main elements distinguished by their being in the three different physical states. Rocks form the *solid* portion, the continents and the bed of the oceans. This is part of the *lithosphere*. The *liquid* portion is almost entirely in the form of oceanic water, although a small proportion is on land in rivers and lakes. This liquid part is the *hydrosphere*. Finally, the *gaseous* part is the *atmosphere*, and this consists of air with some impurities such as smoke, dust and water vapour (although the last is often included in the hydrosphere for convenience' sake).

Much animal and plant life finds the hydrosphere a very agreeable environment, but most of the more advanced types live on land, the floor of the ocean of air. The conditions which must be fulfilled for life to flourish as we know it are very strict, and much of the interest and value of meteorology lies in the study of the ways in which these conditions are fulfilled and maintained.

GASES AND PRESSURE

The atmosphere is a gas. The fundamental distinction between a gas and a liquid is that, whilst the latter has a fixed volume, a gas always fills the whole of the space which is offered to it. Its molecules are much more loosely held together than are liquid ones, and so it is able to expand and contract very much more readily. Individual molecules move with high velocities in all directions within the space occupied by the gas, and many of them collide with the bounding walls of the volume. So many thousands of millions of molecules hit the side walls of the container that it is impossible to distinguish individual impacts, and the total result appears to be exactly the same as a steady push exerted over the whole area. The individual blows thus merge together, and this is what is termed *pressure* in a gas.

Total weight of air
above is :
14·7 lbs. per sq. in.
or
1·03 kg. per sq. cm.

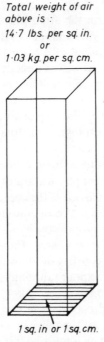

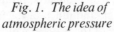

1 sq. in or 1 sq. cm.

Fig. 1. The idea of
atmospheric pressure

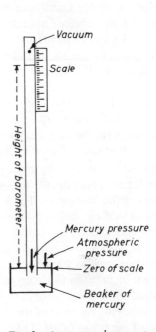

Fig. 2. A mercury barometer

In the case of the atmosphere at ground-level, it is possible to imagine the pressure as being the result of the weight of the air above, and we say that normal atmospheric pressure at sea-level is approximately equal to 14·7 lb per sq inch (1·03 kg per sq cm) (Fig. 1), but even in this case it is nearer reality to consider that the pressure is caused by the impact of the molecules on the unit area of surface.

When a gas is compressed to, say, half its previous volume, the pressure is doubled, because the molecules are now nearer together and there are twice as many impacts per square inch. Thus the pressure exerted by a particular mass of gas is inversely proportional to the volume it occupies. This is *Boyle's Law*, and is only true when the temperature does not change.

The velocity of the molecules is a measure of the *temperature* of the gas. The hotter the faster. Faster molecules naturally bombard with greater vigour, and if the volume of a particular mass of gas remains unchanged whilst its temperature rises, the pressure increases because of the molecules' increased vigour.

In meteorology, pressure is measured by a barometer which may be one of two principal types. In the *mercury barometer* the atmospheric pressure may be balanced by a column of mercury whose length varies with change of pressure. Mercury is used because it is the heaviest liquid and thus requires a shorter column than any other. The top surface of the mercury has a vacuum above it, so the atmosphere does not press on that as it does on the mercury surface in the small, open beaker, as seen in Fig. 2. An arrangement is provided by which the level of the mercury in the beaker may easily be adjusted so as to give a constant zero for the scale. This scale does not extend to the whole length of the tube, for the pressure, and therefore the level of the mercury at the top of the tube, varies only between fairly small limits.

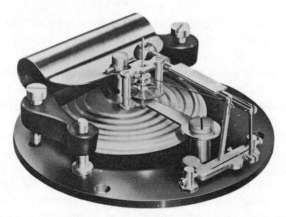

Fig. 3. An aneroid barometer

The second type of barometer is known as the *aneroid* and is now always used when a portable instrument is required. It is pictured in Fig. 3, and consists essentially of a small circular box from which the air has been evacuated but which contains a spring (sometimes inside the box but more often outside it) which prevents it from being completely squashed by the atmospheric pressure. As the latter varies, the box is compressed or expands a little, and a system of levers magnifies this and moves a pointer round a dial. The dial is marked in millimetres of mercury to correspond to a mercury barometer, or in *millibars* or even feet (metres) of altitude.

Millibars are the unit now almost universally employed in measuring pressure in meteorology. One millibar equals a pressure of 1,000 dynes per sq cm or rather more than 1 gm per sq cm, and since average atmospheric pressure is about 1·03 kg per sq cm, this means that it is the same as 1,013 millibars.

Clearly there will be a decrease in pressure as one ascends within the atmosphere, since there is gradually less and less above. This decrease is at the rate of about 1 inch of barometric height per 900 feet rise (1 cm per 100 metres very nearly). Aneroid barometers marked in feet or metres in this way are frequently used in reconaissance surveying and always used as altimeters in aeroplanes. The disadvantage in surveying is that each height to be determined must be climbed, whereas with a theodolite it is possible to survey heights from a lower level, and thus save considerable time and energy.

SOLAR HEAT: ENERGY

Gases contain stored energy because of the motion of their molecules. This energy is the heat which they contain, and radiant heat coming from the Sun is able to increase this energy by being absorbed by the gas. The first effect of the arrival of solar heat is an increase in the speed of the molecules and thus the gas pressure rises and the amount of energy it contains increases We call this a rise in *temperature*.

Almost the whole of the energy on Earth, including that possessed by animals and plants is derived from the Sun. It is solar heat which raises ocean water to the top of mountains, perhaps to provide hydro-electric energy; it is solar heat which provides the energy by which plants may build simple chemicals into complex ones and so grow; and it is plants which provide food for animals which cannot synthesize the simple chemicals themselves. Even when we burn coal or oil we use solar energy. In this case it is stored energy, for the mineral was a plant millions of years ago, and it is the solar heat of those times that provides the warmth of burning the coal or oil today.

WATER VAPOUR

Although the molecules of a *liquid* are much more tightly held together than they are in the case of a gas, they are still quite loose as compared with the molecules of a solid. It is for that reason that a liquid can easily take up the shape of any container in which it is placed, whereas a solid more or less retains its own shape.

When solar heat reaches the surface of a mass of water, whether it be the ocean, a lake or a river, the water is warmed. This means that the molecules move a little faster than before, and consequently a few of them escape from the surface. They become a small fraction of the atmosphere and are known as *water vapour*. This is a completely dry substance until it is converted back into water, and whilst a vapour it behaves very like a true gas.

As more and more solar heat arrives and gives more and more energy to larger numbers of molecules, more and more of them escape from the liquid surface. The amount of vapour in the air increases. Since these molecules are dashing hither and thither in an entirely disorderly fashion, some of them accidentally dive back into the liquid water and are captured by it. When the amount of vapour in the air has reached a certain quantity per unit volume, as many molecules return to the liquid as leave it, and the total amount of vapour no longer increases. The vapour is then described as a *saturated vapour*.

For water, the amount of saturated vapour per unit volume in the space above it is a quite definite quantity for a particular temperature, but if the temperature rises, then the liquid molecules speed up and thus escape even more readily and the amount of vapour required to produce saturation increases. Thus air at a higher temperature holds more vapour when it is saturated than does air at a lower temperature. Figure 4 shows these amounts.

Since gases are very light substances and difficult to weigh, it is more usual to measure their quantities by the pressure which they exert, and the same table gives the corresponding pressures. Thus if the vapour pressure is 0·34 lb per sq inch (24 gm per sq cm) and the temperature is 20°C (68°F) the vapour is saturated and the amount then present (nearly ½ ounce per cubic yard) is the maximum amount that the space can hold at that temperature. If there is a sudden fall in temperature, the air will be able to hold less vapour than it possesses, and the surplus will be thrown out in the form of minute droplets of water, producing mist, fog or cloud according to the circumstances. Thus if the temperature falls to 10°C (50°F) the vapour will remain saturated with $\frac{1}{4}$ ounce per cubic yard, and the other $\frac{1}{4}$ ounce will have been precipitated as mist.

When the temperature of water reaches boiling point, the maximum vapour pressure equals the atmospheric pressure on the water surface and the molecules of liquid are able to escape very freely. The liquid almost explodes, but the rate of gasification is limited by another important energy factor.

LATENT HEAT OF VAPORISATION

When the molecules of a liquid break away and become a vapour or gas, they move very far apart compared with their previous spacing. The gas occupies a much larger volume than the liquid from which it was formed. Since the molecules attract one another, energy is required to force them farther apart, and this energy (again ultimately supplied by the Sun) is known as the *latent heat of vaporisation*. Whilst the heat arriving is used in this way to separate the molecules, it does not accelerate them, and thus the temperature is not raised. The amount of energy required is very considerable, and in the case of water, it takes just about as much energy to convert any particular amount of it into vapour as is required to raise the temperature of the same amount from cold tap temperature to boiling point.

Vaporisation thus consumes heat and it may sometimes do so by cooling its surroundings. This is the reason why it seems much cooler on the beach in summer when you come out of the water than before you went in. After bathing, your body is wet, and the film of water covering you vaporises fairly quickly (that is, you dry off), so that the latent heat required for this vaporisation is extracted from your skin, and you are correspondingly cooled.

Evaporation thus causes cooling, and, conversely, condensation causes warming.

RELATIVE HUMIDITY

When air is not saturated, the amount of vapour within it is measured as relative humidity. *Relative humidity* is the amount of vapour actually present compared with the total amount required to saturate the air at the same temperature. For example, if the temperature is 30°C (86°F), Fig. 4 shows that a cubic yard of air could hold 0·82 ounce of vapour. If there is actually only, say, 0·34 ounce present, then the relative humidity is 34/82 = 41 per cent. The same result is obtained if pressures are used instead of actual quantities. Relative humidity thus may also be described as the pressure exerted by the actual vapour present compared with the maximum vapour pressure at that temperature. The ratio is normally expressed as a percentage.

Temperature		Mass of saturated vapour		Pressure		
°C	°F	oz/cu yard	gm/cu metre	lb/sq in	gm/sq cm	mm of mercury
35	95	1·06	39·2	0·81	57	42
30	86	0·82	30·4	0·61	43	32
25	77	0·62	22·8	0·46	32	24
20	68	0·46	17·1	0·34	24	18
15	59	0·34	12·7	0·25	18	13
10	50	0·25	9·3	0·18	13	9
5	41	0·18	6·8	0·13	9	7
0	32	0·13	4·8	0·09	6	5

Fig. 4. Quantities and pressures of saturated water vapour at various temperatures

If the same air cools to 25°C (77°F), its capacity becomes 0·62 ounce per cubic yard, and the air is 34/62 = 55 per cent saturated. This is with the same actual quantity of vapour present, for it is the holding power that has changed (decreased). By the time the air has cooled to 15°C (59°F), it will have become saturated, and any further cooling will result in the formation of water droplets.

Relative humidity is a very important factor in many meteorological processes, as well as in biological ones (a stuffy room is primarily one with a high relative humidity).

It is usually determined by means of a *wet-and-dry bulb thermometer*. This is pictured in Fig. 5. It consists of two ordinary thermometers mounted an inch or two apart. One has its bulb wrapped in a wick, the other end of which is in a small beaker of water. This is the wet bulb, and the evaporation from the wick causes cooling, so that the wet bulb thermometer gives a lower temperature than the dry one. The amount of this lowering is controlled by the drying rate of the wick, and this is in turn determined by the relative humidity of the surrounding atmosphere.

In the extreme case when the atmosphere is saturated, it can hold no further vapour and so no evaporation occurs, and both thermometers read the same. The less the relative humidity, the greater the difference in the two readings, and tables are available which give

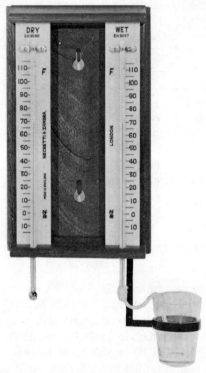

Fig. 5. A wet-and-dry bulb thermometer

the relative humidity for any two temperatures. For example, if the dry bulb reads 20°C (68°F), and the wet bulb reads 5°C (9°F) lower, then the table states that the relative humidity is 60 per cent. Difficulty in reading the thermometers to fractions of a degree, make accuracy by this method impossible, and one usually gives the relative humidity to the nearest 5 per cent. This is quite sufficient for all ordinary purposes.

CHAPTER THREE

Temperature and Stability

EQUAL radiant heat from the Sun may raise the temperature of different substances and surfaces by different amounts. This is due to several factors, the most important being the nature of the surface, the specific heat of the substance and its conductivity.

Some surfaces absorb a greater proportion of the incident rays than do others. Snow and firn (see p. 219), both brilliantly white, not only reflect sun*light*, but also reflect almost the whole of the fairly short wavelength, radiant heat rays from the Sun. Consequently the snow and firn are scarcely warmed. It is for this reason that people who are climbing snowclad mountains are often very hot, not only from the strenuous efforts they are exerting, but also because they are being warmed twice – once directly from the sunshine and a second time from the heat reflected from the white surface. At the same time as the climbers are so hot, the snow is probably showing no signs of thaw!

It is consequently quite difficult to raise the temperature of snow and firn by means of solar heat, although longer wavelength radiant heat coming from rocks, which have themselves absorbed the Sun's heat, is absorbed by the snow, and this is a very effective aid towards melting. References to important glaciological features which depend upon this selective absorption are made on p. 263, footnote.

Darker rocks and vegetation do absorb solar radiation and are warmed by it. The atmosphere, however, is almost transparent to it, and it has been estimated that only about 10 per cent of the total radiation coming from the Sun is absorbed in the atmosphere. Accordingly the air is scarcely warmed by sunshine and this is one of the reasons why the air is cooler the higher we climb a mountain. Most of the warmth acquired by the air comes from contact with the ground, and the presence of a warm ground surface is of the greatest importance.

GROUND TEMPERATURE

Factors which regulate the temperature of the ground surface are:

(1) the energy output of the Sun, (2) the distance of Sun from Earth, (3) the transparency of the atmosphere, especially the presence or absence of cloud cover, (4) the angle of incidence of the Sun's rays, (5) the length of daylight, (6) the reflecting power of the ground surface, (7) the specific heat of the ground material, and (8) the conductivity of the ground material. There are others also.

The *energy output* of the Sun varies by as much as 10 per cent, but the other factors appear to have much more effect upon the heat received on the ground. Variations of solar output may have led to climatic change in the past, especially to the Pleistocene Ice Ages, but they seem to have little quick effect.

Similar comments apply to variations in *distance* from Sun to Earth. This is a maximum in the beginning of July, when it is about 94·5 million miles (152 million kilometres), and a minimum early in January, when it is about 91·5 million miles (147 million kilometres). These are variations of less than 2 per cent from the mean, and whilst they must make northern hemisphere winters a little warmer than they otherwise would be, and the summers cooler, the effect is very slight.

The *transparency* of the atmosphere varies considerably from day to day according especially to the amount of water vapour, dust and smoke there may be within it. Turbulence very often spreads the last two, but this affects only the local and not the total transparency. The presence or absence of cloud, mist or fog, naturally has a very great effect upon the amount of solar heat reaching the ground surface. When one considers that in temperate moist climates, such as that experienced by Britain, the difference in temperature between a summer heat wave and other summer days is mostly due to greater transparency of the atmosphere, one realises how much may be stopped by the cloud cover.

There is another effect which is allied to transparency, and that is the effect of *thickness of atmosphere* traversed. When the Sun is overhead, the rays pass through the atmosphere by the shortest route, but when they arrive obliquely they pass through a much greater thickness, and the absorption is correspondingly greater.

The *angle of incidence* of the sunshine is important as a variable which modifies the concentration of the rays as they reach the surface. The angle may be the result of the direction of the sunlight (a function of latitude, time of year and time of day) or of the aspect of the ground. Figure 6 illustrates the former, and Fig. 7 the latter.

When the circular beam of Sun's rays strikes the Earth obliquely,

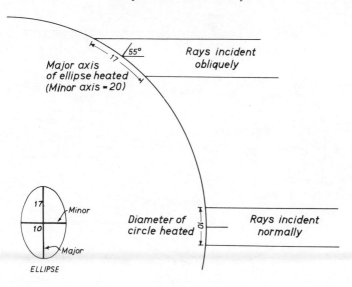

Fig. 6. *Thermal effect of angle of incidence of heating rays*

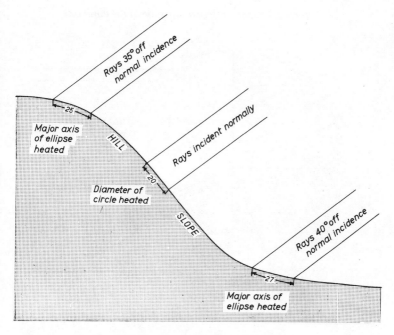

Fig. 7. *Thermal effect of aspect*

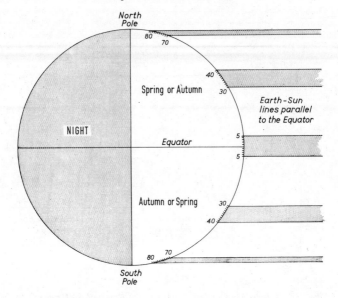

MARCH AND SEPTEMBER

Fig. 8. Thermal effect of latitude at the equinoxes

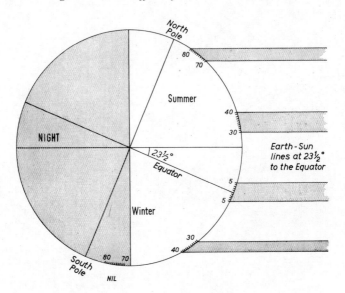

JUNE

Fig. 9. Thermal effect of latitude in June

so as to make an angle with the vertical (55° in the case of the oblique rays in Fig. 6), the surface covered is roughly an ellipse and with a series of ellipses all with the same length of minor axis, the areas are proportional to the lengths of the major axes. These are inversely proportional to the cosine of the angle of obliquity. Since 1 / cos 55° = 1·7, the area to be warmed by the oblique rays carrying the same amount of heat as the direct ones (incident normally) is 1·7 times as great and the warming effect is that much less powerful. Differences in the altitude of the Sun, resulting from differences in latitude, are the first conditions to affect the type of climate experienced by a particular locality.

Differences resulting from variations of the altitude of the Sun at different times of the year produce the *seasons*. Figure 8 shows how places at different latitudes at the *equinoxes* (when the axis of the Earth and the Earth–Sun line are at right-angles to one another about 21 March and 21 September) receive different concentrations of sunlight and thus different intensities of heat. Figure 9 shows the variations which occur at the same places in June.

Another way of demonstrating the effect is used in Figs. 8 and 9, where 10 degrees of latitude are taken at various places and the width of the band of solar heat is drawn. This width is proportional to the cosine of the angle the vertical to the locality makes with the Earth–Sun line. Fig. 10 gives the ratios of the quantities of heat received at the various sites at the equinoxes and in June and December.

It is interesting to note the two periods (June and December) each

Locality	Angle with Earth–Sun line (degrees)			Heat intensity (width of heat-supply band) (Vertical Sun = 1)		
Latitude	June	March and September	December	June	March and September	December
75°N	51½	75	98½	0·62	0·26	NIL
35°N	11½	35	58½	0·98	0·82	0·52
0°	23½	0	23½	0·92	1·00	0·92
35°S	58½	35	11½	0·52	0·82	0·98
75°S	98½	75	51½	NIL	0·26	0·62

Fig. 10. Heat intensities at different latitudes and seasons

year during which the equator receives less, and the two periods when it receives more, heat, although the fluctuations are slight. The distinction between summer and winter at latitude 35° N and S is well brought out, as also is the nil figure for winter at the two polar sites.

These figures only measure one factor which determines climate, and amongst the many others that are also involved, two are: (1) the fact that very oblique rays pass through a much thicker layer of atmosphere and so are reduced still further in intensity, and (2) during the polar summer, the Sun may shine twenty-four hours a day continuously for some time, so that the low intensity is greatly compensated for by the high continuity of solar warming.

The *length of daylight* is determined by latitude and season, and in high latitude countries such as northern Canada and Scandinavia, the summer temperature is often much higher than would be expected, because of these long hours of low-altitude, and therefore weakened, sunshine. By analogy, a small gas jet lit for a long time can raise the temperature of a pan of water perhaps to as high a temperature as can a short-time powerful jet. Plants in these environments grow twenty-four hours a day, and become mature, flower and seed much more successfully than would be anticipated.

ADIABATIC COOLING AND THE DRY ADIABATIC LAPSE RATE, DALR

When any gas expands, its molecules move farther apart and, just as in the case of the conversion of water to vapour, energy is required to carry out this dispersion. When a portion of gas is surrounded by other gas which is also expanding, there is nowhere to obtain this energy excepting from within itself. Consequently, when a gas expands in this way, it is cooled. Conversely, when it is compressed, it is warmed.

Supposing that a mass of air rises from the ground for several thousand feet (hundreds of metres). As it rises, the pressure becomes less and less. By the time it has risen, say, 5,000 feet (1,500 metres) the pressure will have decreased from 14·7 lb per sq inch (1·03 kg per sq cm) at ground level to about 12 lb per sq inch (0·84 kg per sq cm), and the gas will have expanded correspondingly. The energy required to perform this work will have cooled the gas through about 15°C (27°F), so that if it had begun its ascent at 20°C (68°F), it will have cooled to 5°C (41°F).

This is termed *adiabatic cooling*, and the loss of 10°C per 1,000 metres (5·4°F per 1,000 feet) rise is the *dry adiabatic lapse rate*. This is often abbreviated to DALR.

SATURATED ADIABATIC LAPSE RATE, SALR

Because it is cooled on rising, the capacity of the air to hold vapour becomes smaller, and at a certain temperature this will equal the amount of vapour it actually contains. The air will have become saturated.

Adiabatic lapse rate		°C per 1,000 metres	°F per 1,000 feet
Dry	DALR	10	5·4
Saturated	SALR	6	3·5

Fig. 11. Dry and saturated adiabatic lapse rates

Further cooling, as the air continues to rise and expand, will result in some of the vapour being thrown out in the form of *water droplets*, which, if sufficient in quantity, will constitute a cloud. The change of the excess vapour into liquid liberates latent heat of vaporisation, and this partially counteracts the expansion cooling. The effect is that the rising air, while it remains saturated, and therefore throws out vapour as it continues to rise, cools at the rate of about 6 C per 1,000 metres (3·5 F per 1,000 feet) of ascent. This is the *saturated adiabatic lapse rate*, referred to as SALR (Fig. 11).

If the air subsequently descends, it is warmed at one of these adiabatic lapse rates. It will warm at the SALR so long as it is 'impregnated' with sufficient water droplets to vaporise and keep the air saturated. As soon as this ceases to be so, it warms at the DALR instead.

CHINOOK (FOEHN) WINDS

This accounts for the fact that a mass of air very often becomes much warmer after it has passed over a mountain range on which much of its water was extracted in the form of rain. Suppose the air on approaching the mountain is at 25°C and with a relative humidity of 55 per cent, so containing 12·7 gm of vapour per cubic metre (see Fig. 4). Working in metric units because of the simpler arithmetic, this air, climbing the mountainside and cooling by the DALR (Fig. 11) will have reached 15°C by the time it has risen 1,000 metres (Fig. 12). At this temperature, this air will be saturated (Fig. 4).

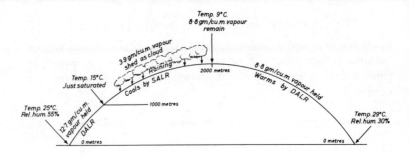

Fig. 12. Warming and drying of air as it passes over a mountain

As it continues to rise above this height, it will cool according to the SALR, and by the time it reaches 2,000 metres above its starting level, it will have cooled to 9°C and will still be saturated. It will now contain a considerably less amount of vapour than originally, since all the time it has cooled whilst saturated it will have thrown out the excess vapour to form cloud and thence rain. It will in fact now contain about 8·8 g vapour per cubic metre.

Supposing that it now descends the far side of the mountain to the original level, but that the water droplets have all been extracted in the form of rain. It will warm up at the DALR, and thus in descending 2,000 metres will become 20°C hotter. It will finish at 29°C, and its relative humidity will have dropped to 30 per cent, both because it is hotter than at the start and because it has actually lost vapour.

Winds that meet high mountain ranges roughly at right-angles, and so are forced to cross over them, pass through this series of stages and finish on the far side as warm, dry winds. Such winds are so important as snow-melters and in connection with agriculture that they have been given special local names. In North America coming down the eastern side of the Rockies, they are known as the *chinook* winds, and in the Swiss Alps as the *foehn*.

EVIRONMENT LAPSE RATE, ELR

The DALR and SALR both give the temperature changes which rising or falling air will experience, but it is well known that the stationary air above a particular locality is usually found to be progressively cooler as one ascends through it. This is discovered when climbing a mountain on a calm day. The rate at which this occurs is known as the *environment lapse rate* or ELR, and may be of any value within limits, may vary for each several hundred feet of ascent, and may even be reversed in the sense that for a few hundred feet it may become warmer as one continues the ascent. A reversed ELR is known as a *temperature inversion*.

Suppose that the ELR at a particular place on a particular occasion is, for simplicity, the same for each of the first several hundred metres of ascent. Again using the metric system for simplicity, suppose that this ELR is 12°C per 1,000 metres. Figure 13 shows on the left-hand side the temperatures of the stationary, environmental air at various heights. If the ground-level air has a low humidity and starts to rise, it will cool according to the DALR, and will acquire the different temperatures marked in the middle column at the various heights. It will be noticed that at every level it will be warmer than the environment, and so will be lighter, and will continue to rise. This is a case of *absolute instability*, and a strong up-current will occur.

Metres	ELR = 12°C/1,000 m	DALR = 10°C/1,000 m	SALR = 6°C/1,000 m
1,500	2°C	5°C	11°C
1,000	8°C	10°C	14°C
500	14°C	15°C	17°C
0	20°C	20°C	20°C

Fig. 13. Unstable air rises through an environment with a high ELR

The right-hand column shows the similar set of figures for saturated air, and it is seen that in this case at every level the rising air again finds itself warmer, and therefore lighter, than its environment at that level. This too is an instance of absolute instability.

In these examples, ELR was greater than both DALR and SALR. It is obvious that ELR could be less than SALR, or it could lie between DALR and SALR, or could vary at different heights. If ELR is less than SALR, any rising air, such as for instance might be driven up a mountainside, will find itself cooler than its environment at all heights and the air mass will tend not to rise. It is *stable*. When the value of ELR lies between DALR and SALR, the mass is stable so long as it rises unsaturated, but is unstable if it is saturated. This is called *conditional instability* (Fig. 14).

DALR		SALR
ELR greater than DALR	ELR between DALR and SALR (uncommon)	ELR less than SALR
UNSTABLE AIR	CONDITIONAL INSTABILITY	STABLE AIR

Fig. 14. Conditions for instability and stability

Figure 15 gives two examples of conditional instability. Suppose the ground air temperature is 20°C and ELR is 8°C per 1,000 metres as shown on the left. Suppose further that warm air at 22°C is introduced at ground-level with a relative humidity such that it will become saturated at 12°C.

Being warmer than the environment, it will rise. At 500 metres, it is still 1°C warmer than the environment, but at 1,000 metres it is just equal and is about to lose its upward impetus. However, just at

Metres	ELR = 8°C/1,000 m		Cooling at SALR			Cooling at DALR
2,000	4°C	6°C				
1,500	8°C	9°C		7°C		
1,000	12°C	12°C Saturated	12°C			
500	16°C	17°C	Cooling at DALR	17°C		
0	20°C	22°C		22°C		

Fig. 15. Conditional instability and conditional stability

Fig. 16. Clouds forming under conditional instability

this level it becomes saturated and starts to cool at the SALR, so that by 1,500 metres it is again warmer than the environment and so continues to rise to 2,000 metres and beyond, providing the ELR remains constant. This is an example of *conditional instability*, the condition in this case being that the rising air becomes saturated at 12°C (or sooner).

Figure 16 is a photograph of such conditions where the air rises and cools at first at the DALR and then suddenly starts to throw out vapour to form cloud and rise vigorously at the SALR. This gives the clouds flat bases at the saturation level and considerable vertical development above, so as to form tall cumulus clouds.

If, however, the 22°C air indicated in Fig. 15 had a saturation temperature at about 6°C or below, as shown on the right-hand side, conditions would have been altered. In these circumstances it would never reach 1,500 metres, for it would become cooler than the environment as soon as it tried to rise above 1,000 metres. It would be unstable to 1,000 metres and then become stable. This is a case of conditional stability at 1,000 metres.

At a *temperature inversion,* any rising air will naturally find itself surrounded by a considerably warmer environment and will tend to sink back again. It will be very stable.

The same applies to an environment when it remains at the same temperature for a range of height. In other words the ELR is zero. This is termed an *isothermal layer.* Since ELR is less than SALR, these are very stable conditions.

The ELR varies from place to place and from time to time. It is increased either when the upper layers of air are cooled (such as by radiation from clouds or by the inflow of cooler air at a high level), or when the ground layers are warmed (either by contact with warmer ground or by the inflow of bottom layers of warmer air). As the ELR slowly increases conditions may change from its being less than the SALR to its first lying between the SALR and the DALR, and then to its being greater than the DALR. The air mass will start stable, acquire conditional instability, and pass into absolute instability.

Stable air prevents much mixing and permits smoke, dust and mist and fog to stay near the ground, whilst unstable air means much vertical mixing, the dispersion of impurities and the production of good visibility.

CHAPTER FOUR

Clouds and Precipitation

SOME of the conditions which lead to the change of water vapour to water droplets in the atmosphere have already been described in the previous chapter. If the temperature is low, ice crystals are produced instead. In either case, *clouds* are formed and often the finer particles become larger so as to fall to the ground as rain, sleet, snow or hail. The meteorologist uses the all-embracing term *precipitation*.

CLOUD TYPES

There is an almost infinite variety in the kinds of cloud which may be produced, but it is possible to classify them to some extent, although each of the major classes has numerous subdivisions. It is often difficult to determine to which class some of the intermediate forms should belong. The following paragraphs are to be taken more as descriptions of the various types rather than as definitions, and are a simplified version of the classification adopted in 1956 by the World Meteorological Organisation, WMO, an international agency of the United Nations.

The clouds are first divided into three levels, and then subdivided.

Mostly high clouds composed of ice particles. Base at from 3 to 8 miles (5 to 13 kilometres) in temperate regions, higher in tropical and lower in polar regions.
Ci – Cirrus – Fibrous filaments, feathery or narrow bands of white or mostly white cloud (see Fig. 17).
Cc – Cirrocumulus – Parallel patterned or rippled white cloud sheet without shading (often a 'mackerel' sky).
Cs – Cirrostratus – Transparent, whitish cloud veil covering all or part of the sky. Often giving a halo round the sun.

Mostly medium high clouds. Base at from 1½ to 4 miles (2½ to 6½ kilometres) in temperate regions (NOTE: Overlaps in height with cirrus clouds).

B   25

Fig. 17. Cirrus cloud

Ac – Altocumulus – White or grey sheet cloud with shading, often in rounded masses with a pattern about three times as coarse as for cirrocumulus. Often producing 'fleecy' cloud (see Fig. 18).
As – Altostratus – Greyish cloud layer covering all or part of the sky. No solar halo (compare with cirrostratus).
Ns – Nimbostratus – Grey or dark cloud layer from which rain or snow is usually falling. Obscures the Sun.

Mostly low clouds composed of water droplets. Base at from zero to $1\frac{1}{2}$ miles ($2\frac{1}{2}$ kilometres) in all regions.
St – Stratus – Grey cloud layer often producing drizzle. Sun sometimes visible through it. No halo.
Sc – Stratocumulus – Grey cloud layer or patches with non-fibrous rounded masses of darker cloud with a coarser pattern than altocumulus.
Cu – Cumulus – Detached 'cauliflower' clouds with sharp edges, very white when sunlit, dark at the base, which is nearly horizontal (see Fig. 16).
Cb – Cumulonimbus – Larger than cumulus especially vertically and often with the top parts spreading out to form an *anvil cloud,* the typical thunder cloud (see Fig. 19).

Fig. 18. Banded altocumulus cloud

Fig. 19. Anvil cloud

It is also possible to classify clouds into three types according to their form instead of according to their height. These three forms are: stratiform, cumuliform and cirriform. Figure 20 compares the two methods of classification.

	High clouds	Medium clouds	Low clouds
Stratiform – thin	*Cirrus* *stratiformis*	*Altocumulus* *str.*	*Stratus* *Stratocumulus* *str.*
– thick	*Cirrostratus*	*Altostratus* *Nimbostratus*	
Cumuliform			*Cumulus* *Cumulonimbus*
Cirriform	*Cirrus* *Cirrocumulus*		

Fig. 20. Comparison of two methods of cloud classification

Of the *stratiform clouds*, stratus itself is the one formed at the lowest level of all, and in fact is often closely related to fog. It produces gloomy weather often of several days' duration, and is one of the most difficult meteorological conditions to overcome at airports. Like other stratiform clouds, it is the result of a stable atmosphere with cooling over a wide area.

The commonest forms of cirrocumulus, altocumulus and stratocumulus are all of the variety known as *stratiformis* (abbreviations: *Cu str*, *Ac str* and *Sc str*), and the mackerel or fleecy effects produced by these clouds often give an attractive appearance to the sky. They are probably the cloud patterns most remarked upon by the non-technical. These types are all fairly thin clouds. Figure 18 is a typical example of *Ac str, altocumulus stratiformis.*

Thick stratiform clouds are all clouds of uniform nature with little internal variations in structure. They are cirrostratus, altostratus or nimbostratus. Heavy continuous rain usually falls from nimbostratus.

Cumuliform clouds, unlike stratiform, are the product of an unstable atmosphere. The cooling which has produced them always results from rising air currents. The commonest type is the 'cotton-wool' cumulus cloud which often occurs with fine weather during the summer, and is not usually associated with any precipitation. Such clouds are also known as *fine-weather cumulus*. Cumulonimbus is the result of very vigorous growth of a cumulus cloud. They become very tall but eventually reach heights where there is a cessation of upward currents, and then begin to spread out sideways.

Cirriform clouds occur only in the higher levels and result from slowly rising air. Very often they have descending streaks of cloud which produce a varied pattern of attractive tails and wisps. These clouds are always tenuous as compared with others, and least is known about their origin.

An artificial cloud which is quite often seen nowadays is the thin streak of *vapour trail* or *contrail* which may be formed behind a high-flying aeroplane. This may be produced in several ways, but the commonest and most easily observed results from the condensation of vapour in the exhaust gases of the engine. These cool, and precipitation of water droplets or ice crystals occurs, to persist for several minutes before evaporation causes them to disappear. The duration of their existence is determined by the humidity and temperature of the part of the atmosphere within which they were formed.

FORMATION OF CLOUDS

All clouds are produced by cooling. The different types which have just been described are determined by the varied ways in which cooling may occur. Cooling by mixing is relatively rare, for if two air masses of different temperatures meet one another, there is much more tendency for the warmer, and therefore lighter, mass to override the cooler, heavier one, than for the two actually to mix. Uprising currents produced by such meetings are often of the type resulting from *depressions* (see p. 77).

Air may be warmed by passing over warm ground, and in this way it becomes unstable and *convectional* uprising currents are produced. This is well illustrated by *land* and *sea breezes*, in which the land warmed during the day causes uprising and leads to a breeze blowing from the sea to the land; and the cool land at night leads to uprising over the sea and a breeze in the reverse direction.

The third way in which up-currents may be produced is by the air being compelled to ride over such an obstacle as a mountain range. These produce *orogenic up-currents* and *orogenic clouds*. They are the cause of the high rainfall of mountain regions (see Fig. 12).

PRECIPITATION

Precipitation is the general term used by meteorologists to describe any particles which fall from clouds, whether or not they reach the ground. In suitable circumstances, the falling particles are vaporised before they make contact with the surface, and such streams of falling particles are known as *virga*.

Naturally the ice crystals or water droplets which compose any cloud are always falling relative to the air amongst which they exist, but the maximum rate at which they can pass through this air is so slow that cloud descent may be ignored. Cloud droplets vary in diameter considerably – from one-25,000th to one-500th of an inch (0·001 to 0·05 mm) – and their terminal velocity is between $\frac{1}{4}$ inch and 16 yards per minute (6 mm and 15 metres per minute).

It is necessary for the particles to grow larger before they can leave the cloud and fall sufficiently fast to become precipitation. There is more than one way in which this growth may occur. In the case of ice crystals in a cloud which also contains water droplets, the former grow at the expense of the latter. Water droplets may become larger by collision, since a cloud is composed of droplets of different sizes and they will be descending at different speeds and so will merge with one another. The average size of a cloud droplet is generally less than one-2,500th of an inch (0·01 mm) in diameter, and it requires a million of these to produce a small raindrop one-25th of an inch (1 mm) in diameter.

The terminal speed of such a drop is 21 feet per second or $14\frac{1}{2}$ m.p.h. (6·5 metres per sec), and consequently, when it has grown to such a size, it soon falls out of the general cloud and descends towards the ground as rain. The conditions which are particularly favourable to the formation of drops from droplets are: (1) a variety of droplet sizes, (2) a large number of droplets, (3) a moderate up-draught to prevent the drop from falling out of the cloud before it has reached an adequate size, and (4) a cloud of considerable vertical thickness, again to give the drop time to acquire a good size.

We generally distinguish between *rain* (with drops larger than one-50th inch (0·5 mm) diameter, *drizzle* (with smaller drops), *snow*, *sleet* and *hail*. Only six of the ten major types of cloud described earlier in this chapter commonly give rise to precipitation as is shown in Fig. 21, although occasionally other types may do so.

It will be noted from this table that persistent precipitation comes in general from stratiform clouds. It lasts for a considerable number of hours, and is generally not of very great intensity. On the other hand, short, severe showers, generally lasting less than one hour, almost invariably come from cumuliform clouds.

	May produce persistent falls of:
Altostratus	rain, sleet or snow
Nimbostratus	rain, sleet or snow
Stratus	drizzle
Stratocumulus stratiformis	drizzle, sleet or snow
	May produce showers of:
Cumulonimbus	rain, sleet, snow or hail

Fig. 21. Cloud types most likely to produce precipitation

The effect of mountains on precipitation has already been described on p. 20, and this is well exemplified in Britain where the rainfall of 38 inches (97 cm) per annum at Morecambe becomes as much as 69 inches (175 cm) at Ambleside.

Rain-shadow, the result of extraction by mountains over which the wind has passed, is illustrated by the lighter rainfall of Yorkshire as compared with Lancashire, but this is only one example, and any mountain mass over which a rain-bearing wind passes produces this result.

THUNDERSTORMS

A special type of sudden shower is the *thunderstorm*. This is produced by a cumulonimbus cloud in which the powerful up-current is sufficient to prevent the fall of normal-sized raindrops. This results in much break up of the drops, the passage upwards of the smaller fractions, and an interplay between water and ice particles. Recent research has shown that the distribution of charge through a thunder cloud is as shown in Fig. 22, and that this is different from the distribution which had previously been considered to exist.

A number of different theories have been put forward to explain the formation of these charges, and it is highly probable that different processes operate at different stages of the storm. The lightning is the electric discharge of these very high potentials (believed to be about 100 million volts). The heavy rainstorm occurs when the upward current slackens sufficiently to permit the large water drops, which have already been formed, to fall to the ground.

MIST AND FOG

Mist and *fog* are not merely low cloud, for the latter is always formed by cooling due to air rising, whereas the former is the result of air of sufficiently high humidity being cooled by passing over cooler ground.

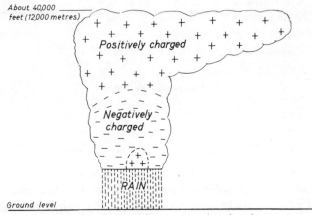

Fig. 22. Electric charges in a thunder cloud

The ground may become cooled at night by radiation so as to produce *radiation mist* or *fog*. This is encouraged by the absence of cloud, which acts somewhat like a blanket and discourages radiation from the ground. Alternatively, warmer air may be blown over cooler ground and so be cooled to produce an *advection mist* or *fog*.

The particles of water in mist are smaller and fewer than in fog, and visibility is usually not less than 1,100 yards (1,000 metres). The amount to which visibility is reduced in a fog is partly controlled by the size of the particles. Numerous small particles, especially if smoke particles are present also, lead to very poor visibility. Fog requires a relative humidity of 90 per cent or higher, whereas mist may occur with a value as low as 80 per cent.

Haze also reduces visibility, but is due to particles of smoke or dust in the atmosphere, and not to water droplets. Industrial areas and desert regions (where dust storms may occur) are particularly subject to haze.

DEW AND FROST

It is obvious that for fog to be formed so as to be at least several feet in thickness above the ground, there must be sufficient turbulence for that thickness to be cooled. If, however, the air is quite calm, only the layer immediately in contact with the ground will become cooled, and water may be formed directly on the cooler objects. This is *dew*. It is important to realise that no falling of water is involved. It is a contact process. However, not all the water found on plants in the morning results from condensation from the air. Much of it is *guttation dew,* that is, water which has been exuded from the leaves in the normal process of transpiration, and which, during the period of high humidity in the adjacent atmosphere, has not been evaporated.

Frost occurs when the temperature falls below 0°C (32°F) before the air becomes saturated. In that case, further cooling produces the direct deposition of ice crystals on the cold surfaces, and their gradual growth through the night produces a layer of frost.

CHAPTER FIVE

Air Currents and Air Masses

BESIDES varying from day to day at any one place, the atmospheric pressure changes from point to point over an area at any one time. Lines drawn on a map through places which at a given moment have equal atmospheric pressure are termed *isobars,* and these are familiar on the maps seen in the daily television weather report and forecast and in many newspapers.

Because change of altitude in itself causes a change in atmospheric pressure at ground-level, maps drawn to indicate the pressure distribution on the actual ground over an area at any one time show a combination of weather and altitude distribution. In order to simplify this, it is usual for the meteorologist to adjust the observed pressure at each place to what it would be if it were at sea-level. The effect of altitude is thus removed and the maps show the meteorological elements only.

GEOSTROPHIC WIND

If pressure were the only force operating, air would tend to move directly across the isobars from high pressure to low, and this would be the ground surface wind. The examination of any weather chart which marks isobars and wind directions will, however, show that this is not what actually occurs. The winds blow more or less along, instead of across, the isobars in such a direction that (in the northern hemisphere) the low pressure area is on the left of the direction of the arrow.

This effect is produced by the Earth's rotation, which turns the wind direction through a right-angle. This is known as the *Coriolis effect,* and the resulting wind is known as the *geostrophic wind.* This wind blows directly along the isobars with a velocity proportional to their spacing – the closer they are together, the faster the resulting wind.

The direction in which the geostrophic wind blows was first described by Buys Ballot more than a century ago, and what came to be known as *Buys Ballot's law* stated that if, in the northern hemisphere, you place your back to the wind, low pressure is on your left (on your right in the southern hemisphere).

The theoretical geostrophic wind is more or less identical with the actual wind at altitudes of over 1,500 feet (460 metres) above the ground, but below that ground friction has an influence. This

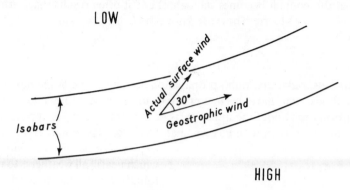

Fig. 23. *The geostrophic and actual surface winds*

opposes the Coriolis force, and thus the actual wind direction near the land surface is generally in a direction at about 30° to the left of the geostrophic direction in the northern hemisphere. It thus blows roughly along the isobars, with a tendency towards the area of low pressure (see Fig. 23). The angle is as low as about 10° over the sea where the friction is less. Over land at ground-level the wind-speed is about one-third the speed which may be calculated for the geostrophic wind. At sea it is about two-thirds.

It is useful to remember that, as a result of the above facts, the wind blows round a depression in an anticlockwise direction in the northern hemisphere, and round a region of high pressure (anticyclone) in a clockwise direction.

OTHER WINDS

Land and sea breezes have already been described (see p. 29), and it must be clear that local land configuration plays an important part in what are usually minor changes in wind direction. Houses and other obstacles cause deviations, whilst the pattern of hills, mountains and valleys deflects the wind to a somewhat larger extent. Powerful funnelling effects may be produced if the configuration is suitable, and this is the origin of the *mistral*, which is a steady wind often of considerable velocity which blows down the lower Rhône valley – and often follows steamers sailing south from Marseilles, much to the discomfort of their passengers.

Gentle breezes are produced at night in hilly districts if the higher ground cools more rapidly than the more sheltered low. Then the cooler air drifts down into the valley, and if the contours are such that this cool air becomes stagnant there, it often results that a *frost hollow* is produced. These are known as *katabatic winds*.

Rockets, radar and radio propagation are only some of the modern methods that have been employed to disclose more and more information about the upper parts of the atmosphere. It appears to be in layers, each with its own characteristics. The lowest layer, the

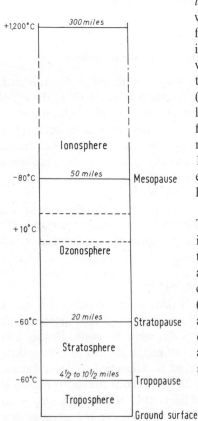

troposphere, is the one within which nearly all weather is to be found. Here are the clouds, here is precipitation, and most of the winds. In this layer, temperature falls with increasing height (see Fig. 24), and the upper limit of the troposphere varies from about 3½ miles (5½ kilometres) at the Poles to about 11 miles (18 kilometres) at the equator, with rather lower levels in winter than in summer.

Above this is the *stratosphere.* The boundary between the two is the *tropopause.* In the stratosphere, temperature remains approximately constant with change of height at −60°C (−75°F) with fluctuations of about 20°C (36°F) either colder or warmer at different times and places. In general in the stratosphere it is warmer over

Fig. 24. Layers of the atmosphere

the Poles than over the equator. The stratosphere reaches upwards to a height of something like 20 miles (30 kilometres), when it passes, at the *stratopause,* into the next layer which is variously known as the *ozonosphere, mesosphere* or *upper stratosphere.*

So far as is known, this shows at first an increase of temperature with height, then a warm layer, perhaps 6 miles (10 kilometres) thick, where the temperature is of the order of 10°C (50°F), followed by another layer through which it falls again to about −80°C (−110°F) at a total height above the ground of about 50 miles (80 kilometres). This is the *mesopause,* and above this is the *ionosphere* with temperature increasing with height so that at about 300 miles (500 kilometres) it is of the order of 1,200°C (2,200°F).

The differences in the temperature gradients both in magnitude and in sign in these various layers are due first to the fact that, in the troposphere, heat exchanges mainly occur as the result of vertical air currents, or convection, whereas above that it is by radiation and absorption. The variety of changes in temperature which occur is also linked with the physical state of the gases at those low pressures and when they are subject to high intensity radiation from the Sun – for we must always remember that the atmosphere acts very like a filter, in much the same way as the photographer's filter which he places in front of his lens to cut out colours or wavelengths which he does not wish to reach his film. In particular, there is a layer at about 16 miles (25 kilometres) which absorbs most of the ultra-violet solar rays, which are very powerful above this level, and, if they got through to the Earth's surface, would kill all life.

WINDS IN THE UPPER AIR

Fascinating though this exploration of the high atmosphere may be, nevertheless it is with the troposphere that we are concerned. At altitudes in this of the order of $3\frac{1}{2}$ miles ($5\frac{1}{2}$ kilometres), there is a narrow 'lane' of fast-moving air perhaps 200 miles (300 kilometres) in width circling the Poles at speeds averaging more than 60 mph (100 km/h) and reaching 115 mph (180 km/h) in places.

At a somewhat higher altitude, there is a larger circular stream of air with a more complex pattern and an average speed approaching 120 mph (190 km/h) with speeds as high as twice this not uncommon. This is at a height of about 6 miles (10 km) and is mostly over latitude 30°. It is known as the *sub-tropical jet stream,* whereas the other is the *circumpolar jet stream.* Both these streams blow in a

general easterly direction, and their heights, velocities and localities
vary to some extent with the season of the year.

Similar jet streams occur in the southern hemisphere, and it is
probable that others remain to be discovered at even greater altitudes. They have a profound influence upon the weather of the
localities that are situated beneath them, but exactly how this
operates remains to be discovered.

MEASURING WIND VELOCITIES

To measure *wind velocities* at considerable heights is a matter of
varying, and generally complex, techniques. At ground-level it is a
much simpler matter. Instruments which do this are known as

zontal, radial spokes (see Fig. 25). The whole 'wheel' is rotated by

Fig. 25. Cup anemometer

the wind, and measures not only the wind-velocity by the speed with
which the wheel turns, but also measures the total *run* of the wind.
It does not distinguish direction.

The *pressure-tube type* of anemometer (see Fig. 26) is more sensi-
tive and can be more accurately calibrated. It is capable of measuring
rapid fluctuations in velocity, and is excellent therefore for recording
individual gusts. Both draw graphs on record paper, and there are
also other types.

Note that wind is described by the point of the compass *from* which it comes, and that if this direction changes in a clockwise direction, the wind is said to *veer*. If the change is anticlockwise, the wind is said to *back*. Thus a southwest wind may back later to become south.

Fig. 26. Pressure-tube anemometer

PLOTTING WIND FREQUENCIES

Figures 27, 28 and 29 show three ways that are commonly employed to plot the frequencies of wind from various directions at a particular station. The location selected for this example is Holyhead, Anglesey. Figure 27 gives the greatest amount of information, is easy to read in detail, but rather difficult to read if generalities are what is required. It is plotted by drawing lines from the sides of the octagon as zero, one line for each month, the length of the first line representing, as a percentage of the total January observations, the number of occasions on which the wind was blowing from that direction. The eight lines for January, in the eight different directions, together with the figure for calms for January (2 for this station), add to 100, and the same is true for each month.

Thus this diagram shows the directional distribution of wind for each month and the lines for different months are comparable only (1) when we assume that the months are of equal length (and within the accuracies of plotting this is reasonably true, and (2) when we remember that these are frequencies of observation and that no reference is made to wind-velocity. For example, the winds from the northwest show the same frequency (9 per cent) for both January and February, but this might not mean that the same *amount* of wind came in the two months. One of the months might have gentle breezes for 9 per cent of the time, whilst the other had gales for the same proportion of the period.

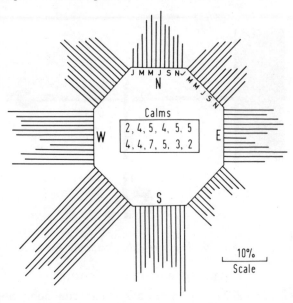

Fig. 27. Octagon diagram of percentage monthly wind frequencies for Holyhead

The *wind-rose* diagram (Fig. 28) gives the same information but on an annual, instead of a monthly, basis. The zero for each radial line in this instance is the circumference of the station circle. The *polar* diagram (Fig. 29) is the same as the rose, excepting that the zero for each measurement is the centre point, and instead of the radial lines being actually drawn, their 'envelope' is shaded in. This produces a more dramatic picture, which is perhaps thereby easier to remember and compare with other stations, but it is more difficult to read than the rose.

All these diagrams show the percentage frequencies of occasions on which wind comes from the different directions, and for Holyhead it is clear that wind most often comes from the southwest, with west and south not far behind, and that the least frequent winds come from the southeast. The octagon shows more detail than this, and, for example, shows that southeasterlies are particularly rare from May to August.

Such diagrams, as has already been hinted, are far from sufficient for most geomorphological studies where wind is important. In coastal work, what is important is not only which is the most

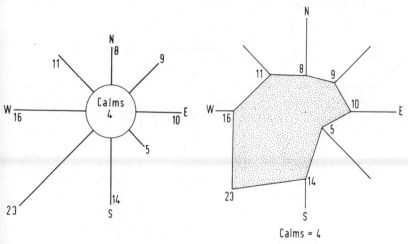

Fig. 28. *Rose diagram of percentage annual wind frequencies for Holyhead*

Fig. 29. *Polar diagram of percentage annual wind frequencies for Holyhead*

frequent direction of wind, but which is the most frequent direction of strong winds, gales, etc. From the point of view of coast erosion, the direction in which the gentler winds come is of no importance whatever, winds below a certain velocity being quite ineffective in this process. The diagrams do not compare directional frequencies of winds of various velocities, nor do they compare total quantity of wind (that is miles run) either within themselves or when diagrams for several stations are being compared.

AIR MASSES

The lower atmosphere obtains most of its heat, not directly from solar radiation, but indirectly from the ground, as already explained (p. 13). Apparently about two-thirds of the lower atmosphere's heat reaches it from the ground and one-third from the Sun direct. This is important, for it results in large continental areas tending to be places where atmospheric conditions vary but little from point to point, and where air stagnates for a while and thus has the opportunity to acquire characteristics which reflect the locality and are fairly uniform throughout its bulk. Such volumes of air are known as *continental air masses*.

Besides forming over the great land areas, air masses also occur over oceans, and in such cases they naturally have a high humidity and are known as *maritime air masses*.

Symbol	Name of mass	Characteristics in source region	Further history
A	Arctic	very cold, dry	stationary
AA	Antarctic	ditto	ditto
Pc	Polar continental	cold, dry	moves towards Tc or Tm, becoming unstable
Pm	Polar maritime	cold, moist	ditto
Tc	Tropical continental	hot, dry	moves towards Pc or Pm, becoming stable
Tm	Tropical maritime	warm, moist	ditto
Em	Equatorial maritime	hot, very moist, unstable	stationary

Fig. 30. Types and characteristics of air masses

Masses occur in four principal latitudes. Those at the poles are termed *arctic* or *antarctic,* and like the *equatorial* air masses, they move their location but little. Between these are *polar* and *tropical* air masses. The latter originate in a belt centred on the tropics, both north and south of the equator, and tend to drift slowly to regions of somewhat higher latitude.

The *polar air masses* received their name before the existence of static air masses at the Poles themselves was appreciated, and thus the adjective *polar* has now become something of a misnomer. Having been used for so many years, it would, however, be most confusing to change it now.

These polar air masses originate in high latitudes centred approximately on latitude 60° north or south, and tend to drift to regions of lower latitudes. They thus in time meet the tropical air masses moving in the opposite direction, and the war which rages between the two is the cause of the very variable weather conditions of these middle latitudes, of which more will be said in Chapter 9.

A list of the principal types of air mass and their characteristics is given in Fig. 30, and the effect of the various masses on the climates of different parts of the world is largely the subject of the following chapters.

During their movement from the source area to another, it may well be that a particular air mass may have the opportunity to spread over a wider area, in which case it is said to experience *divergence,* with the result that slow subsidence of upper layers of air occurs so that there is a tendency for these upper layers to become warmer and acquire a lower relative humidity. They thereby become more stable.

On the other hand, when the tropical and polar masses approach one another, there is some congestion, *convergence* occurs, with accompanying instability. These two processes are of very great importance in determining the type of climate a particular area experiences.

Part Two

The Elements of Climatology

CHAPTER SIX

The World's Climates

AFTER the foregoing brief introduction to some of the principal facts of meteorology, it is possible to discuss the world's climates in broad, general terms and attempt some kind of classification. This has as its object simplification and generalisation, and an approach towards easy description and identification. In the present instance, it seeks to collect together the vast number of available records, to reduce them to some sort of order and so to make it possible for the student to obtain an impression of the ways in which climate changes as one moves about the world.

Classification can be empirical or systematic. An *empirical classification* is one which takes no account of cause or origin. It merely groups together those varieties which are similar to one another without regard to the way in which they may have come into existence. One very often later discovers that by doing this, one has inadvertently put together items with common origins. Thus the empirical classification is very often found to make scientific sense. For example, in classifying plants, one might separate all those whose flowers had, say, six petals from those which had four, and so on. This would be based purely on description, and would not necessarily bear any relationship to the evolutionary origin of the different types. In the early stages of knowledge of any subject, it is often only possible to classify empirically, since causal relationships are not at that time understood. Such classifications have often led to important scientific discoveries.

Nevertheless, the only truly scientific classification is a *genetic, causal* or *systematic* one. In this case, items with the same origin are placed together, and they cannot be classified until their origin is known.

In attempting a classification of the world's climates, these problems and difficulties arise, together with others. The demarcation on a map of climatic areas suggests two erroneous things. First, that the climate is the same over the whole of any one area, and second, that it suddenly changes as one passes over the boundary line. Neither is true, and of course all lines between climatic regions should be broken ones to indicate no sudden change, and the colours, if any, with which adjacent areas are tinted should blend gradually one into the other. For practical reasons, this is not convenient, so it is necessary to use such maps with caution.

Again one is supposing that one knows what is meant by the word *climate*. It has been defined as the average weather, but like many other averages, it may well be that it never actually occurs, nor does the same average in different localities always mean the same thing. For example, two places may both have the same average annual temperature of, say, 20°C, but one may have an annual range of 10° and the other 30°, so that the average summer temperatures at the two places may be 25° and 35° respectively, with corresponding winter temperatures of 15° and 5°, producing two very differing climates. It is for this reason that most atlases print isothermal maps for January and July, and similarly rainfall maps for the same two months, instead of for the whole year, for it is just as important to know something of when the rain falls as it is to know the total amount. Two places in Britain, one notorious for the fact that it always seems to be raining and the other popular holiday resort both have in fact the same annual rainfall, but one has hours and hours of drizzle and the other short periods of heavy, thundery rain which is soon over.

Climate, too, is the sum total of all the weather factors, which include temperature, hours of sunshine, rainfall, wind-velocity and direction, their distribution through the year, the reliability of each of these factors and the occurrence of other characteristics, such as fog, frost and so on. Then again, the same rainfall in places of differing temperatures does not have the same effect on the plants and animals living there, for in hot areas so much more of the precipitation is lost by evaporation that but little is available for plant growth.

Perhaps the one aspect of nature that best summarises all these variables is the ecological range of plants growing in any locality, although here again these are affected by other conditions besides climate, such as the nature of the soil, angle of slope, aspect and so on.

In the following chapters we shall consider climate quite separately from plant growth. The influence of climate on the morphology of an area is seen throughout the middle part of this book, and the combined influence of landform and climate in determining the plant and animal inhabitants of an area is the subject of the final part.

CLIMATIC CLASSIFICATION

Simple, broad climatic classification is very old. For many centuries the equatorial, temperate and arctic zones have been recognised by man, and their rough connection with latitude has been realised. The fact that some places are desert, others are tropical forest, others grow palm trees, or broad-leaved deciduous trees, or conifers, or even no trees at all: these simple aspects of biogeography, too, have long been realised.

The difficulty in making a more precise classification has partly been one of lack of climatic information for numerous sites. Even today, for many parts of the world only temperature and rainfall records are available, and these are often unreliable, or the instruments may not have been sited so as to obtain a true result that is typical for the area.

Perhaps the most used classification is the one designed by *Wladimir Köppen,* a German climatologist who lived from 1846 to 1940. He published his famous classification first in 1900, and then revised it in 1918. Each type was precisely defined in terms of temperature or rainfall, or a combination of the two, using various formulae. The limits of each type were thus quite definite and rigid. The classification was entirely empirical, since it made no reference to causation.

The primary division was into four types, separated by temperature differences, and a fifth, which seems rather out of line with the others, for it did not depend on temperature, but on aridity – it included all dry climates. They were:

Type A, *tropical climates,* in which every month had a mean temperature over 18°C (64·4°F).

Type B, *dry climates,* in which, in general, evaporation exceeded the precipitation. This included both steppe and desert, and the boundaries were determined by formulae involving both annual rainfall and mean annual temperature.

Type C, *warm temperate climates,* in which the mean temperature of the coldest month was below 18°C (64·4°F) and above −3°C (26·6°F).

Type D, *snow climates,* climates with severe winters, with the mean temperature of the coldest month below −3°C (26·6°F), but with the warmest month's mean temperature above 10°C (50°F).

Type E, *polar climates,* in which the mean temperature of the warmest month was below 10°C (50°F).

These were then subdivided into twenty-four main types, to which code letters were given. The second letter described in general the precipitation régime, and a third, the temperature and length of the summer. Thus, Dfb indicated a severe winter climate (Type D in the definitions just given), with adequate precipitation throughout the year (f), and a short, warm summer (b).

Another much-used system was designed by Thornthwaite, and published in 1931 and 1933. This system pays more attention to vegetation types, and the sufficiency or otherwise of precipitation throughout the year. He introduced the idea of *potential evapotranspiration,* which is the amount of moisture that would be removed from the soil, both by direct evaporation into the air and indirectly by transpiration by plants, providing there were an ample supply of water available in the soil. It is clearly dependent upon the temperature, and clearly the *water need* of an area is greater in regions of high temperature.

By comparison of this with the *water supply* (precipitation) through the seasons, the type of vegetation which may be able to flourish in an area may be deduced.

The Thornthwaite classification of climates is based on the monthly potential evapotranspiration in relation, separately, to the monthly temperature and the monthly precipitation. For the former, he obtained six temperature types:

A′	tropical	D′	cool temperate
B′	subtropical	E′	snow climates
C′	warm temperate	F′	ice climates

and from the latter, five humidity types:

A	rain forests	D	steppelands
B	forests	E	deserts
C	grasslands		

To these he added a third symbol to indicate the precipitation régime:

r	sufficient precipitation all the year
s	insufficient precipitation in the summer
w	winter
d	all the year.

So that, for example, BB's indicates a subtropical forest climate with insufficient rainfall in the summer.

The calculation of the monthly potential evapotranspiration figures from the available data has proved difficult, and although the classification is regarded as very important, especially since it considers precipitation in connection with how useful or otherwise this will be, nevertheless it has not yet been used to the full extent to which it is likely in the future.

A number of simplified systems have also been used, and the more recent ones have attempted to relate the type to their origins, so as to produce genetic classifications. This cannot lead to such definite boundary lines as do the empirical ones, and although it does introduce some apparent vagueness into the classification,

EQUATORIAL CLIMATES
(Dominated by equatorial air masses, Em, with some influence from tropical maritime and continental masses, Tm and Tc)
1 Equatorial climate (Af)
2 Tropical wet-and-dry climate (Aw)
3 Monsoon climate (Am)

TROPICAL CLIMATES
(Dominated by tropical air masses, Tm and Tc)
4 Humid subtropical climate (Cfa)
5 Tropical and subtropical grassland climate (BSh)
6 Hot desert climate (BWh)

TEMPERATE CLIMATES
(Interacting or alternating tropical and polar air masses, Tm, Tc and Pm, Pc)
7 Mediterranean climate (Csa or Csb)
8 Marine temperate climate (Cfb)
9 Continental temperate climate (Dfa, Dfb, Dwa or Dwb)
10 Temperate grassland climate (BSk)

ARCTIC (ANTARCTIC) CLIMATES
(Dominated by polar or arctic air masses, Pm, Pc, A or AA)
11 Subarctic climate (Dfc)
12 Arctic climate (ET)
13 Polar climate (EF)

Fig. 31. Major climatic types (Gresswell)

nevertheless it may be nearer to what actually occurs in nature. Fig.
31 shows the scheme used in this book, and is a slight revision of
one first published in 1961.[1] It has been possible to employ more or
less the same areal boundaries in the chapters on vegetation which
form the final part, and to facilitate comparison the Köppen
(approximate) equivalents are given alongside each type (Fig. 31).
Figure 32 gives the key to the Köppen code letters that have been
used, although the fuller definitions for the first letters have already
been stated.

FIRST LETTER
A   Tropical climates
B   Dry climates
C   Warm temperate climates (Mesothermal)
D   Snow climates (Microthermal)
E   Polar climates

SECOND LETTER
S   Semi-arid climate
W   Arid climate
F   Ice-cap climate
T   Tundra
f   adequate precipitation throughout the year
m   monsoon-type precipitation
s   summer a dry season
w   winter a dry season

THIRD LETTER
a   hot summer
b   warm summer
c   cool, short summer
h   hot and dry
k   cold and dry

Fig. 32.   Key to (some parts of) the Köppen letter code

[1] In R. Kay Gresswell, *Revision Outlines of Geography – Physical and Mathe-
matical* (Hulton Educational Publications, reproduced here with permission).

CHAPTER SEVEN

Equatorial Climates

THE accounts of each climatic type which follow are necessarily very generalised. Cautionary remarks regarding maps of climatic regions have already been given, but in addition there are local variations in climate from mile to mile; the weather experienced is often far from the climatic average; the proximity of sea modifies the conditions, as also does altitude, angle of slope and aspect. Everyone is experienced in this kind of effect, for we all know the minor deviations from the general daily forecast which modify the weather in our own home districts. Similar variations on a larger scale apply to climatic regions, but with these notes in mind, the following give some idea of what is experienced in each of the areas delimited.

The six maps showing the world distribution of climates adopted here are placed where seems most appropriate in the text. They are: Africa, Fig. 33, p. 54; South America, Fig. 35, p. 57; North America, Fig. 40, p. 65; Australia, Fig. 43, p. 68; Europe, Fig. 46, p. 73; and Asia, Fig. 57, p. 83. Figure 31 gives the table of types.

1. EQUATORIAL CLIMATE

This climate occurs on both sides of the equator for a few degrees in width in Central and South America, Africa and the Far East. It reaches the west coast of Africa, but not the east because of the mountain barrier east of the Congo. It touches both coasts of Central America and northern South America, where, however, the physical features prevent continuous development from west to east.

These areas are all located in the *equatorial calms* or *doldrums* at the approximate convergence of the *trade winds* from northerly and southerly directions. This, coupled with location in the parts of the world receiving the greatest amount of insolation, produces hot ground with very warm, unstable air, which may be either the local equatorial air mass, Em, or tropical masses, Tm, drifting slowly towards the equator. The instability produces a heavy rainfall, most often of a thundery type, storms commonly occurring in the after-

noon when the ground, and thus the lower air, has been strongly
heated by the day's sunshine.

Total annual rainfall varies, but is always copious (often between
60 and 80 inches (150 and 200 cm) per annum), and there is no dry

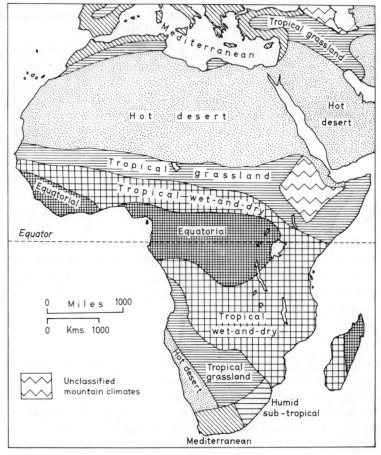

Fig. 33. The major climatic regions of Africa

season. The high temperature reduces the effectiveness of the rainfall
and produces high humidity, although there is invariably an ample
supply of ground moisture for plant growth.

The high altitude of the Sun throughout the year (never more than
$23\frac{1}{2}°$ off the vertical at midday (see Fig. 9) ensures that there is no
seasonal relief from the heat. One of the chief characteristics of this

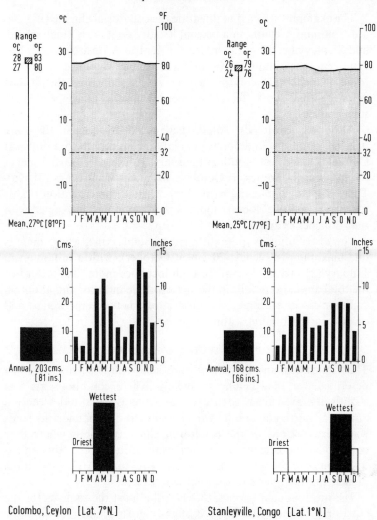

Colombo, Ceylon [Lat. 7°N.]   Stanleyville, Congo [Lat. 1°N.]

Fig. 34. Equatorial climate – Data for Colombo and Stanleyville

climate is its extreme monotony. Not only is the time of sunrise and
sunset almost unchanging throughout the year, but the mean temperature is almost constant from month to month. In fact, the
difference between day and night conditions is virtually the only
variation. Mean temperature is about 27°C (80°F), although the
daily range is often as great as 10°C (18°F). This results from the
great radiation losses during the hours of darkness.

Equatorial climates

The examples selected to illustrate the equatorial climate (Fig. 34) are Colombo, Ceylon, in a coastal locality on a fairly small island, and Stanleyville, far in the interior of central Africa. Naturally this results in some diminution of rainfall at Stanleyville, although it still totals 66 inches (168 cm) for the year. At the same time, the altitude of more than 1,500 feet (450 metres) results in slightly lower temperatures.

Although, as already stated, there is no dry season, there are marked variations in amount of rainfall from month to month. At Colombo, the driest month is February with just less than 2 inches (5 cm), and the wettest is October, with nearly 14 inches (35 cm). There is a second maximum (in May), when the precipitation almost reaches 11 inches (28 cm), and a second minimum in August with only 3 inches (8 cm).

The distribution is quite different at Stanleyville, where there is one maximum (8 inches: 20 cm in October), with a minimum in January ($2\frac{1}{4}$ inches: $5\frac{1}{2}$ cm). In both localities more than a third of the total annual rain falls in the wettest three months, and about an eighth in the driest three. This gives a ratio between the wettest and driest quarters of almost three to one.

2. TROPICAL WET-AND-DRY CLIMATE

The tropical wet-and-dry climatic areas more or less flank those just described, for they belong to regions where conditions are just slightly removed from equatorial, and this is in latitudes centred about 15° north and south of the equator. It also bounds the landward terminations of the equatorial climatic regions where they come to an end because of the increasing altitude. Thus this type is to be found in the highlands of eastern equatorial Africa and in the higher, *chapada,* parts of south central Brazil.

The mean annual temperature is still almost the same as for the equatorial climate, the range is slightly greater and there may be considered to be summer and winter seasons, although of course the whole year is hot. During the summer (June to August in the northern hemisphere and November to January in the southern), these areas are dominated by equatorial maritime air masses, Em, and there is a heavy rainfall of the order of 10 inches (25 cm) per month, whilst in the 'winter' tropical continental air masses, Tc, take over, and the climate becomes very dry. This is the origin of the descriptive term *wet-and-dry* in distinction from the equatorial climate. The daily range of temperature is again greater than the

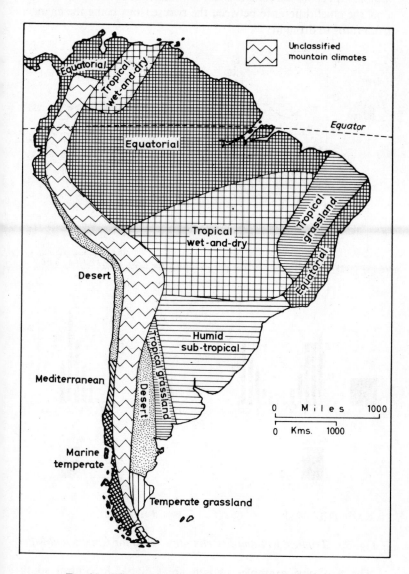

Fig. 35. The major climatic regions of South America

annual range, but the climate is not so monotonous as the equatorial one, the chief difference between the two seasons being the change from rains to drought.

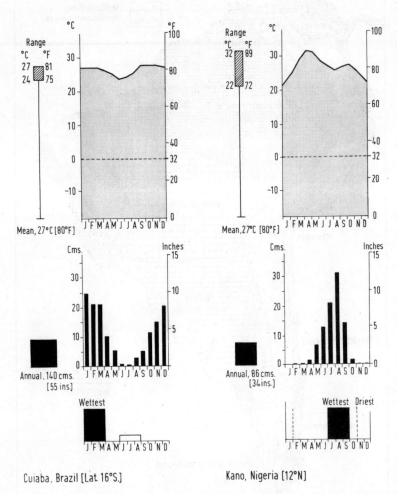

Fig. 36. *Tropical wet-and-dry climate – Data for Cuiaba and Kano*

The two type examples chosen are Cuiaba, in central south Brazil, and Kano, in Northern Nigeria (Fig. 36). Both these have a mean annual temperature of 27°C (80°F) with a 4°C (7°F) annual range at Cuiaba and 9°C (17°F) at Kano. At Cuiaba, nearly half the annual rain falls in January–February–March (summer), whilst at

Kano three-quarters comes in July–August–September (again summer). At Cuiaba, $1\frac{1}{2}$ inches (4 cm) is the total precipitation for the
winter quarter of the year; at Kano there is virtually none. In both
cases, the wet quarter has the effect of lowering the temperature by
a few degrees on account of the cooling effect of the tremendous
amount of evaporation which then occurs.

3. MONSOON CLIMATE

The monsoon climate is a variant of the tropical wet-and-dry, but
with a still greater difference between the wet and dry seasons. There
have been attempts to include this climate as an integral part of the
wet-and-dry type, but the name has been used with its quite definite
meaning for so long that it is probably not now possible to abandon
it, nor may this be desirable. It is under the influence of the same air
mass in the winter, the tropical continental, Tc, but either the
equatorial or the tropical maritime, Em or Tm, takes over in the
summer.

The special areas most famous for this climate are India, and
Siam and Viet-Nam. Local relief has a considerable effect as always
in producing further variants, and, for example, the Western Ghats
have an exceptionally high precipitation during the appropriate
months and lead to a rain-shadow area on their eastern side.

Bombay and Rangoon are selected as type stations (Fig. 37). In
both cases the temperature for the whole year still reaches a high
average, being 27°C (81°F); both have their coolest months, 24°
and 25°C (76° and 77°F), in January; and both find that the evaporation resulting from the heavy summer rains lowers the temperature
by some 3°C (6°F). Consequently, May and April respectively are
the hottest months at 30° and 31°C (86° and 87°F). In Bombay, July
is down to 27°C (81°F), with a slight rise after the rains have
slackened in October. In Rangoon, July is 26°C (80°F), again with a
slight rise in October, although the rains do not really come to an
end there until the middle of November.

The monsoonal character is well brought out by the fact that
nearly three-quarters of the whole year's precipitation is received
during the months of June–July–August in both cases, and less than
one per cent falls in the February quarter.

As already stated, the monsoon climate is only a somewhat
extreme variety of the tropical wet-and-dry, and it may perhaps be
better to consider rather that this is the local name given in certain
parts of Asia to the one climate.

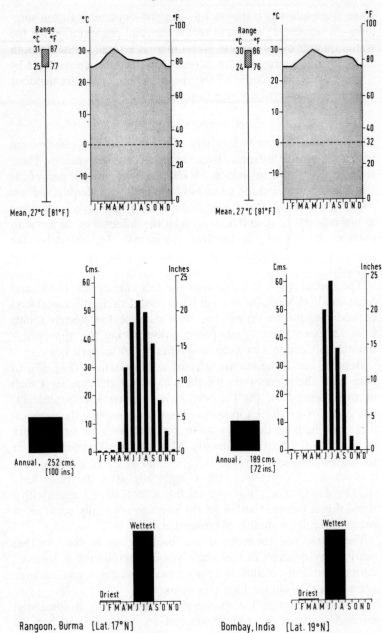

Fig. 37. *Monsoon climate – Data for Rangoon and Bombay*

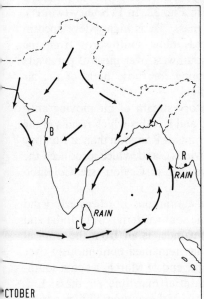

OCTOBER

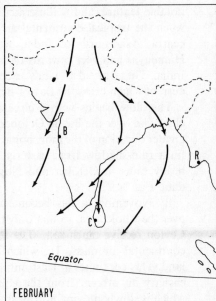

FEBRUARY

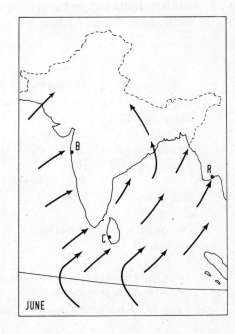

JUNE

Fig. 38. *Winds over India and the Bay of Bengal*

The complete change in wind direction which occurs in India is a notable feature, and is illustrated in Fig. 38. In February (winter), when the tropical continental air mass, Tc, is highly developed in central Asia north of India, winds blow southwards from the Himalayas and veer towards the southwest over most of peninsula India. These are dry winds excepting for those parts of the air current which cross the Bay of Bengal.

This flow begins with a circulatory stream of air moving anti-clockwise over the Bay in October, and it is this which results in the greater duration of the monsoonal rains at Rangoon than at Bombay (in a rain-shadow from easterly winds), and which produces the heavy rains in October and November in Ceylon (see Colombo data, Fig. 34).

By November it has become a continuous northeasterly wind over the whole area, so that only the southeastern part of India and Ceylon receive much rain. The remainder is air from the tropical continental air mass, Tc, which has remained continuously over land. This continues at least until the end of March, when a south-easterly air stream from the equatorial maritime air mass, Em, which is slowly moving northwards with the summer Sun, produces southwesterly winds north of the equator. These begin to invade southern India and gradually creep northwards to bring the rains to the Bombay district by June.

	1 Equatorial	2 Tropical wet-and-dry	3 Monsoon
Mean annual temperature	27°C (80°F)	27°C (80°F)	27°C (80°F)
Annual range	2°C (3°F)	5°C (9°F)	5°C (9°F)
Annual rainfall	High 70 in. (180 cm)	High 50 in. (130 cm)	High 70 in. (180 cm)
Wet quarter contains*	one-third	one-half (summer)	three-quarters (summer)
Dry quarter contains*	one-eighth	very little (winter)	very little (winter)

Conversions are approximate only in this generalised table.
* Of the annual precipitation.

Fig. 39. Equatorial Climates – Generalised typical characteristics

The equatorial climates as a whole are summarised in the generalised characteristics table shown in Fig. 39. From this it will be seen that the mean annual temperature of this group of climates tends to be around 27°C (80°F), with a very small annual range at the equator itself, increasing to the order of 5°C (9°F) farther away. For the equatorial climate, the wettest quarter of the year is only 2 to 2½ times as wet as the driest quarter. This is a fairly even distribution. On the other hand, the tropical wet-and-dry and the monsoon climates each have very heavy rainfall during the wettest quarter with very little indeed during the driest. Given the climatic data for an individual station it is very often difficult to distinguish between tropical wet-and-dry and monsoon climates, and in fact it is often much more a matter of personal or geographic regional decision than scientific reality.

When considering the table given in Fig. 39, note that in the last two lines, the fraction corresponding to an equal distribution of rain throughout the year would be one-quarter. The fractions in the wet quarter must therefore always be one-quarter or greater, and those for the dry quarter one-quarter or less.

CHAPTER EIGHT

Tropical Climates

4. HUMID SUBTROPICAL CLIMATE

THE humid subtropical climate is important as occurring in the southern states of U.S.A., in southern Brazil, Uruguay and much of Argentina, parts of the east coast of South Africa and Australia, and southeastern China (where it is known as the *China type*). All these are areas which man finds of great use to him in the raising of food, and the natural vegetation types that occur will be described in Chapter 35.

Compared with the equatorial climates, the humid subtropical, in spite of its name, is a much drier zone. All its areas are dominated by the influence of the tropical maritime air masses, Tm, which move slowly to higher latitudes, and, coming from the oceans, are heavily laden with moisture. They occasionally meet with polar air masses during the winter months, but for much of the time even then, and during the whole of the summer, it is tropical maritime air alone which affects these areas.

When the different masses meet, the tropical rides over the polar, to produce frontal weather which will be explained under the marine temperate climate (p. 77). This, and the fact that in any case the Tm masses are tending to rise as they move towards higher latitudes, results in adiabatic cooling with consequent increase in relative humidity, the formation of cloud and precipitation.

Summer temperatures in these areas may be as high as in equatorial regions, but the winters are considerably cooler. Mean annual temperature range is of the order of 10°C (about 20°F) or more, total annual rainfall tends to be rather less than (and is sometimes as low as half as much as) is typical of the various equatorial climates. Although there is a marked summer or later summer maximum of rainfall, there is no period of drought. This is exemplified by the generalised figures, which give one-third of the total rain falling in the wet quarter and one-fifth in the dry. These are only just above and below one-quarter, the fraction for equal distribution of rain through the year.

Fig. 40. The major climatic regions of North America

All these areas are within the influence of the trade winds for much of the year, but in southeast China there is a strong monsoonal effect on account of the very large size of the Asiatic continent. This causes the winter winds, which blow from the Asiatic high, to bring very dry air, with a resulting dry period (at Shanghai only one-tenth of the annual rain falls in the driest quarter). There is a complete reversal in wind direction in the summer, when there is low pressure in the interior of Asia and moist air is drawn in from the ocean (two-fifths of the annual rain falls in the summer quarter at Shanghai).

C 2

This is known as the *China type,* and although it has these monsoonal characteristics, it is not a true monsoon because of the cooler winters and the fact that the dry quarter is less dry than in the true wet-and-dry monsoon type.

The two selected stations are Pine Bluff, Arkansas, and Montevideo, Uruguay (Fig. 41). In spite of the fact that the former is 9° of latitude farther from the equator than is Montevideo, its mean annual temperature is as high (17° and 16°C) (63° and 61°F), although, being more distant from the sea, its annual range is twice as great as at Montevideo. Nearly one-third of the annual precipitation falls in the wettest quarter (early winter) in each case, and about

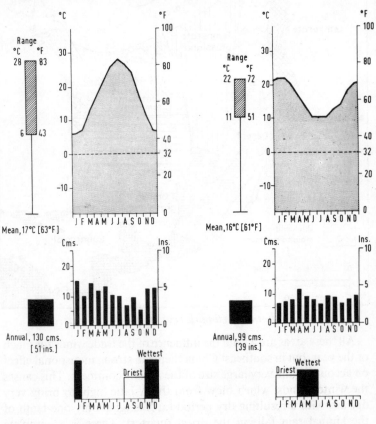

Pine Bluff, Arkansas, U.S.A. [Lat. 34°N.]   Montevideo, Uruguay [Lat. 25°S.]

Fig. 41. Humid subtropical climate – Data for Pine Bluff and Montevideo

one-fifth comes in the driest three months (autumn). There is thus no great variation of rain through the year, the wettest month being no more than twice as wet as the driest.

5. TROPICAL AND SUBTROPICAL GRASSLAND CLIMATE

Both the tropical grassland and the hot desert (which follows) are dominated by tropical continental air masses, Tc. These are generated over the great continental areas astride the Tropics of Cancer and Capricorn. They consist of warm to hot air with a very low humidity.

The tropical grassland climatic areas lie between the tropical wet-and-dry and the hot deserts, and thus stretch roughly latitudinally from Cape Verde to the Ethiopian highland, and from Benguela to Bulawayo across Africa, and in western Asia from near the Black Sea to the Persian Gulf. Because of the presence of the great mountain ranges of the Andes and Rockies, this climatic region lies more north-and-south in the Americas. In the States, it stretches from the coast in the northwest corner of the Gulf of Mexico northwards until it merges into the temperate grassland climatic belt. In South America, it reaches from Fortaleza in northeast Brazil to the Brazilian Plateau, and in Argentina it forms the western side of the Pampas. In Australia, the tropical grassland lies to the north of the hot desert climate and variants, the subtropical grassland and subtropical semiarid climates, lie to the east and south.

Only one sample station has been selected for this type (Fig. 42).

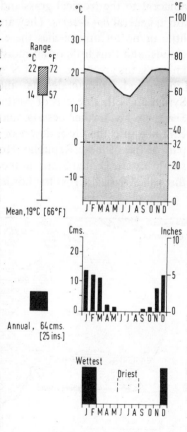

Bulawayo, Rhodesia [Lat. 21°S.]

Fig. 42. Tropical grassland climate – Data for Bulawayo

Bulawayo, Rhodesia, at 4,400 feet 1,300 metres) above sea-level, has a mean temperature of 19°C (66°F) with an annual range of 8°C (15°F). Its rainfall distribution is its important characteristic. Out of an annual precipitation of 25 inches (64 cm), 15 inches (38 cm) or 60 per cent fall in the wettest three months, summer, and none at all in the driest three, winter.

6. HOT DESERT CLIMATE

As source regions for continental tropical air masses, Tc, the areas adjacent to the tropical grasslands farther away from the equator are in general *hot deserts*. They are regions of high pressure, so that little or no air approaches these belts within the height range of clouds, and thus little or no moisture is brought to them. The best known is the great arid area of North Africa, comprising the Sahara, Libyan and Arabian deserts, and continuing eastwards into the Syrian and other deserts of Arabia. East and south of the Caspian Sea there are further deserts, and, with a slight break only, these continue into the Gobi desert of Mongolia and the northernmost part of the Chinese Republic. Hot deserts are also to be found in southwestern United States in the Great Basin, passing southwards through Arizona across the border into Mexico.

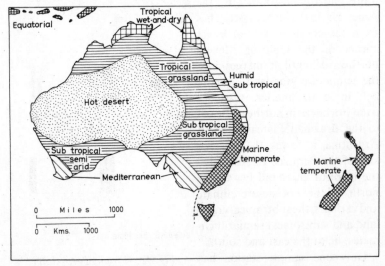

Fig. 43. The major climatic regions of Australia and New Zealand

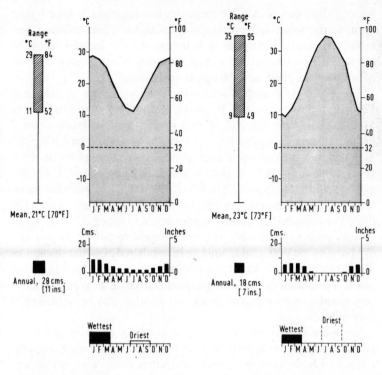

Fig. 44. Hot desert climate – Data for Alice Springs and Baghdad

Because of the lesser land masses in the southern hemisphere and the consequent greater influence of coastal climatic effects, deserts there are smaller. In South America, there is the desert area of Patagonia, as well as the small Atacama desert, which is mainly due to the high relief features of the Andes. The Kalahari of South Africa is well known but is not entirely devoid of vegetation and has the Namib desert on its western side. There are also the extensive desert regions of the interior of Australia.

The term *hot* is applied to all these deserts to distinguish them from the *cold deserts* of arctic regions. In the latter, the lack of vegetation is due to the low temperatures which virtually prohibit plant growth, whereas those just listed are all aridity deserts. Temperature is not only controlled by latitude, but is also influenced by the amount of cloud cover (as well as by several other factors), and in the arid

regions this being small, temperatures are in general a little higher
than in the lower-latitude tropical grassland climatic areas previously described. Mean annual temperature is around the 20°C
(about 70°F) level, but the annual variation becomes on the whole
about twice as great as for tropical grasslands.

The two type examples selected are Alice Springs in Northern
Territory, Australia, and Baghdad, Iraq (Fig. 44). The former
averages 11 inches (28 cm) of rain a year, and the latter about 7
inches (18 cm). Eleven inches is a very low rainfall indeed when the
high temperatures are taken into account. Alice Springs has January
as its hottest month 29°C (84°F), and July its coldest 11°C (52°F),
giving an annual range of 18°C (32°F). Baghdad, in the other hemisphere, has the reverse months for hottest and coldest, with 35°C
(95°F) in July and 9°C (49°F) in January, a range of 26°C (46°F).

With such a low rainfall, it is meaningless to talk of the wet and
dry parts of the year, and it must be remembered also that the figures
quoted for mean annual rainfall are only the averages for a period of
years. The actual fall is very irregular indeed. One year may have
considerably more than the mean, and another may be virtually dry
throughout.

These are areas of subsiding air, and adiabatic warming lowers the
relative humidity even further. This, coupled with the high temperatures, makes the potential evapotranspiration very high indeed and
always much more than the precipitation. Consequently the ground
is very dry, with little or no vegetation.

	4 Humid subtropical	5 Tropical grassland	6 Hot deserts
Mean annual temperature	20°C (70°F)	20°C (70°F)	20°C (70°F)
Annual range	10°C (20°F)	10°C (20°F)	10°C (20°F)
Annual rainfall	moderate 45 in. (115 cm)	small 25 in. (65 cm)	very low 5 in. (13 cm)
Wet·quarter contains*	one-third (late summer)	two-thirds (summer)	very irregular
Dry quarter contains*	one-fifth	very little	very little

Conversions are approximate only in this generalised table.
* Of the annual precipitation.

Fig. 45. Tropical Climates – Generalised typical characteristics

The tropical climates as a whole are summarised in the generalised characteristics table shown in Fig. 45. Although the generalised mean annual temperature is stated to be 20°C (about 70°F) in each case, in fact the tropical grasslands are a little cooler than either the humid subtropical or the desert climates. The amount of the annual range is significant. The humid subtropical has a rather even rainfall distribution throughout the year; the tropical grassland has very little in its driest quarter; and very little meaning can be attached to distribution of precipitation in the case of the hot deserts. The fundamental characteristic of the tropical climates is that they are all determined by tropical air masses alone, and in this they differ from both the equatorial and temperate groups which flank them on either side.

CHAPTER NINE

Temperate Climates

7. MEDITERRANEAN CLIMATE

IT is interesting to trace the various climatic regions in which famous civilisations of the past and present have been or are located. There has perhaps been a tendency to move through the millennia to cooler areas, and this may very well be linked with changes in mode of life, involving the progressive mastery of temperature control by clothing and the heating of buildings, and especially may it be linked to the change to industrialisation in the latest phase.

The type centre of the Mediterranean climate is naturally the Mediterranean itself, the heart of the Greek and Roman empires. It is one of the most distinctive of all climatic types, often described by the well-known phrases 'warm, wet winters' (the three w's), and 'hot, dry summers'. This is a fairly accurate description and the half-yearly change is due to the areas coming under the influence of different air masses.

In the winter half of the year, the Mediterranean areas are dominated by polar maritime air masses, Pm, and in the summer by tropical maritime, Tm. It might be thought that since both of these are maritime in origin, the distribution of precipitation would be fairly uniform over the twelve months, but in fact since the Pm masses move to lower latitudes, their lower layers are warmed and thus become unstable, so that instability rain results. On the other hand, the tropical masses moving polewards have their lower layers cooled and become very stable, with the result that precipitation is thereby inhibited. As already stated, the winters are cool and wet (half to three-quarters of the annual rain falls in the wettest three months of the year), and the summers are warm and dry (with one-twentieth of the annual total being a typical proportion).

The Mediterranean is located between the hot desert areas and the marine or continental temperate climates, and with the shift of the seasons it alternately acquires the characteristics first of the one and then of the other. During the winter it receives southwesterly winds (northern hemisphere) which bring with them the moisture that provides the winter rain, especially to those sections towards the west of the continents. In the summer, the polar air has moved northwards, to be replaced by the tropical maritime, with its great stability and consequent dryness.

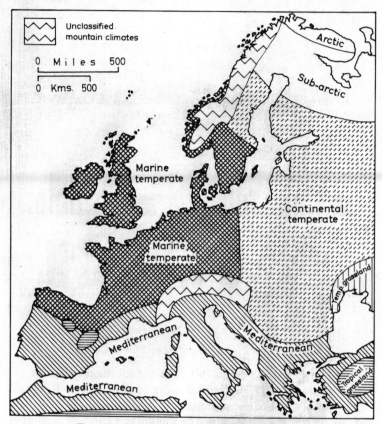

Fig. 46. The major climatic regions of Europe

This type of climate occurs in five areas in addition to the name area, the Mediterranean itself. The remaining areas are: the middle west coast of the United States, especially in the Californian valley; and, in the southern hemisphere, the middle west coast of Chile, the Cape Town to Port Elizabeth coast of South Africa, and around both Perth and Adelaide in Australia.

Rome and Perth (Australia) are the two localities selected as being typical (Fig. 47). These have hottest months with temperatures of 24° and 23°C (76° and 74°F): July and January; and coldest 7° and 13°C

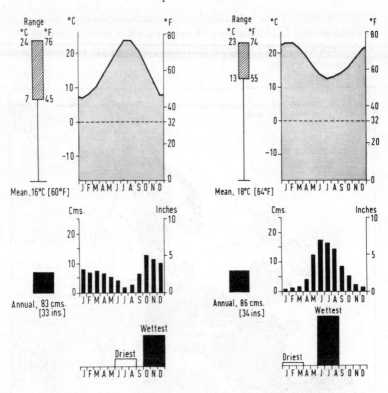

Rome, Italy [Lat. 42°N]   Perth, Australia [Lat. 32°S.]

Fig. 47. Mediterranean climate – Data for Rome and Perth

(45° and 55°F): January and July. The annual ranges are thus 17°
and 10°C (31° and 19°F). Perth is more equable than is Rome on
account of its immediate proximity to a large ocean mass, which
extends both north and south. The rainfall is 33 and 34 inches (83
and 86 cm) per annum respectively, with rather less than half during
the wettest quarter in Rome (October to December) and more than
half at Perth (June to August). In the driest months (summer), Rome
has about one-tenth of the annual total, and Perth about a twentieth.

8. MARINE TEMPERATE CLIMATE
(often known as cool temperate oceanic)

The three temperate climatic types now to be discussed are chiefly
distinguished by their relative proximity to the sea and the ameliorat-

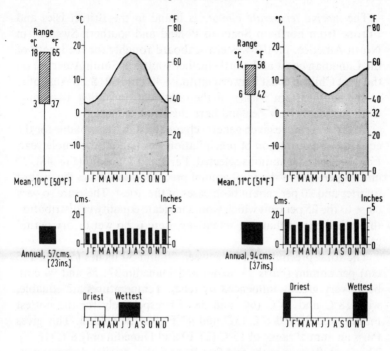

Paris, France [Lat. 48°N.]　　　　Dunedin, New Zealand [Lat. 46°S.]

Fig. 48. Marine temperate climate – Data for Paris and Dunedin

ing effects of onshore winds. With increasing distance from the coast, precipitation decreases and annual range of temperature increases. The three are thus distinguished as marine, continental and grassland climates, the last name indicating the relative absence of trees.

They are perhaps the most variable climates in the world both from point to point and from moment to moment, and the latter is especially the case with the marine temperate so that it has been said not to be a climate at all, but merely a succession of days with differing weather. This is due to the area being one where polar and tropical maritime air masses regularly meet and react with one another. Continental air masses of both polar and tropical origin are also (but less frequently) involved. These are the regions of depressions and anticyclones, where the weather forecast rarely extends for more than twenty-four hours ahead, and where long-range forecasting can be couched in nothing more than the very vaguest of terms.

The *marine temperate climate* is found in the British Isles and Europe from northern Spain to Poland and southern Sweden; in North America, on the western seaboard roughly for the length of the Canadian coast and a little farther south; in South America, on the west Chilean coast between latitudes 40° and 50° S; in Australia, in the southeastern corner of the continent, including Tasmania. Both islands of New Zealand have this same climate.

So far as it can be given general characteristics, it is notable for the equality of distribution of precipitation throughout the whole year. For the two type stations selected, Paris and Dunedin (Fig. 48), 27 and 28 per cent of the total annual precipitation falls in the wettest quarter and 20 per cent in both cases in the driest. These are so very close to the 25 per cent which would indicate equality of distribution through the year that one might say there is no wet or dry period at all.

The total precipitation is between 20 and 50 inches (50 and 125 cm) per annum (Paris 23 inches and Dunedin 37: 58 and 94 cm), being very greatly influenced by relief. Temperatures are equable, with 18°C and 14°C (64° and 58° F) respectively for the hottest month, and 3° and 6°C (37° and 42°F) for the coldest. This gives Paris an annual range of 15°C (27°F) and Dunedin only 8°C (16°F). This is a reflection of the fact that Paris is already slightly 'continen-

	Approximate distance from Atlantic	Mean annual temperature	Mean annual range of temperature	Mean annual precipitation
	miles (km)	°C (°F)	°C (°F)	inches (cm)
Valentia	nil	11 (51)	8 (15)	56 (142)
London	250 (400)	11 (51)	13 (24)	25 (64)
Paris	250 (400)	10 (50)	16 (28)	23 (58)
Hamburg	700 (1,100)	9 (48)	18 (38)	29 (74)*
Berlin	850 (1,350)	9 (48)	20 (36)	23 (58)
Vienna	900 (1,450)	9 (49)	22 (39)	25 (64)
Belgrade	1,200 (1,900)	11 (52)	24 (43)	24 (61)
Bucharest	1,500 (2,400)	11 (51)	26 (47)	23 (58)
Odessa	1,700 (2,700)	9 (49)	27 (48)	16 (41)
Astrakhan	2,500 (4,000)	9 (49)	32 (58)	6 (15)

Conversion, especially miles to kilometres, approximate.
* Additional precipitation from proximity of North Sea.

Fig. 49. The change from marine to continental climate across Europe talised' by being in the centre of its country instead of on the coast, and so is drier and slightly less equable. This tendency continues across Europe until the climate may be considered to have become continental.

The preceding table (Fig. 49) shows this effect. All the stations have a mean annual temperature between 9° and 11°C (48° and 52°F), and the increase in annual range coupled with decrease in annual precipitation as distance from the Atlantic becomes greater and greater is most striking. The distances given from the ocean in the first column are only approximate and there are occasional side influences such as proximity of the North Sea or the Mediterranean.

Depressions – Duplex Weather

The inconstancy of this marine temperate climate is due, as already stated, to these being areas where two air masses impinge upon one another, and where there may be said to be more or less constant warfare between them. The tropical mass is naturally considerably

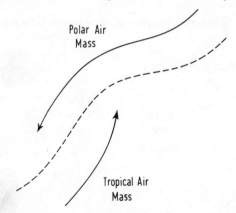

Fig. 50. Polar and tropical air masses converge

warmer than the polar, and consequently it tends to ride over the latter. This results in adiabatic cooling and thus precipitation. At the same time, the ground-level boundary between the two air masses tends to become curved in plan, with the warmer air within the concave side of the curve (Fig. 50). This becomes emphasised to the state shown in Fig. 51, and a *depression* is formed. The ground-level air streams within these masses are already moving in the directions shown by the arrows in Fig. 50, and the development of the curved

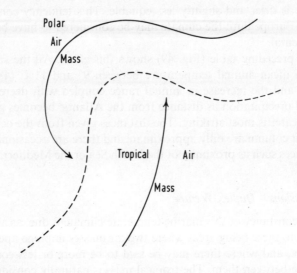

Fig. 51.   The second stage in the development of a depression

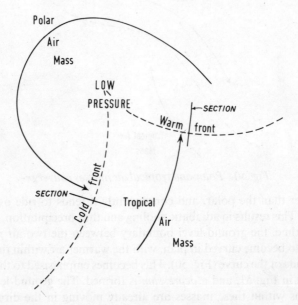

Fig. 52.   A fully developed depression

boundary results in their being deflected to produce a roughly circular pattern as shown in Fig. 51. This is the anticlockwise wind movement around the centre of a depression. The centre of the curve becomes sharpened, and is a centre of *low pressure*. The two sections of the boundary are now termed the *cold* and *warm fronts* respectively (Fig. 52). The diameter of the depression shown in Fig. 52 is normally of the order of 500 miles (800 km) when in western Europe.

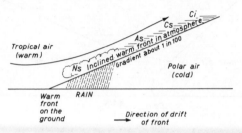

Fig. 53. Section through a warm front. In this diagram, as in Figs. 54–6, the gradient of the front is considerably exaggerated

The warm air in the *warm sector* crosses the boundary and immediately begins to ride over the cooler air. Figure 53 shows a section across this boundary drawn at the point indicated in Fig. 52, and from this it is seen that precipitation, generally in the form of rain, is produced just over the warm front. Much the same effect occurs at the cold front, due to the cool air burrowing underneath the warmer, and thus lifting the latter off the ground. Figure 54 shows a section through this, the position being located on Fig. 52. Again rain is produced on the cool side of the ground contact of the boundary.

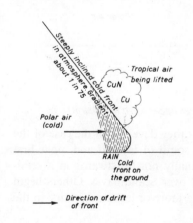

Fig. 54. Section through a cold front. (The CuN and Cu are often replaced by Ac, As and Ns cloud in Britain)

As these processes continue, more and more of the warm sector is lifted off the ground, until, when the cold and warm fronts meet, the depression is said to be *occluded*. The process continues even beyond this point, and the two volumes of cool air begin to overlap one another, the cooler of the two remaining on the ground and the other, slightly warmer, being lifted up. Figures 55 and 56 show the two types of such occluded depressions. In both cases there is a continuous area of rain.

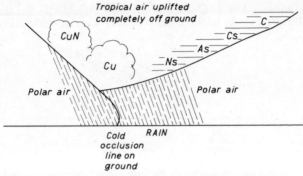

Fig. 55. An occluded depression (cold occlusion)

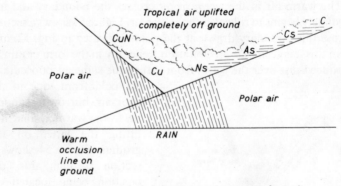

Fig. 56. An occluded depression (warm occlusion)

Depressions of this kind drift as they develop. In the case of the British Isles, they often originate south of Iceland and move first southeastwards, then east, and finally northeastwards in a semicircular arc until they are centred over Scandinavia. Others begin north of the Azores, and move in a more or less straight line to the same destination.

As a typical depression passes, the wind is first from the southeast, then, if the centre passes on the southern side of the observer, the wind becomes northeasterly and finally northerly, the weather probably remaining fairly dry throughout. If the centre passes on the northern side of the observer, the wind veers to become southwest and eventually northwest, and in the meantime there will be two periods of rain, as first the warm, and later the cold, front passes over. If the depression is occluded, there will be a longer and more severe period of rainfall. Between the passing of the warm and cold fronts, there will be a rise in temperature.

The term *duplex weather* may be used to indicate that two air masses are involved in its production. This contrasts with *simplex weather,* such as belongs to most of the other types of climate already described and also to the marine temperate on other occasions when only one air mass is involved, as will be described below.

There are endless varieties of duplex weather. Depression may follow depression, minor (secondary) depressions may develop within major ones, depressions may be of varying intensities, may be increasing in intensity or may be filling up. All these produce a multitude of weather types.

Anticyclones

Anticyclones may be described as produced by simplex weather conditions in the sense that they are occasions when only one air mass is present. This may be either the tropical maritime mass, Tm, which has moved a little northward from the Azores, producing a warm anticyclone or region of high pressure, or it may be polar air, producing a cold anticyclone.

A *warm anticyclone* over the British Isles generally coincides with a deep depression in Icelandic areas. It is a time of upper air convergence which brings air together at a faster rate than divergence at low levels can remove it. There is a general subsidence of air, and with this there is adiabatic warming and a decrease in relative humidity. Consequently precipitation is rare and temperatures are high at ground-level. The wide spacing of the isobars leads to very low wind velocities. This may lead to the formation of considerable *radiation fog,* which may only be two or three hundred feet (a hundred metres) deep, but which may be persistent in winter. In summer, there is sufficient heating to disperse it during the daytime. Summer heat waves in Britain are mostly periods of warm anticyclonic weather.

A *cold anticyclone* is due to the southerly drift of polar air and, unlike the warm anticyclone, is a shallow feature of the atmosphere so far as the cold conditions are concerned. At a height of something of the order of 2 miles (say, 3 kilometres) the 'lower than normal' temperature ceases, and above this level the anticyclone does not show itself in the upper air pressure charts. Cold anticyclones occur in Britain chiefly in winter, they very often more form a ridge than a circular area, winds are light, moving in a clockwise direction, with clear skies and low temperatures.

Snow and Frost

Temperate climates are ones in which the incidence of snow and frost tends to become important, and wherein extensive cloud cover, as well as fog is to be found.

The incidence of *snow* is very greatly influenced by relief. Ben Nevis (4,406 feet, 1,359 metres) has an average of 170 days a year with snow lying on the summit, but at low levels, the expectation in the Shetlands is 25 days per year, in northern England about 13, and in Cornwall 5. A map of amount of snowfall in such areas as the British Isles, northern Europe or the States, is almost the same as a contour map of the relief.

Frost too is important especially for certain crops which are killed off by it in the autumn. New growth may be destroyed by individual late frosts in spring. There are approximately 100 days per year with frost at Glasgow, and the same number occur in such widely scattered places as Northumberland, Cambridge and London. The importance of local variations, in this case the influence of sea, is shown by the fact that Clacton-on-Sea, a mere 50 miles (80 kilometres) from Cambridge, has only 60 frosts a year. The Channel Isles have as few as 27, and the Isle of Man 44. These may be compared with 240 days with frost each year along the U.S.–Canadian border, and approximately 200 days in Iowa (continental temperate climate).

In most of the marine temperate climate regions, the sky is more than two-thirds covered with cloud during the whole year.

9. CONTINENTAL TEMPERATE CLIMATE

The major distinction between the continental and marine temperate climates is that the former has a greater annual range of temperature, very often twice as large, either because it is far from the sea and its ameliorating effects, or because it does not experience onshore winds even if it be near the coast.

This climate is to be found therefore in two types of area. The major inland one comprises eastern Europe with a great tongue stretching far into Asiatic U.S.S.R. The eastern seaboard type occurs as most of the United States and Canada roughly between latitudes 40° and 50° N and east of about longitude 95° W. Most of Manchuria and Korea and some adjacent areas also have this climate.

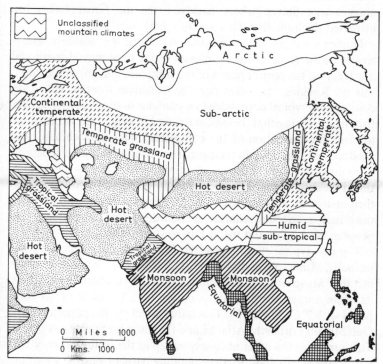

Fig. 57. The major climatic regions of Asia

These areas are under the influence of both polar continental, Pc, and tropical maritime, Tm, air masses, but there is somewhat less cyclonic development than in marine temperate climates. The two air masses often remain rather more distinct from one another, with the polar air generally dominating in the winter, and the tropical in the summer.

The American area of the continental temperate climate is under the influence of polar continental and maritime air through the whole year, the former having northern Canada as its main source region, and the latter originating over the North Atlantic Ocean. We have already seen that the tropical maritime, Tm, over the Caribbean Sea produces a humid subtropical climate in the southern States, but it may spread northward into the middle and northern States at any time and so produce warm, moist weather, or with convergence on the polar mass, produce depressional or duplex weather.

The polar air alone produces cold spells of weather in winter with clear skies and stable air. There is little precipitation excepting in the northeastern States, where passage over the Great Lakes has increased the humidity. This is anticyclonic weather.

Duplex or depressional weather occurs in the northern States largely as the result of the air masses which have moved south and north across the central plains of the continent and have met alongside the Rockies, very often near the Canadian frontier. Here they develop into typical depressions very similar to those described over Britain, excepting that, being continental in origin, they contribute towards the formation of the continental temperate climate, and produce less rain than do their maritime counterparts. Such depressions may start from almost any latitude of the States, but as already stated the commonest is near latitude 49° N. All travel southeast and then eastwards with an increasing northerly tendency, so that by the time they reach the Atlantic seaboard by far the majority are between New York and the St Lawrence estuary.

The two typical stations selected for this climatic type are Minneapolis, Minnesota and Moscow, U.S.S.R. (Fig. 58). In spite of the fact that Moscow is 11° of latitude farther north than Minneapolis, its mean annual temperature is only 3°C (5°F) lower (4° as compared with 7°C: 39°, 44°F). This is due largely to the presence of the Gulf Stream drift in the Atlantic and the warm air that passes over it. This produces the great northerly sweep in the isotherms over that part of the ocean and the corresponding parts of Europe which are under the influence of that air, and its effect reaches even as far east as Moscow. This is known as the *Gulf of Winter Warmth*. This is particularly important in winter, and we may contrast the mean January temperatures at Bergen, Norway and Churchill, Hudson Bay, both on latitude 60° N. They are 1°C (34°F) and −30°C (−22°F) respectively.

The warmest month at both selected stations is July, and the coldest January. Minneapolis reaches 22°C (72°F) in summer and Moscow 19°C (66°F). The coldest month has the same mean temperature, −11°C at both stations (Minneapolis 13° and Moscow 12°F). Thus the winters are very similar as regards temperature, but Moscow has the cooler summer.

The two stations are also very alike as regards precipitation. Minneapolis has 28 inches (71 cm) a year, and Moscow 21 inches

(53 cm). The wettest quarter is either in summer or late summer, and produces about two-fifths of the year's total. The driest is mid-winter, and has only about an eighth of the annual fall.

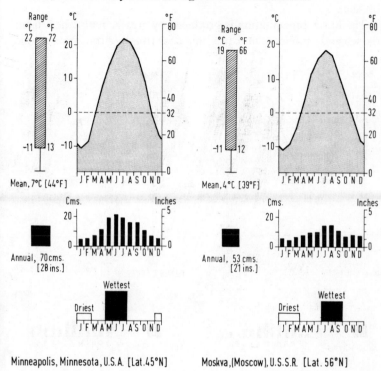

Minneapolis, Minnesota, U.S.A. [Lat. 45°N]   Moskva, (Moscow), U.S.S.R. [Lat. 56°N]

Fig. 58. Continental temperate climate – Data for Minneapolis and Moscow

This climatic type may therefore be considered to be closely related to the marine temperate, but is modified by the relative absence of marine effects, so that the temperature range is much greater and the precipitation is both less and less evenly distributed.

10. TEMPERATE GRASSLAND CLIMATE

This climatic type is dominated by prairie and steppe landscapes, although the drier portions tend towards semidesert. It is by far the driest of the temperate climates, although its temperature conditions are somewhat similar to those of the continental temperate. These grasslands are to be found between the Rockies and the continental temperate in America, in a small area in southern Argentina, and in a large area, generally to the south of the continental temperate climate, in U.S.S.R., stretching from the Black Sea to the very centre of Asia.

The lower precipitation is produced by greater remoteness from the sea and supplies of moisture, and it is virtually a transitional zone

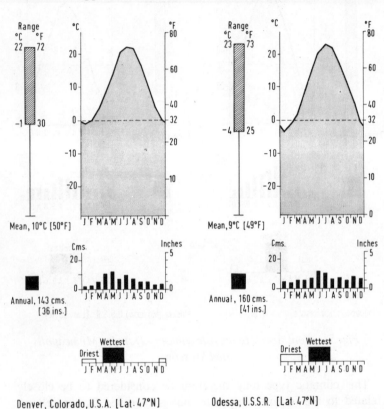

Denver, Colorado, U.S.A. [Lat. 47°N]   Odessa, U.S.S.R. [Lat. 47°N]

Fig. 59. Temperate grassland climate – Data for Denver and Odessa

between the continental temperate and the hot desert climates. In the States, the annual rainfall illustrates this. At the eastern edge of the zone, it is about 30 inches (75 cm) a year, and this falls off progressively to near 10 inches (25 cm) by the time the desert area is reached. This greatly influences the vegetation as will be seen in Chapter 36.

Like other temperate climates, it too is controlled by both polar and tropical air masses, but in this instance both are of continental

	7 Mediterranean	8 Marine temperate	9 Continental temperate	10 Temperate grassland
Mean annual temperature	15°C (60°F)	10°C (50°F)	7°C (45°F)	7°C (45°F)
Annual range	10°C (20°F)	10°C (20°F)	25°C (50°F)	25°C (50°F)
Annual precipitation	small	moderate	moderate	small
	20 in (50 cm)	30 in (75 cm)	25 in (60 cm)	20 in (50 cm)
Wet quarter contains*	one-half	one-quarter	two-fifths	one-half
	(winter)	(late summer)	(late summer)	(early summer)
Dry quarter contains*	one-twentieth	one-quarter	one-eighth	one-eighth
	(late summer)	(varies)	(winter)	(winter)

Conversions are approximate only in this generalised table.

* Of the annual precipitation.

Fig. 60. Temperate Climates – Generalised typical characteristics origin, Pc and Tc, and this again emphasises the dry conditions that prevail.

Two typical stations are Denver, on the eastern side of the Front Range of the Rocky Mountains at nearly 5,300 feet (1,600 metres), and Odessa, U.S.S.R. (Fig. 59). The low altitude of the latter, and its proximity to the Black Sea compensate for the fact that it is 7° of latitude farther north than Denver. Consequently their mean annual temperatures are 10° and 9°C (50° and 49°F) respectively, with the hottest month July in each case at 22° and 23°C (72° and 73°F), and the coldest January, at −1° and −4°C (30° and 25°F), producing annual ranges of 23° and 27°C (42° and 48°F). The total annual precipitation is 14 and 16 inches (36 and 41 cm) respectively, with early summer the wettest (just over half the year's total), and mid-winter the driest with about an eighth in each case.

The four temperate climates are summarised in the generalised table shown in Fig. 60, and this should be compared with the other similar tables in Figs. 39 and 45.

CHAPTER TEN

Arctic Climates

11. SUBARCTIC CLIMATE

The great width of the northern part of America and Eurasia results in huge areas of land which are far from the sea and which become very cold in winter, with the ground covered with frozen snow and therefore dry. These two areas thus become the source areas for the so-called polar continental air masses, Pc (the word *polar* as already explained on p. 42, being something of a misnomer). This air is dry, very cold and stable. It is a region of light winds and little cloud, although a certain amount occurs in summer.

One area of the subarctic climate stretches from the southern half of Alaska, across Canada south of Hudson bay, and into Labrador. Newfoundland falls into this type, although greatly modified from the typical examples, on account of its insular nature and the consequent moderating effect of the neighbouring ocean. The second area occupies most of the northern half of Finland, and, from somewhat south of the White Sea, it is bounded on its southern side by a line which lies diagonally between latitudes 60° and 50° N, so that, passing a little north of Omsk, it roughly follows the Mongolian frontier and continues to Kamchatka.

The data for the two selected typical stations tell their own stories (Fig. 61). These two localities, one, Eagle, on the frontier between Alaska and Canada, and the other, Yakutsk, in the eastern centre of Asiatic U.S.S.R., have mean annual temperatures of −4° and −11°C (24° and 12°F) respectively, with hottest months July at 15° and 19°C (59° and 66°F). The coldest is January at −26° and −43°C (−15° and −46°F), giving a mean annual range at Eagle of 41°C (74°F) and 62°C (112°F) at Yakutsk. These tremendous ranges, coupled with the absolute coldness of the winters, are sufficient to distinguish this particular climate from all others. It is one in which the continental nature of the thermal régime is most pronounced.

The total precipitation is light in both instances, with 11 inches (28 cm) a year at Eagle and 14 inches (36 cm) at Yakutsk. These figures are in water equivalent, for naturally most of the fall is in the

D   89

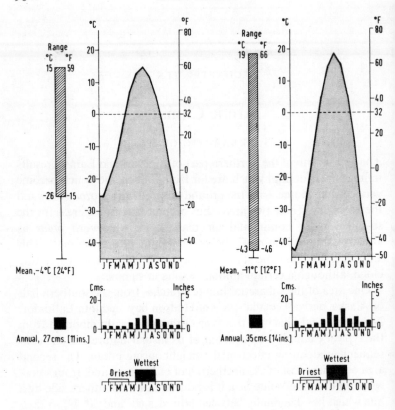

Eagle, Alaska [Lat. 65°N.]   Yakutsk. U.S.S.R. [Lat. 62°N.]

Fig. 61. Subarctic climate – Data for Eagle and Yakutsk

form of snow, the greatest amount being in the summer, when just about half the annual amount falls in three months. There is very little snowfall indeed in the winter. The 'driest' quarter is late winter, and in both localities these receive in all one-tenth of the annual total.

12. ARCTIC CLIMATE

The northernmost part of U.S.S.R. and the northern part of Canada, as well as almost the whole of Greenland, experience a climate which is colder still in the summer, but whose winters are often warmer than the extreme continental type of the subarctic climate. Even at this high latitude this is partly due to the closer proximity of the sea, and also because of the effect of the near-by polar air mass. These regions largely lie within the arctic circle, and thus they experience the curiosity of continuous daylight in summer with the opportunity of continuous sunshine, and the dread of the equally continuous night-time of winter.

The result of this is that Spitsbergen, for example, cools continuously from July, the warmest month at 6°C (42°F), until the beginning of the following March, by which time the temperature has fallen as low as −19°C (−2°F). For the whole winter there is no sunshine to provide any warming effect whatever. Then quite quickly the daylight period becomes long, and soon it stretches through the twenty-four hours of each day. This means there is no night-time to cause a daily cooling period, and the (admittedly low-powered) Sun shines continuously, to provide a summer temperature as high as 6°C (42°F). This produces an annual range of 24°C (44°F) with a somewhat unusually shaped curve.

Precipitation, almost wholly in the form of snow, is light (equivalent to 12 inches (30 cm) of water per annum), and mostly falls in the winter.

13. POLAR CLIMATE

Apart from the fact that it is cold throughout the year, with the temperature always below zero centigrade and with extremely cold winters, little is known of the actual polar climate. No long-period records have been kept, although the existence of the polar air masses may well have a very considerable influence on climates some distance away. The centre of Greenland is a continuous ice cap, and this constitutes a polar climate even though it stretches southwards beyond the arctic circle.

The generalised summary for the arctic climates is given in Fig. 62.

Permafrost is a characteristic of the ground condition in arctic regions. This is the state when the ground-water is frozen within the soil and never thaws, even during the summer. When there is a slight surface thaw there is still permafrost below. Although the upper-most yard (metre) of the regolith (see p. 111) in Spitsbergen thaws out during the summer, there is still permafrost below. The great depth of permafrost has the useful effect of rendering the coal-mines of Spitsbergen perfectly dry, since all water within the rock is frozen. The walls, floor and roofs of the passages in these mines are all wonderfully white from a thick layer of frost as the ventilation air is cooled below its dew-point by the cold rock.

In most cases the depth of the *lower* surface of permafrost is unknown. It is certainly greater than 1,000 feet (300 metres) over most of the arctic climate areas, and the region of permanently frozen subsoil extends well into the subarctic zone, although there in most cases the surface itself thaws during the summer. The existence of permafrost is of first importance both in the weathering of rocks and in the control of vegetation.

	11 Subarctic	12 Arctic
Mean annual temperature	−1°C (30°F)	−7°C (20°F)
Annual range	35°C (60°F)	25°C (45°F)
Annual precipitation	small	small
	10 in. (25 cm)	10 in. (25 cm)
Wet quarter contains*	half (summer)	two-fifths (winter)
Dry quarter contains*	one-eighth (early summer)	one-eighth (summer)

Conversions are approximate only in this generalised table.
* Of the annual precipitation.

Fig. 62. Arctic Climates – Generalised typical characteristics

CHAPTER ELEVEN

Changing Climates

THE location and character of the various types of climate described in the previous chapters have not always been the same as they are at the present time. The single fact that there have been ice ages during the last half million years demonstrates the far greater extent of the cooler regions at those times, with a somewhat lower temperature in the remaining areas, and a compression of the climatic belts between the glaciated parts and the tropics.

Not only did these climatic changes lead to a great increase in areal dimensions of the ice cover, they also led to an equally large increase in ice volume, with a consequent shortage of water in the oceans and a lowering of ocean-level, as is described in Chapter 28. The changes in temperature modified the weathering processes on land, and the lowered sea-level extended the river courses over the newly exposed coastal land and often led to rejuvenation. Clearly too, the vegetation zones moved their location farther from the poles, so that, for example, southern England and northern France acquired a periglacial type of vegetation.

The reasons for these and other changes, even sometimes to warmer climates than the present, are still by no means determined, and the whole subject is one of divergent views and controversy. This mainly arises from the complexity of the series of variables which bring about the final climatic result.

It is not even firmly established whether a general rise in temperature or a lowering is required to initiate an ice age. A rise in temperature greatly accelerates evaporation from the ocean surface, and this leads to increased cloudiness, which, while producing greater precipitation, which is certainly necessary to initiate an ice cover, nevertheless also leads to decreased cooling of the land or ice surface because of the cloud blanket, and this might prevent the increase or even the continued existence of the ice. On the other hand, the increased cloud might greatly reduce the amount of insolation reaching the surface and thus reduce the melting of any ice that existed.

The difficulties are at once apparent. The whole climatic complex is a matter of very delicate balance between a considerable number of interacting factors, and a slight change in any one of them sets up a whole series of following changes, in a kind of chain reaction, which may eventually even react back to the initial stage in a cyclic kind of way. No doubt it is something similar to this which causes the great fluctuations of weather that are more noticeable in some parts of the world than in others.

Climates are changing even today. It is known that during the sixty years prior to about 1940, air temperatures have been rising at least in Europe and possibly throughout the world more or less continuously, so that during that period they have become about half a degree centigrade warmer throughout the year (with about twice as much increase in the winter season). There is some evidence that this rise has now ceased, but this is not certain. During the same period, almost every glacier shrank in size, so that it is normal to find recently abandoned terminal moraines beyond the present limits of the ice. It has been calculated that the area of ice in Switzerland has reduced by a quarter in the same period.

Ocean-level is slowly rising, probably as the result of melting ice, although the possibility of tectonic changes affecting the depths of the ocean floor cannot be ruled out.

All these changes are very slow, and precise measurements of temperature, ocean-level and so on, have generally not been made over a sufficiently long period to give a certain picture.

More is known about the changes which have occurred over much longer periods of time. It is possible to determine past temperatures by the record of types of vegetation to be found in bogs and the like, and it is also possible to make a direct determination of the temperature prevailing at the time when certain organic remains were living by the ratio of various oxygen isotopes. It seems likely that during the Upper Cretaceous and the Eocene, temperatures in Europe and the States were about 12° to 15°C (21° to 27°F) warmer than they are today. A decline set in about the middle of the Oligocene, which accelerated during the Miocene and Pliocene, so that by the end of the latter, temperatures were almost the same as at present.

During the Pleistocene, temperatures fell some 9°C (16°F) lower than the present during each glaciation. The amount of this fall in temperature varied with the intensity of each individual period.

The last ice sheet more or less completed its decay in Britain about 12,000 years ago, with short glaciers remaining in the cirque hollows on mountain sides until approximately 8500 B.P.[1] In the meantime, rock hollows in the Lake District and other mountain areas became lakes. This was followed by a continued rise of temperature to the warmest period since the decay of the ice, known as the *climatic optimum*. It coincides with the highest post-glacial sea-level, the Tapes stage of Scandinavia or the Flandrian or Hillhouse stage of western Europe and Britain. This was about 6000 B.P.

In historic times, the Roman period appears to have begun with a slightly warmer climate than today, deteriorating later. There have been frequent warmer and cooler periods since, with much of the fourteenth, fifteenth and sixteenth centuries slightly warmer than now; the seventeenth century distinctly cooler, and a brief period of warmth in the mid-eighteenth, followed by a cooler period which seems to have ceased about 1850. Throughout Norway, there are marked terminal moraines far beyond the present glacier limit, and these are known to date from 1740 and 1830 respectively, the latter not marking so great an extent of ice as the former.

[1] B.P. = years before the present.

Part Three

Weathering and Rivers

CHAPTER TWELVE

Weathering

THE term *weathering* has acquired a technical meaning and does not simply refer to the action of the weather upon rocks. It is conveniently, although somewhat arbitrarily, used in contrast with the term *erosion,* and perhaps the simplest distinction is to say that in weathering the agent performs its action merely by being present, whereas in erosion it does so primarily as the result of its movement. Thus more or less stationary air, water and ice are weathering agents, but when they act because they are moving so as to be wind, rivers, waves, currents, glaciers and so on, they are erosive agents.

Thus somewhat curiously, wind is excluded from weathering, and perhaps equally incongruously is the inclusion of the destructive action of plant roots, etc.

Weathering processes may broadly be divided into *physical* and *chemical.* The various processes of physical weathering may in turn be placed in two groups – those resulting from temperature changes, and those resulting from fluctuations in the water content of rocks.

FREEZE–THAW

(a) *Block Production*

One of the most important of these processes is known as *freeze-thaw.* Ice has a 9 per cent larger bulk than the water from which it was formed, and thus a water-filled joint or other crack in a rock is widened by that amount on freezing. When thaw follows, there is room for additional water, which in turn produces further widening of the joint when freezing occurs again.

The more frequently the temperature of the rock crosses the freezing point, the more effective this process is, assuming that water is present. If no rebound occurs on melting, and if the whole of the expansion takes place sideways and not along the length of the joint, the width of the crack is given by the formula $1 \cdot 09^n w$, where n is the number of times the water has frozen and thawed, and w is the original width. This shows that a crack could be widened to a little

99

Fig. 63. Joints widened by freeze-thaw action

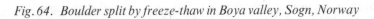

Fig. 64. Boulder split by freeze-thaw in Boya valley, Sogn, Norway

Fig. 65. Felsenmeer *on the slopes of the Hardangerjokul, Norway*

more than double its original width by ten freeze-thaws. Figure 63 shows joints that have been widened in this way, and Fig. 64 shows a block about 5 feet (1·5 metres) high that has been split in two by this process.

Freeze-thaw is most important in climates which have a large number of cold nights with temperatures below, and days with temperatures above, 0°C. In such climates the small amount of water required is generally available. It is ineffective in very cold polar climates, since thaw is infrequent, and in tropical regions, since freeze is equally rare. It is probably the most effective of all weathering agents in temperate climates, such as those of western Europe, including Britain, and of much of northern United States and southern Canada.

Eventually the joint may be widened sufficiently to detach the piece of rock from the mountain mass, and it may then be in such a location that it will tumble down the slope under the action of gravity. In this way, scree or talus slopes are formed (see figures in Chapter 14). A fairly gentle slope prevents or at least hinders dispersal of the fallen blocks, and the ground may then merely obtain a scatter of boulders. Such an area is generally given the German term *felsenmeer,* and this is seen in Fig. 65, where no solid rock is visible, and boulders of all sizes are scattered with no particular orientation.

Note their angular shape – corrasion has not yet begun their rounding.

The process is sometimes known as *frost action*, but this is an unfortunate term, since it has no connection with frost excepting that it may well often occur on a frosty night, simply because frost and freeze-thaw both require somewhat similar climatic conditions.

(b) *Granular Disintegration*

An even more effective type of freeze-thaw occurs with porous rocks when the whole volume, impregnated with water, freezes and subsequently thaws. This needs to occur only a few times with an individual rock before complete disintegration occurs. The previously solid rock mass breaks up into a granular heap, which is soon washed away after the next rainstorm. This occurs with artificial stone such as concrete road-kerbs if they are porous.

FROST-HEAVING

Frost-heaving is a phenomenon that is closely related to granular disintegration, inasmuch as it also is caused by the freezing of water, which on this occasion saturates a sand or clay soil. Being already unconsolidated, the increase in volume results in a rise in the level of the ground surface. Gates then scrape on ground which they normally just clear as they swing, and roadways are heaved up several inches into irregularities which greatly inconvenience traffic. For this reason, concrete and tar macadam pavings are often unsatis-

Fig. 66. Frost-heaved road near Oslo

Fig. 67. Stone polygons on low ground in Spitsbergen

factory in regions where freeze extends several feet deep in the winter. Figure 66 shows a main road only a few miles from Oslo in the condition to which it had deteriorated by the time of spring thaw. In such localities, pressed stone roads are usual, and when thaw comes road-scrapers can easily level out the ridges that remain. This effect is particularly bad where the ground is formed of clay, because of its high retention of water and consequent large expansion on freezing. On important highways that cross clay soils, it is now usual to excavate the clay to a depth below the limit of winter freeze, and refill with irregular stone blocks between which drainage will be easy. Very little heaving then occurs.

Patterned ground, such as is shown in Fig. 67, is thought to occur by the same processes. Winter freeze lifts the ground irregularly and at the same time the frozen surface, probably snow-covered, is slippery and any stones thereon slide down-slope to become concentrated in the hollows, and so produce a rough hexagonal pattern. The hexagons seen in this figure are about four feet across. The ground between is clay, and the individual stones are mostly about 2 inches (5 cm) across. The clay sinks, by decrease in volume, as the ice within it turns to water in the summer, so that the stones are then upstanding by a few inches. Such phenomena occur in glacial and periglacial areas and at altitudes above 3,000 feet (900 metres) in cool temperate climates.

ARIDITY SHRINKAGE

Variations in the water content of porous rocks and soils often have important effects. Swelling occurs with the presence of the water, and shrinkage during dry periods. The shrinkage may produce cracks such as are shown in Fig. 68 penetrating the surface of a mud, and these provide conditions favourable to freeze-thaw, gravitational break-up and erosive removal. They are sometimes known as *desiccation cracks*.

Shale rocks contain a large clay fraction, and this may swell and contract alternately by wetting and drying, so that it breaks off in thin flakes. Cliffs of shale rocks such as occur at Robin Hood's Bay, Yorkshire, continually rain small pieces of rock down to the beach below by this process.

THERMAL FLUCTUATIONS

Alternate expansion and contraction due to temperature changes, especially when confined to the outer layers of rock, may often produce breakdown in the rock itself without the aid of water. This process is termed *exfoliation,* and results in a thin skinlike layer of rock peeling off the general mass. When the rock is relatively free from joints, and especially if it is igneous and thus not stratified in the usual sense, this peeling may develop an onionlike pattern (see Fig. 69), and result in rounded forms. The knobs seen here are about 5 feet (1·5 metres) across.

Fig. 68. Aridity cracks in alluvial clay

Fig. 69. Exfoliation peeling in a glacial climate, Mjolfjell, Norway

There has been dispute as to whether this is in fact actually due to temperature changes. Laboratory experiments, in which rocks were subjected to rapid and considerable alternation of heat and cold, failed to produce any exfoliation until the cooling was accompanied by a water-spray, and it has been suggested that some chemical action also occurs. It is, however, difficult to imagine how water on the rock surface can lead to a slab of rock several inches thick peeling off an unjointed mass as does often happen, other than by producing spot-cooling and thus uneven contraction and stresses which are sufficiently strong to break the rock.

There is no doubt that exfoliation, that is onion-peeling, does occur, whether or not it is purely an effect of a temperature gradient within the rock. Exfoliation domes are found in a wide variety of climates. The Sugar Loaf Mountain of Rio de Janeiro is an oft-quoted example within the tropics, but there are several fine examples in many temperate climates such as Jodalsnuten, 3,070 feet (936 metres), near Stalheim, Norway (Fig. 240). The detail example illustrated in Fig. 69 is situated in a subarctic climate immediately adjoining a glacier.

There is, of course, also always the possibility that some apparent exfoliation owes its origin to load release.

LOAD RELEASE FEATURES

Another type of physical breakdown is due to unloading. Rocks that were formed at considerable depths below the surface (and thus particularly plutonic rocks) were produced under considerable pressure, and it is easy to visualise that when this is released by the removal of the load by erosion, the rock may expand and so crack to form joints.

The same applies to sedimentary rocks that have been subjected to considerable pressure by further deposition above them. This often happens, and for example the Cambrian, Ordovician and Silurian rocks of central Wales totalled nearly seven miles in thickness. The lower members of such a series may well be expected to develop joints in precisely the same way, when pressure is later removed by erosion.

SOLUTION WEATHERING

Solution weathering lies on the borderline between physical and chemical weathering. The phrase is often quite incorrectly given to some types of chemical weathering, but it should be confined to those instances where the rock passes into solution in water without chemical modification. It is clear that only certain rocks, chiefly *evaporites* such as anhydrite, gypsum and rock salt, are soluble in this way. As a weathering process this now chiefly occurs in semi-arid regions, since in humid regions any such surface deposits have already been washed away.

CHEMICAL WEATHERING

Chemical weathering involves actual chemical change. The product is generally soluble in water, and thus the chemical change is fol-

Fig. 70. Grikes and clints and surface chemical weathering above Malham Cove, Pennines

lowed by solution. The best known is the weathering of limestone. The calcium carbonate is converted by carbon dioxide in rainwater into calcium bicarbonate. Calcium bicarbonate is soluble in water. Thus rainwater removes limestone.

Limestone is a non-porous rock although it is highly permeable. This is because it is well-jointed and surface water can enter the rock by way of the joints. Most removal of rock occurs where most water passes, and thus the joints are widened, their exposed edges are rounded and the well-known pattern of *grikes* (= widened joints) is produced, with *clints*, the remaining limestone, between. Notice that the widening of the joints in this instance is accomplished by the actual removal of rock and not, as with freeze-thaw, by the movement of the rock.

It very often happens, as is the case in Fig. 70, that the weathering is of two types. Besides the widened joints already described, there are also smooth concavities and flutings on the top surface of the *pavement*. Such concentrations of water as would be required to produce this pattern could only have been obtained whilst the rock was covered by soil, which, while permitting it, would at the same time slow down the movement of water. Subsoil weathering also occurs with granite in much the same way, as is described below.

In limestone regions, it is usual for almost the whole of the rainfall to pass underground and extensive caverns are produced by this chemical weathering (see Chapter 15).

Other varieties of chemical weathering tend to be somewhat complex, since in most cases they are in fact composed of a series of reactions which follow one another. *Hydration* occurs when water is adsorbed in the form of water of crystallisation; *hydrolysis* involves the use of water to form a hydroxide; the hydroxide is usually then converted into a carbonate by the carbonic acid in rainwater (this is *carbonation*); *oxidation* involves atmospheric oxygen, but hydration and hydrolysis are almost always associated with it.

The importance of all these reactions is that the products are either soluble in water, or that the parent rock is broken down into granular form, either because the whole product is much larger in size than the original, or because some of the minerals present have expanded by their change whilst others have not. The mosaic no longer fits, and so it collapses. This is the case with granite, where by a series of reactions, the felspar is converted into clay, and the quartz and mica fall apart, even though they have not themselves been altered. Fig. 71 shows a granite boulder one foot (30 cm) in diameter that has been completely disintegrated in this way, and Fig. 72 shows more or less isolated granite blocks that are all that remain of a former continuous mass. Besides vertical flutings, there are often groovings on the top surfaces of granite, supporting the

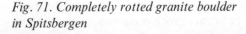

Fig. 71. Completely rotted granite boulder in Spitsbergen

*Fig. 72. Granite mountain topography in the Black Hills,
South Dakota*

idea that the decay occurred beneath a cover of soil in the same way
as with the limestone shown in Fig. 70.

Tors almost certainly afford a somewhat similar example of subsoil rot. They are upstanding masses of rounded and dissected
granite forms particularly well known on Dartmoor, although they
occur in many other localities. These could not have obtained their
present pattern by means of sub-aerial weathering or erosion. Wide
joint-spacing slowed down the chemical decay of the tors, close
joint-spacing encouraged the decay of the areas between them, and
normal mass wastage and sheet erosion have removed the rotted
material, leaving the tors themselves now projecting above the
general surface.

The tor seen in Fig. 73 is Bismarck Rock at Mwanze on the edge
of Lake Victoria, Tanzania. It is a perfect example of this kind of
feature. The rotting occurred whilst the tor was covered, rejuvenation removed the material (which was much more fully rotted
because of close jointing) from above and around it, and later Lake

Fig. 73. Bismarck Rock granite tor, Lake Victoria

Victoria came into existence and partially drowned it, so as to form an island.

It is possible to find tors whose granite is in various states of decay, and quarrying near Princetown, Dartmoor, has exposed buried granite which is so rotted that it crumbles at a touch. If this were to have become exhumed naturally, it would soon have collapsed completely, and clearly it is an example of advanced decay. These are probably the conditions which prevailed at one time between the existing tors.

Tors may also occur in rocks other than granite. There are torlike features in sandstone in parts of the Pennines where great crags of rock may project from the relatively steep hill slope. These have almost certainly developed in quite a different way, probably by the discontinuous erosion of a resistant layer of rock which otherwise would have stood out as a kind of shelf along the hill side.

The various chemical processes all require the presence of water, and thus they scarcely occur at all in deserts, whether these be hot tropical deserts, or frozen polar regions. The rate at which chemicals react is controlled both by temperature and by concentration. Reactions generally proceed faster at higher temperatures.

The most important attacking chemical is dilute carbonic acid in the shape of rainwater. At 25°C (76°F) 0·8 cc of carbon dioxide will dissolve in 1 cc of water, but at a temperature just above freezing as much as 1·7 cc will so dissolve. This means that in localities very near 0°C rainwater is twice as strong a solution of carbonic acid as it is in tropical regions. This additional concentration just more than counteracts the slowing down in the reaction rate because of the low temperature. Thus the effectiveness of rainwater as carbonic acid is very nearly the same in all climates where it occurs.

REGOLITH

The sum total of these various ways in which massive solid rock is broken into pieces of varied size by weathering processes is to produce a layer of unconsolidated material which covers the larger part of the land surface of the Earth. This is known as the *regolith*.

Besides this weathered rock that is still more or less in its original position, the regolith includes other loose material comprising the products of erosion and transportation, such as aeolian, fluvial, glacial and marine deposits of all kinds, including loess, alluvium, boulder clay (till), beach material and so on. Essentially all these are parts of the original regolith that have been moved a greater or lesser distance from their place of formation, and in general they have been modified by rounding, fracture, etc., so reducing their calibre during their journey. Much of the regolith may have existed as such for millions of years, and during that period may well have been moved from place to place many times. If it were possible to learn the story of a single grain of sand, it would indeed be a fascinating and involved tale.

Regolith is often considered to include organic substances that have been derived from plants and animals living upon it, but it is better to consider this to be a *soil*, especially when it has remained in one locality for a sufficient length of time to develop a definite stratification within itself (see Chapter 33).

CHAPTER THIRTEEN

Mass Movement

ONLY a small fraction of the total land surface, even in a district well provided with rivers, is occupied by channelled, flowing water. The movement of the regolith on the intervening areas is by means of one of the processes known under the collective title of *mass movement*.

In all cases, mass movement is downhill and obtains its energy from gravity. With a particular gradient, the principle factors which accelerate the rate at which the actual movement occurs are those that serve to reduce frictional forces, mostly by way of lubrication. Mass movement can in fact take place at almost any rate, but in practice it is convenient to divide it into two types, the first, which may be termed *creep*, in which the movement is so slow that repetitive surveys over a period of years are often the only way of detection, and the second, termed *slip*, where the movement is so fast that it may often deserve the description *catastrophic*.

CREEP

Creep, although slow, is virtually continuous in one form or another, often within the whole mass of the regolith, so that the total movement is great in magnitude and therefore importance. It may broadly be classified as either *soil creep, sheet wash* or *solifluction* (see Fig. 74).

(a) *Soil Creep*

This refers to slow downhill movement by downwash by moving water. It may be confined to the surface layers, or it may permeate the whole thickness of the regolith.

Surface creep occurs after every shower of rain, when water moves downhill on the surface and drags individual grains of soil, or, by removing soil from the downhill sides, enables small stones to topple or slip a little way. By this type, different parts of the surface move at different rates, due to local ease or difficulty, and so at the accumulation points small terracettes may be formed. An example of micro-terracettes is shown in Fig. 75, where the carex gives the scale, being bent over by the downwash from a recent rainstorm.

Terracettes may become much larger than those seen in this illustration, and Fig. 76 gives an example from the Pennines. The rock beneath is Carboniferous Limestone, and although it is possible that the terracettes may sometimes image a stepped rock face behind, this is not necessarily the case. When artificial stripping prior to

MASS MOVEMENT

Creep
a Soil creep
b Sheet wash
c Solifluction

Slip
a Mass boulder slip *or* scree collapse
b Mud flow
c Straight shear slope-collapse
d Rotational shear slope-collapse
e Subsidence

Fig. 74. The principal types of mass movement

quarrying exposes the rock surface, this normally turns out to be a fairly smooth slope whose minor irregularities bear no relationship to the terracettes that lay upon it.

Water percolating within the mass of the regolith may drag individual grains of soil along with it. Since there is no free passage, this is a slow process, but nevertheless it is of very considerable magnitude when the total is considered. Vegetation reduces the rate of both these processes.

Fig. 75. Micro-terracettes on a hill slope near Finse, Norway

Fig. 76. Terracettes near Bakewell, Derbyshire, England

Sporadic movement of material of larger calibre may be a secondary result of soil creep. Pebbles and boulders creep chiefly by the removal of smaller material from their down-gradient side, so that they slip or topple. Each individual move is so short that little momentum is gained.

(b) *Sheet Wash*

In monsoon and other areas of heavy downpours, it is normal for the regolith to become temporarily saturated, and all further rain thus remains on the surface. It is no rare occurrence for the whole area of a fairly gentle slope to be covered by a continuous sheet of water, even several inches in depth, flowing downhill at sufficient speed to erode and transport large quantities of the fine material. Such mass movement is known as *sheet wash* or *sheet flood,* and is of major importance in many regions far outside the tropics, in fact it is considered by some to be the dominant factor in the production of smooth slopes in most parts of the world, including semi-arid areas and those which have a temperate climate. Further comment will be made on these points in the next chapter.

(c) *Solifluction*

This form of mass movement occurs when the surface soil thaws out for a few inches in depth after it has previously been frozen. The top soil then retains all its surface moisture, since the underlying material is still ice-bound and is thus impermeable. The result is a downhill movement of this top material *en masse* over the well-lubricated smooth, iced layer below. A wet ice surface is virtually frictionless, and a slope as gentle as three degrees is sometimes sufficient to promote solifluction. It is common in mountainous parts of Britain, but more important in slightly colder climates. Although it accounts for the movement of large volumes of material, it is invariably too slow to be discerned without measurement.

Solifluction deposits characteristically show little rounding of the individual pieces (see Fig. 77). There is generally a rough orientation which gives some appearance of stratification, and where the material has met a hollow, or where it has been deflected by projecting, immobile boulders or outcrops of solid rock, it may be *festooned*. Solifluction deposits are generally known in Britain as *head*, although when composed of chalk rubble the term most often used is

Fig. 77. *Solifluction deposit near Cader Idris, Wales. Total height shown is about 3 feet (1 metre)*

combe rock (also spelt *coombe rock*). The American term *congelitur-bate* is almost synonymous.

Visual evidence of one or more of these various types of movement is often provided on pasture hillsides, where a contour wall may act as a barrier and collect material on its uphill side, where as a result the wall appears to be quite low, but has a high drop on the downhill side.

SLIP OR CATASTROPHIC MOVEMENT

As is the case with most classifications, the two categories of mass movement merge into one another. On the whole, slip is discontinuous, but when it does occur many thousands of tons of material move a considerable distance in a short time – in minutes or at the most in a few hours.

Such movements might almost come under the term *avalanche,* but strictly this should be restricted to snow slips. These true avalanches have several causes. They may occur when snow on a steep slope slips because of a reduction in friction between it and the ground or other snow beneath. If a mountain-slope is snow-covered, and a slight thaw occurs, followed by a re-freeze, and another storm brings further snow, this upper layer of snow is particularly liable to slip on the thin, virtually frictionless sheet of ice that separates the two layers. Alternatively, spring melt may allow water to percolate beneath the snow and so remove the friction by lubrication.

Another type of avalanche is due to overloading. More and more snow falls or is blown on to the slope, until eventually the weight is greater than the frictional forces can resist and the whole mountain-side of snow comes roaring down into the valley.

Some slopes are more susceptible to snow avalanches than others, and the local inhabitants are usually well versed as to which are the danger areas, and when weather conditions that are likely to promote such falls are prevailing. It often happens that a slight movement, such as the passage of a skier, may be sufficient to trigger off a great avalanche.

This brief account serves to illustrate the causes of rock slides of various kinds, where the material which moves is part of the regolith clothing the mountainside, and where no fracture of solid rock is involved.

The primary causes are lubrication, over-loading and over-steepening, and an individual slip is often caused by a combination of all three.

Lubrication takes two forms. The mere presence of a large amount of contained water not only reduces the friction with the underlying bedrock, but also greatly lessens internal friction within the sliding mass. Both of these greatly facilitate slip.

Over-loading occurs when more and more rock debris is added to a scree slope, or, and this occurs more often, when heavy rain has loaded the regolith with an exceptional weight of contained water. This occurs more readily with clays or clayey sands than with gravels or boulder heaps, which drain more rapidly.

Over-steepening is generally the result of erosion at the toe of a slope by fluvial or marine action. Slip then occurs to restore the original angle.

The importance of the trigger type of cause of the actual slip must be emphasised, and again there is the resemblance to avalanches. The conditions favourable to slip gradually build up over a long period of time, perhaps years or even centuries, and as the limiting point is more and more closely approached, a progressively slighter cause will be capable of 'triggering off' the catastrophic movement.

There are several types of slip and these were listed in Fig. 74. The first two refer to regolith movement, but the third and fourth (and probably the fifth) involve actual rock fracture.

(a) *Mass Boulder Slip or Scree Collapse*

The original formation of scree slopes is discussed in the next chapter, but once they are present they are liable to sudden, catastrophic slip. This may be caused by any of the conditions just described and the movement may consist merely of a slight settling, often confined to the lower parts of the slope, or it may involve the whole height of the scree so that the toe spreads farther across the ground below, and also so that the top of the scree descends a little, exposing solid rock to the vagaries of weathering. This is the *free-face* which subsequently feeds the scree (see next chapter).

(b) *Mud Flow*

Contained water is particularly important when the regolith is largely clay. Clay can retain a considerable quantity of water, and if the proportion exceeds a certain amount, the whole mass can change into a kind of sludge. When the material begins to slide, the resulting agitation results in a sudden decrease in viscosity so that the whole mass behaves more or less like a fluid. This is known as *thixotropy*, and the material comes rolling down the hillside at tens of yards per

Fig. 78. Mud flow at Alum Bay, Isle of Wight, England

Fig. 79. Straight rock slide below Brixdal glacier, Norway

hour. This effect can occur in sands and other fine-grained materials as well as with clays. A mud flow of this type is seen at Alum Bay, Isle of Wight (Fig. 78).

(c) *Straight Shear Slope-collapse*

The types of mass movement so far described have been concerned with the regolith. Continual erosion of the base of a solid rock out-crop can, however, lead to such an amount of over-steepening that the bedrock itself collapses. Marine cliff erosion is one type of such an over-steepened landform. In this condition, the rock strength is insufficient to permit so steep a slope to be stable, and fracture occurs, followed by collapse.

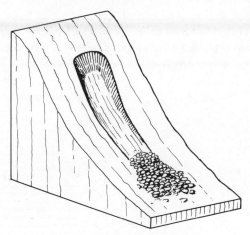

Fig. 80. Rock slide tongue

A combination of circumstances may well prevail in the sense that, for example, freeze-thaw expansion of the joints may be weakening the rock itself. Sudden rock slip may well occur as the combined result of these two conditions.

A straight *rock slide* may occur as is shown in Fig. 79 where the debris from the scar which forms the white square at the top has come tumbling down the mountainside and has destroyed all the trees in its path. This produces a *rock slide tongue,* as is shown in Fig. 80.

The two almost vertical side walls of a recently deglaciated valley (see Fig. 81) were created by ice erosion when the space between them was occupied by ice, so that there was a solid, either of rock or

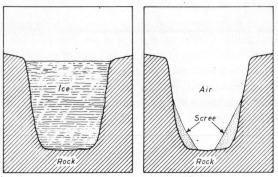

Fig. 81. LEFT: U-*shaped valley formed with glacier supporting the perpendicular side walls,* RIGHT: *Collapse to form deglaciation screes when only air between the side walls*

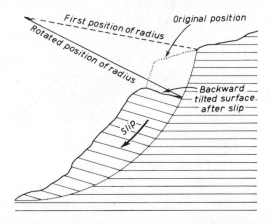

Fig. 82. Rotational shear slope-collapse

ice, throughout. When at last the glacier melts away, the pair of walls are left unsupported with only air between. They are then too steep to be stable, and in most instances a partial collapse occurs quite soon.

This gives rise to the more or less continuous scree which so typically lines both sides of many deglaciated U-shaped valleys (Fig. 83). These screes cover what lateral moraines may have been

Fig. 83. Valley choked with deglaciation screes. Sognfjord, Norway

left by the glacier, and, since their formation is rapid and is followed by the quite distinct and much slower freeze-thaw supply of further debris blocks, such forms may be termed *deglaciaton screes*. They often almost choke their valleys.

(d) *Rotational Shear Slope-collapse*

Many examples of rock slope collapse take a different pattern. This is usually *rotational shear*. The cliffs at Folkestone Warren on the south coast of England, the valleyside at Edale, Derbyshire, and the escarpment at Sutton Bank, Yorkshire, are but three examples of this type of collapse.

Instead of breaking up in a general tumble of shattered rocks, a single great mass breaks off the slope with a curved crack along which it slips in the way shown in Fig. 82. The mass which has moved has remained more or less whole, and has rotated during its slide, so that the strata, perhaps originally horizontal, are now tilted backwards, as also is the original level top surface, with the result that a small lake often forms on this top surface.

E

CHAPTER FOURTEEN

Slope Development

THE combined result of weathering and mass movement is a *slope*. There are other ways of producing slopes, such as by direct contact with moving ice or water, in the form of a glacier or a river, or by direct wave action on a coast. These forms will be discussed in later chapters.

When we consider the very large proportion of total land surface that consists of slopes produced by weathering and mass movement, it is at first a surprise to discover how little is known about their formation. We soon find, however, that the subject is extremely complex because of the great variety of conditions that may prevail, and we begin to realise how difficult it is to discover what is really happening on a particular slope. A few field visits to slopes in your neighbourhood will illustrate these points.

Slopes may be composed of solid rock, such as many cliffs, the sides of freshly glaciated valleys, and parts of weathering slopes. In the last instance, the solid rock exposure is usually known as the *free face*. This is shown in the upper parts of Figs. 84 and 85. In these two instances, the upright surface was originally produced by glaciers, but what is seen today is the result of weathering, mostly by freeze-thaw.

SCREE

Debris slopes soon accumulate at the toe of a rock slope and so produce *scree*. Both Figs. 84 and 85 show excellent examples of such accumulations. Figure 84 shows a *scree cone* of the type produced when the weathering has been concentrated on one part of the mountainside so as to produce a discharge funnel. When there is little or no assistance from running water, the cone has a constant or *straight slope,* and individual larger blocks may come tumbling down on to the flat ground below, far beyond the limits of the actual cone. One is seen in the foreground of this figure.

Figure 85 shows the profile of a similar scree, and illustrates the straight slope. The telegraph poles give the scale. In this instance the scree is continuous along the length of the valleyside.

Fig. 84. Scree cone and weathering funnel in Tempel Mountain, Spitsbergen

Fig. 85. Straight scree slope in Naeroydal, Sogn, Norway

*Fig. 86. Pedimentation in Red Rock Canyon, south Utah,
United States*

When much of the transport in such instances is aided by down-ward water movement, the profile produced is of concave form, especially in its lower parts, and this is seen in the water-aided screes in Red Rock Canyon, Utah (Fig. 86), where the continuity of the slope across the whole of the hillside, the shallow channels formed in it by small, periodic streams flowing down it, and the damper nature of the less steep lower parts as revealed by the presence of vegetation, are all clearly seen. Such a water-aided scree is termed *alluvial scree*. Above is the free face of horizontal strata capped by a structural horizontal surface.

PEDIMENTATION

The sequence of events for the general retreat of a steep escarpment or similar rock slope is as follows (Fig. 87). Starting with a nearly upright rock face AB, weathering is rapid and scree accumulates faster than it can be removed by other agencies, such as by a scree-toe stream or sheet wash. The *scree* then grows in volume to BCD, and at the same time the *free face* retreats to EC. Since the lower parts of the free face were early masked by scree, and so virtually ceased to experience weathering, the *buried rock face* recedes with height and becomes curved as shown in BFC in the diagram.

If the ratio of scree removal to weathering supply remains constant or decreases, the scree will continue to grow until it reaches the
summit and no free face remains. It more often happens, however,

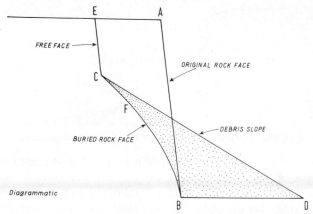

Fig. 87. The geometry of free face and debris slope development

that the ratio increases, for the weathering supply diminishes with a
smaller free face, and in this case the upper limit of the scree may
well remain at a constant height, and the whole feature ECD then
retreats parallel to itself.

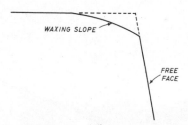

Fig. 88. The waxing slope

Local precipitation may well cause minor erosion of the summit
lip of the free face (Fig. 88), and this is the *waxing slope*.

In semi-arid regions the little precipitation that does occur mostly
takes the form of sudden downpours, often thunderstorms. Sheet
wash (see p. 114) then becomes important and the material of the
lower slopes of the scree is gradually transported over a wide apron
area. This produces a *pediment* (Fig. 89). In Fig. 86 the whole of the
foreground forms the pediment linked with the scree slope by a

change of gradient and a much more continuous cover of vegetation. The whole process so described is known as *pedimentation*.

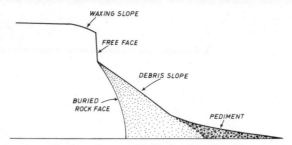

Fig. 89. The four facets of fully developed pedimentation

The rate at which the scree slope is removed is decreased by the presence of vegetation upon it, for this tends to bind the surface layers. Under favourable climatic conditions, such as in temperate humid areas, for example, and especially with rocks which readily break down into material of small calibre, it very commonly happens that the scree slope reaches to the crest line and the free face is entirely covered.

Fig. 90. Straight valley-side slopes near Causey Pike, west of Keswick, English Lake District

Fig. 91. Waxing slope, debris slope and pediment in Derwent valley near Hackness, Yorkshire, England

In these circumstances further debris supply almost or completely ceases, the scree gradually wastes away and the regolith becomes a soil. The whole slope is covered by vegetation, further decay can only occur very slowly by underground rotting and mass movement becomes very slow. This condition very commonly prevails in the lowland hill country of Britain, of much of continental Europe and of parts of the United States. The typical appearance of the hillier countryside is then as shown in Fig. 90, where the friable Skiddaw Slates (Cambro-Ordovician) are so easily eroded that the valley has already had sufficient time to change completely from a glaciated one to a well-developed pluvial one. Note the increase in valleyside gradient in the lowest part of the slopes, indicating an acceleration in fluvial down-cutting due to rejuvenation. This is discussed again on p. 209.

Another example is shown in Fig. 91, where an old horizontal surface at about 500 feet above sea-level is being slowly dissected by the presentday river system whose valley floor lies at 150 feet. There is an abrupt change of gradient between the tree-clad, debris slope, which reaches to the summit (where a short, convex, waxing slope is visible), and the more gently sloping, concave, cultivated pediment. The river Derwent is seen flowing towards the viewpoint in the left centre foreground.

Fig. 92. Craggy ground in Borrowdale Volcanic Series above Blea Tarn, south of Great Langdale valley, English Lake District

Pediment is entirely absent in the slope shown in Fig. 90, owing to the rapid fluvial removal of the debris, and in the Derwent valley much of it is considerably steeper than is the case shown in Utah in Fig. 86. The lower gradient in the latter instance largely results from the greater power of the sheet wash, partly because of the sudden, powerful rainstorms and partly because of the lower percentage of vegetative cover, but the very gentle gradient of the pediment near to the river itself in the Derwent valley should also be observed.

Great divergencies from these typical types occur from gently rolling *plains,* where everything excepting the waxing slope and the pediment has disappeared, through *craggy ground,* where rock slope, irregular perhaps because of a variable lithology, protrudes through a regolith that is insufficiently thick to provide a continuous envelope (Fig. 92), to a *badland* topography (Fig. 93), where vertical free faces dominate over the relatively small debris slope. Bryce Canyon, Utah, consists of limestones and sandstones, and although in a semi-arid area, solution weathering down vertical joints has produced the extreme forms seen in the photograph. Many of the pillars are more than 100 feet (30 metres) in height.

Horizontal bedding leads to stability in such residual forms, and this or a backward tilted strata promotes upright faces in escarpments or cliffs, since individual blocks, even when loosened from the main mass by joints or weathering, then tend to pack firmly. On the other hand, forward tilted strata easily discharge individual blocks, and so lead to a more gently sloping free face.

A slope such as is illustrated in Fig. 89 comprises a convex uppermost *sector*, two straight *segments* and a concave lowermost sector. With further development it is usual for the free face segment to be the first to disappear, and then, being no longer supplied with material, the debris slope almost entirely wastes away, leaving only a thin regolith, which is usually a soil. By this time, the waxing slope and the pediment have joined, and the whole slope comprises a convex and a concave sector with no straight segments between.

This description has dealt only with the most simple cases, and the complexity of any hill slope as found in the field is due to the numerous agencies which may influence, interrupt or modify its development. The variation of lithology from point to point up the slope, climatic variation and the initiation of a new cycle, are only three of many such factors.

Fig. 93. Badland topography in Bryce Canyon, Utah, United States

Fig. 94. Weathering in Andreeland, Isfjord, West Spitsbergen

The original rock slope here has been considered as being a near vertical one. This may have resulted from faulting, from glaciation or it may be a fossil cliff associated with a relative fall in sea-level. Other 'original' slopes may be relics of a previous cycle and their subsequent history will be modified accordingly.

A single scree cone in Spitsbergen was illustrated in Fig. 84, and Fig. 94 shows a mountain face in Andreeland, Isfjord, northwest Spitsbergen, where there is a group of such cones, many of their funnels being doubly compound – small cones in the upper parts coalescing to form few, larger funnels, and smaller, younger ones developing in the sides of these. The scree cones are coalescing and tending to form a continuous scree slope along the length of the steep face.

Spitsbergen has a low annual precipitation (equivalent to $13\frac{1}{2}$ inches (34 cm) of rain per annum) mostly in the form of snow, which on melting percolates through, rather than over, the scree slope, so that no pediment is developed and there is scarcely any vegetation. With its many examples of horizontal strata (Devonian, Carboniferous and Triassic rocks are all seen in Fig. 94) under these climatic conditions, these characteristic landforms have developed and have given the name to the islands. The general precipitous slope is of glacial origin, and truncated spurs may be seen on the lower parts of the exposed free face.

CHAPTER FIFTEEN

Underground Water and Karst Topography

DURING heavy downpours, a considerable proportion of the rain is removed by surface run-off, but in instances of moderate falls much of the precipitation is removed through the regolith as *soil-water,* and in suitable circumstances a considerable amount is also removed by deeper routes within the rock itself. Such water is known as *ground* or *underground water*. It is important to realise that in the case of material of small-sized particles, such as silt and clay, there is a film of water round each grain of the material. This is adherent due to surface tension and does not enter into the movement of water through the mass. In fact it is only under exceptional conditions that this water dries out. Should this have occurred, however, the perfectly dry regolith of fine calibre can thus absorb a considerable amount of water before any starts to flow through it. This retained water more or less fills all the space between individual particles in the case of silts and clays, and it is for this reason that, although they hold a considerable amount, they do not permit water to move through them. Such material is said to be *impermeable,* and water falling upon its surface does not soak in.

This may be contrasted with rocks such as sandstones, where the individual grains, and consequently the spaces between them, are larger. Although the grains still possess their film of water, the spaces are no longer filled by this, and there is room for water to percolate through the mass. Sandstone and similar rocks are thus said to be *porous*.

There are also rocks which are non-porous and yet permit considerable quantities of water to pass through them. These are those which have a well-developed joint or fault system, and the water passes through these often with great ease and at considerable speed. Such rocks, of which limestone is a good example, are sometimes termed *permeable* rocks.

Geomorphologists have borrowed these two words from engineers, who define *porosity* as the amount of water a rock can hold within the pore spaces, and *permeability* as the rate at which water

131

will flow through a rock. Thus a rock is permeable if water can pass through it; porous if it does so through the pore spaces; and there is no term to indicate that it passes through the joints or faults, although *secondary permeability,* a clumsy phrase, has been suggested (*primary permeability* having the same meaning as porous).

SINKS

It occasionally happens when a river passes from one geological outcrop to another that it flows from an impermeable to a permeable rock. Some of its water may then sink beneath the ground, and so reduce the amount that remains in the stream itself. If the ground is sufficiently permeable and the amount of water is not too large it may even happen that the whole of the river disappears underground. It may do so by gradual seepage through its bed, so that there is no definite point at which one may actually see it go, or it may disappear through a wide open *swallow-hole* or *sink*. The famous Gaping Gill and Alum Pot, both on the flanks of Ingleborough in the English Pennines, are two examples of such funnel-shaped sinks, where the stream in each case cascades down the vertical side of the hole, which in both instances is several feet in diameter and more than 200 feet (60 metres) deep. This particularly occurs in limestone country, and an example of such a swallow is shown in Fig. 95 in Dowel Dale in the Pennines, four miles south of Buxton. In this case, no feeding river now remains and the sink is in fact a relic of past times, when

Fig. 95. Limestone topography and sink above Dowel Dale, Derbyshire

Fig. 96. Joint widening in limestone on Ingleborough

there was surface drainage (see *dry valleys,* below). The surroundings of the sink itself, like the protected farmstead on the left, are covered by trees, since the stone wall and the steep slope of the hole discourage sheep and other grazing animals, and tree seedlings have been able to develop. This is an example of the natural vegetation of the area in the absence of herbivorous animals.

Sinks, besides also being called swallow-holes, are known as *pot-holes* (but see p. 152) and *dolina.* In Yugoslavia there are flat-floored depressions, believed to have been produced by a large number of sinks coalescing. These are termed *uvalas* and are often half a mile (800 metres) in diameter. Larger forms of the same pattern are called *poljes,* but there is considerable doubt as to their mode of origin.

The solubility of limestone in rainwater leads to the removal of rock from either side of any joint through which rainwater passes, and thus they become widened, and underground movement of water is made easier and more rapid. The surface of exposed limestone is dissolved as well as the sides of the joints and so the chemical weathering is accelerated. This was described in Chapter 12, and Fig. 96 illustrates clearly that the joints pre-date the widening, for they criss-cross one another perfectly.

CAVERNS AND UNDERGROUND WATER PASSAGES

The same effect also occurs beneath the ground, and thus a whole system of underground passages of varying width and height is developed. During the decay of the glaciers and ice sheets of the ice ages, there was considerably more water to be disposed of than there is today, and it is probable that the major development of the cavern systems, which occur particularly in certain parts of the Pennines and other limestone rocks, may well have taken place at that time. Today many of the underground passages are only occupied by relatively small streams, although they often demonstrate clearly, by the pattern of their erosion and by deposits of clay and other debris high on their sides and roof, that they have passed through a stage when they have been full of water. This may well indicate a time of greater water supply, but one must also remember that the streams have eroded and dissolved their floors, and thus lowered their beds, so that the cavern passage was deepened vertically and the higher parts of the walls were abandoned.

Leaking roofs give rise to the formation of *stalactites* of limestone re-deposited by partial evaporation of the water drops, and a similar formation is often built up on the floor in the form of a wider, stumpier column termed a *stalagmite*. Their presence indicates that that part of the cavern has been free of stream flow since they began

Fig. 97. Sink through pebbles below Malham Tarn. The river is flowing away from the camera

their formation. The rate at which stalactites increase their length is very variable, depending upon the degree of saturation of the percolating water and the rate of evaporation, which in turn is controlled by the natural air currents in the cavern, their rate of flow and their relative humidity.

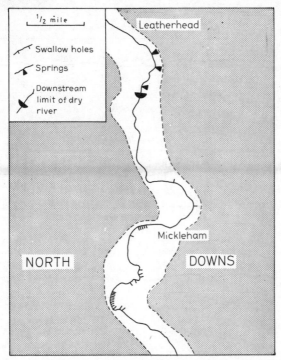

Fig. 98. Sink holes in the river Mole between Dorking and Leatherhead

It often happens that a stream bed continues on beyond the swallow point, and perhaps it is still occupied by a surface flow of water during wetter weather. Figure 97 looks downstream and the continuance of the bed, beyond the point where all the water seeps down through the pebble bed, is clearly seen. This occurs with many rivers, and the Mole is a good example where it crosses the North Downs between Dorking and Leatherhead (see Fig. 98). Its bed is dry for more than 2 miles (3 km) during periods of drought, but becomes a substantial stream during the wet season. There are at least twenty-five points at which water is swallowed, and what length of the bed becomes dry is determined by the capacity of the various underground channels, which cannot of course take more than their size and gradient and the head of water permit. When the river continues throughout on the surface, this indicates that all the underground channels are full to capacity and that there is still a surplus of water that cannot be accommodated, and so remains on the surface.

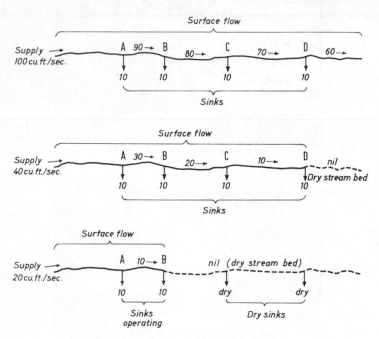

Fig. 99. Stream shortening with drought

Figure 99 makes clear the mechanism by which progressive shortening of the flowing section of river occurs with the onset of drier conditions. Suppose there are four sinks within the river bed at A, B, C and D, each connected with underground channels, each of which can take a flow of, say, 10 cubic feet per second. If the normal flow of the river during wetter periods is, say, 100, all the underground passages will be filled to capacity and 60 cubic feet per second will still remain as a surface river beyond sink D. When drier weather has prevailed long enough to reduce the full river supply to 40 cubic feet per second, the four underground channels will just be able to take the whole of the water, and the river will be dry below point D. When the weather has been drier still, and the full river supply is reduced to 20 cubic feet per second, the first two sinks will be able to take all the water offered, and the river will dry earlier still, at the point B. Thus with drought, the river, originally a continuous one along its whole course, first disappears at D, and then progressively shrinks until ultimately it may vanish even at A.

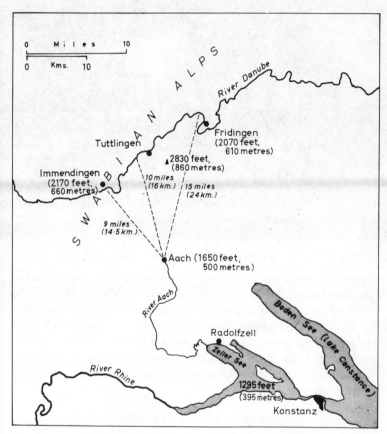

Fig. 100. Water flow from Danube to Rhine

DANUBE–RHINE WATER SWITCH

It is important to realise that the underground routes do not necessarily bear any relationship to the surface valleys, and water that sinks from a particular river does not necessarily rejoin that same river lower down, but may in fact have switched to a different valley altogether. An interesting example of this occurs in connection with the Danube and Rhine. From several points on the bed of the Danube for a 12-mile (19 km) stretch upstream and downstream of

Fig. 101. The escarpment of the South Downs north of Brighton

Tuttlingen (see Fig. 100), a proportion of the water passes underground through the limestone of the Swabian Alps for distances up to 15 miles (24 km) (measured direct), to issue as a powerful spring in the bed of a small lake at Aach, with a flow of about 350 cubic feet (10 cu. metres) per second. From Aach it flows as a surface stream southwards to the Zeller See, and so joins the river Rhine just below Konstanz. Thus the two greatest rivers of western Europe are united beneath the ground.

SPRINGS AND ESCARPMENTS

Whether the underground water be contained in definite streams within limestone or other well-jointed rock, or whether it be within the pore spaces of the general mass of the rock, such as is generally the case with sandstones, the water may well have a downward limit set to it by a change in lithology from a permeable to an impermeable rock. This occurs repeatedly in the Midlands and southeast England, where it is very common for a chalk or limestone to lie upon a clay (for example, Jurassic limestone upon Liassic clay, often with a sand between; Cretaceous chalk and Upper Greensand upon Gault clay), and in such cases the outcrop between the two rocks regularly becomes a line of springs or a general seepage line.

It is very common for the porous rock to give rise to a scarp feature as is shown in Fig. 101, which is a photograph of the chalk escarpment of the South Downs, viewed eastwards from 6 miles ($9\frac{1}{2}$ km) northwest of Brighton. The dip-slope on the left is Upper Chalk (see Fig. 102), which is quite thin at this point, so that most of the scarp slope is in Middle Chalk covered by grass. The line of trees at the foot of the scarp marks the outcrop of a thin layer (about 10 feet: 3 metres) of the harder, but more permeable, nodular Melbourn

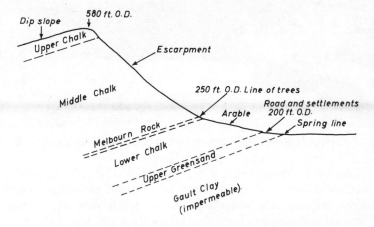

Fig. 102. Geology of the South Downs escarpment

Rock, and this provides the additional moisture to permit tree growth. From this almost to the road, the gently sloping fields are in Lower Chalk, which, as is typical, is too soft to form an escarpment, but the road on their northern (right) side, parallel to the scarp foot, and all the settlements, such as Fulking in the foreground and the little hamlet of Edburton about four fields farther away, are on the much drier Upper Greensand. Water from the various chalks passes through into the Greensand, below which it is stopped by the impermeable Gault Clay that underlies it. This outcrops just to the right of the road, and gives rise to springs which feed two streams identifiable in the photograph by the thin lines of trees which start at the road and pass off the photograph on the right-hand side. One of these is just beyond Fulking, and the other just beyond Edburton.

Repetition of alternate permeable and impermeable beds produces a multiplicity of scarps as is seen in Fig. 103, which shows the twin scarps of Wenlock Edge (left) and Callow Hill (right) with Hope Dale between, as seen from the air looking northeastwards

Fig. 103. *Wenlock and Aymestry limestone escarpments with shale vales between*

from about Craven Arms, which is 8 miles (13 km) northwest of Ludlow. Figure 104 gives a simplified map and geological section across the same area, and it is easy to see that the more massive and permeable limestones form the two escarpments, whilst the three dales are all formed of much more easily eroded shales, which, being also impermeable, have surface drainage.

Wenlock Edge forms a continuous scarp excepting in the foreground, where the small stream (line of trees) in Hope Dale breaks through to the west (left). In mid-distance in Hope Dale, but too small to be visible, are other strike streams, which unite to cut through the Aymestry escarpment to the right as Sefton Batch, and farther away the same feature is repeated in Dunstan's Brook. This combination of strike streams in the shale vales, with breaks through the escarpments, illustrates the way in which such features will eventually be destroyed, and also shows that the drainage through the present scarps must have originated before they were ridges. It is thus superposed (see p. 208). Springs issue from both these scarp foots.

DRY VALLEYS

The level at which lines of springs emerge may also be coincident with the level of the *water table* or upper surface of the *saturated zone* within the rock. This is controlled partly by the relief, the pattern of impermeable rocks and also by the rate of supply of water compared with the rate at which it flows out from the *aquifer*. These factors are particularly important on the dip-slopes which back escarpments.

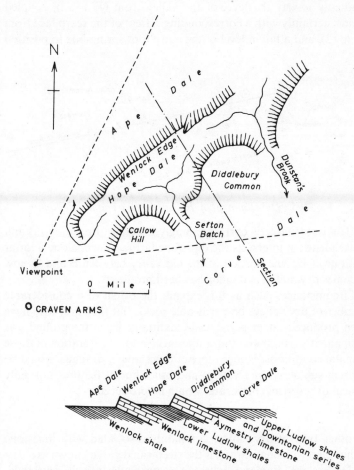

Fig. 104. *Map and section across the Wenlock and Aýmestry escarpments*

Figure 105 illustrates this. There is a spring-line at the foot of the permeable scarp-forming rock at A. The water table within the rock follows profile AEB as is indicated, and thus there is a spring-line roughly along a contour on the dip-slope at B. Below B on the dip-slope, because the rock beneath is saturated, there is surface drainage in spite of the permeability of the stream bed, and valleys are eroded.

There is a subsequent river on the impermeable clay (left), and this gradually lowers the level of the valley from (1) to (2), coupled almost certainly with a corresponding retreat of the scarp face from (1) to (2), and a fall in level of the scarp foot spring-line to position

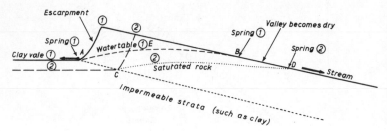

Fig. 105. Development of dry valleys on a chalk dip-slope

C. The water table is correspondingly lowered to position (2) and consequently it intersects the dip-slope farther down, along a lower contour at D. The portion of the old valley between B and D now becomes dry, and a *dry valley* has been produced.

Circumstances such as this explain the origin of a considerable number of dry valleys on permeable rocks, but they may also have been produced under periglacial conditions, when the ground was permanently frozen and thus impermeable for the duration of those climatic conditions. Under those circumstances, drainage would be entirely sub-aerial and valleys and other fluvial features normally typical of impermeable strata, would be produced.

KARST VALLEYS

Another type of dry valley, commonly associated with limestone rather than with chalk areas, is the steep-sided gorge known as a *dale* in Derbyshire, England, where it is particularly well developed. Figure 106 shows such a dry valley (Woo Dale) tributary to the wet valley (Wye Dale), east of Buxton. The dry valley floor, no longer experiencing any substantial erosion, now hangs above the present river valley by a few feet.

Figure 107 is an air photograph of Cheddar Gorge cut in limestone in the Mendip Hills, Somerset. The camera faces northeastwards up the gorge, which dies in the distance on the summit level at about 900 feet (275 metres) o.d. In the foreground the gorge is nearly 500 feet

Fig. 106. *Dry valley in Carboniferous limestone, Derbyshire*

Fig. 107. *Cheddar Gorge, Somerset*

(150 metres) deep, and the limestone is dipping gently towards the east (right), which accounts for the asymmetry of the valley – the downward sloping dip makes discharge easy from the western (left) side. Caverns open into the sides of the gorge, but the gorge itself is virtually dry.

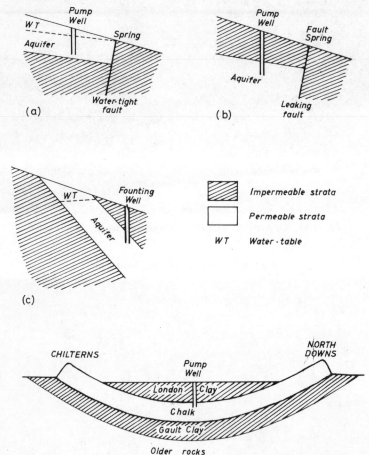

Fig. 108. *Aquifer sections. a. Held by watertight fault; b. Released by leaking fault; c. Trapped aquifer tapped by well; d. Synclinal aquifer*

At various times suggestions have been made that such features are *collapsed caverns,* but many of their characteristics make this impossible as a general explanation. Maybe some limestone gorges have been formed in this way, but in the majority of cases they are valleys which have been cut by surface streams coming from impermeable strata and supplying water at a rate sufficient to prevent complete disappearance underground. Thus the valley was deepened by normal stream erosion, but the valley sides received no lateral surface drainage and thus were not cut back into gentler slopes by mass wastage. A valley which rises on the heights, as does Cheddar, may have been fed by meltwater from adjacent ice.

AQUIFERS AND WELLS

Underground water is much used as a source of domestic and industrial water. The detection of extensive, reliable supplies of underground water is thus a matter of considerable importance. Figure 108 shows some of the ways in which water may be located. Faults may be watertight (Fig. 108a), and thus hold up water, or they may leak (Fig. 108b), and thus let it run away by fault springs. If the ground configuration is such that the surface is below the level of the water table near by, then a well sunk on the low site will produce a founting spring (Fig. 108c). This is the true *artesian well,* although the word is often used for all wells that tap underground water, even though it may have to be pumped (Fig. 108d).

CHAPTER SIXTEEN

Channelled Fluvial Flow

A NUMBER of different factors together determine the flow of water
in an open channel. The energy is provided by gravity, and thus the
gradient of the stream floor and the consequent rate of loss of
potential energy are of first importance. Gradient may be expressed
as a ratio, such as 1 in 60 or 1 : 60, which indicates a fall of 1 foot
in every 60 feet, or as so many feet per mile, or metres per kilometre,
or, as is often the custom with engineers, it may be expressed as a
percentage. A gradient of 2 per cent means a fall of 2 units of length
per 100 of the same units measured horizontally. The terms *grade*
and *slope* are synonymous with the word gradient.

All other factors tend to consume energy, and thus reduce the
speed.

FLOWING WATER

A current of water may move in either of two ways. One is by *laminar
flow,* in which the water may be considered to consist of a series of
superposed layers parallel to the stream bed and in which none of it
changes layer (Fig. 109). This sometimes occurs in thin sheet flooding over smooth surfaces, but is rare in natural streams. The other
type of motion is *turbulent flow.* This turbulence is principally produced as the result of minor irregularities on the floor and banks of
the stream. It is a disorderly, non-repetitive motion and its existence
greatly reduces the rate of flow, both because it increases internal
friction within the water, but also because of the large momentum
changes which it introduces.

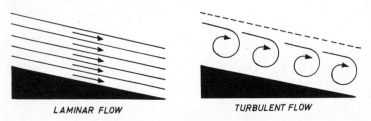

LAMINAR FLOW   TURBULENT FLOW

Fig. 109. Laminar and turbulent flow

146

Turbulence is, however, an important factor favourable to the pick-up and movement of load, as will be described later.

Another factor which reduces flow is *friction* on the bottom and sides of the river bed. Most rivers have more or less rectangular channels in their straight reaches, and the longer the combined length of the bottom and sides (known as the *wetted perimeter*), the greater is the friction for a particular roughness. Simple calculation shows that for a particular size of river (cross-sectional area), the wetted perimeter is least when the river is twice as wide as it is deep (Fig. 110). Thus the best shape for a river with, say, a 32 square foot (or 32 sq metres) cross-section is for it to be 8 feet (or 8 metres) wide and 4 deep. This gives a wetted perimeter of 16 feet (or 16 metres), and any other shape for the rectangle leads to a larger answer.

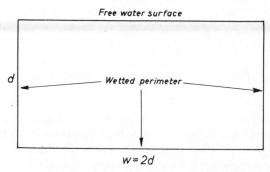

Fig. 110. Least-friction shape for river bed

A further point which this also reveals is that the ratio of the wetted perimeter to cross-sectional area is much less for large rivers than for smaller ones, even when they are all of the best shape, and this means that in this respect large rivers are the more efficient. As a river becomes larger the relative importance of this type of friction becomes less and less, and this is one of the reasons why very large rivers can maintain their flow even although they have a very low gradient, and also why a river in flood flows so much faster than the same one in its normal state – the cross-sectional area (a measure of the motive power) has perhaps doubled because the depth has doubled, but the wetted perimeter has only slightly increased, with the result that the frictional efficiency has become much greater.

The following table (Fig. 111) shows what happens if two rivers A and B join and retain the best two-by-one shape. It is assumed that when the two rivers join there is no sudden change in speed, and thus the cross-sectional area of the combined river is the sum of the two separate ones (Fig. 112). The last column shows that the relative frictional efficiency has increased from $12\frac{1}{2}$ and 10 to 16, which is a numerical way of saying that the friction on the wetted perimeter has increased less than the cross-sectional area of the river. With the individual rivers the total wetted perimeter was $100 + 80 = 180$, but in the combined river this decreased to 128, and this measures the reduction in that type of friction.

River	Cross-sectional area = a = wd	Depth =d	Width = w = 2d	Wetted perimeter = p = w + 2d	Relative frictional efficiency = a/p
A	1,250	25	50	100	$12\frac{1}{2}$
B	800	20	40	80	10
A + B	2,050	32	64	128	16

Fig. 111. Effect of river junction on friction

The nature of the river bed and banks is also of great importance, and the more uneven these are, due to the presence of large stones, boulders or other obstructions, the greater will be the friction. Allowance must be made for a *roughness factor,* and the higher this is the less will be the water velocity.

There remain two other conditions which influence the rate of flow, but both are constant[1] for water, which is the only liquid with

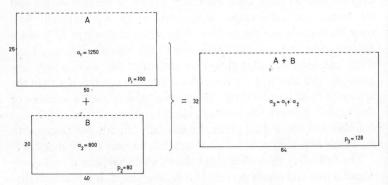

Fig. 112. Separate and combined rivers

[1] They do in fact vary slightly with temperature.

which we are concerned. These are *density* and *viscosity*. The total energy stored in water at, say, the top of a hill is the product of its *density* and its height, and this has all been consumed by the time it finally becomes stationary in the sea.

Viscosity could be described as the stiffness of a liquid. Treacle is more viscous than water, and consequently it flows much more slowly under the same conditions. It is a very interesting and most instructive exercise to consider what differences a change of viscosity in water would make to river flow, and consequently to the resulting fluvially produced topography. If water were as viscous as, say, car gear oil, the whole aspect of our scenery would be changed.

Thus the velocity of the water of a stream is increased: (1) by a steep gradient; (2) by low turbulence; (3) by the cross-sectional rectangle being in the best 2 to 1 proportion (most rivers actually are somewhat shallower than this); (4) by increase in size of the river; and (5) by a low roughness factor for the bed and banks (this reduces turbulence as well as friction).

TRANSPORTATION

The actual movement of water in a river is modified by the fact that it usually transports material along its course. The load may be in *solution, suspension* or it may be *bed load*.

Certain substances are soluble in river water, and when they have been so dissolved, to all intents and purposes they become part of the fluid itself, and move with it until for some reason they may be precipitated. The quantity of soluble salts carried into the oceans in this way is very large when considered in a worldwide setting, and it is probable that the whole of the salts at present contained in the oceans is the result of the accumulation of such soluble loads throughout geologic time. The total salts at present in solution in the oceans is of the order of 40,000 million million tons ($= 4 \times 10^{16}$ tons). This represents an average of about 3·5 per cent of the total weight of the water, but the amount normally present in river water is very much less than this. The dissolved salts are important since they represent the removal of rock in this manner, but they are insufficient to affect the river's flow in any appreciable way.

The *suspended load* consists entirely of material of small calibre. When once a particle has been tossed into suspension in the water, its rate of fall is aided by its effective weight and hindered by the frictional resistance as it moves down through the water. The effective weight is the difference between the actual weight and the buoyancy, and is constant for a particular particle in the water. The resistance increases in proportion to the velocity and so, as the latter increases, a velocity is reached at which the resistance is equal to the effective weight. There will then be no further acceleration and the particle will have reached its *terminal velocity*. Other factors remaining unchanged, the terminal velocity is roughly proportional to the square of the particle diameter, and if the particles are sufficiently small and the stream-velocity sufficiently great, the uplift given by turbulence will be adequate to prevent sedimentation. When a particle is in suspension it moves downstream at the same speed as the water itself, so that its rate of transportation is high.

Material may be moved along the river bottom as *bed load* in several ways. Even large boulders may move by being rolled. This results from the removal of material, probably of smaller size, from the down-current side and even from beneath the individual block, so that it topples over and thus moves a foot or so downstream. The speed is naturally very slow indeed, since a number of years may well elapse between each individual movement of any particular block, but it does occur, and the total foot-tons of material so transported by the river each year is quite considerable.

Push is a more effective method for pebbles of medium size. This results from the impact of the water itself, as well as from impulses received from other material impinging on the upstream side of the pebble. If a supply of pebbles of various sizes is introduced on a river bed, both roll and push may easily be observed.

For sand and gravel the commonest movement is by *saltation*. In this process, individual grains move forward by a series of long, low leaps and when one impinges on the bed it spurts up others which are then propelled forward by the current until they in their turn start off some more. This is the way in which sand in particular is moved by wind, and this aspect of the process will be discussed further in Chapter 29, but it is equally of importance within rivers also.

LOAD

There have been many investigations into the load which a river can carry. The three areas marked in Fig. 113 indicate the stream velocity ranges within which particles of different sizes will be eroded from the stream bed, carried along if already in suspension, or dropped back to the stream bottom. It shows that as the speed increases, medium sized sand is the first material to be picked up. This occurs at a little over ½ foot per second (= one-third mile per hour) (15 cm per sec), and both larger and smaller particles require higher velocities for pick-up to occur, the latter since they form a smoother bed on which the turbulent water finds it more difficult to obtain any 'grip', and also these small particles tend to cling to one another.

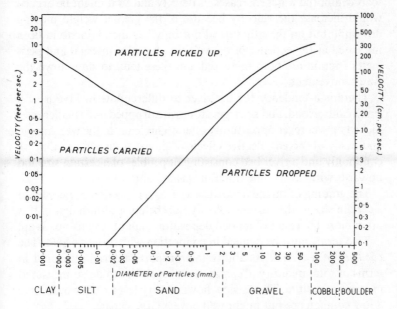

Fig. 113. Relationship between particle size and river velocity required to transport load

Clay, when once deposited, is difficult to pick up again, and requires velocities up to about 8 feet per second (= 6 miles per hour) (2·4 m per sec), whereas when once in suspension it remains so until the water becomes virtually stagnant.

When material is already on the move, there is a lower water velocity which must be reached before *sedimentation* occurs. For medium sand, this is nearly one-tenth the velocity that was required to pick it up, and for smaller particles the ratio of the two speeds is even greater.

The area of the graph between the two lines is the range within which material that has already been picked up will continue to move.

The diagram refers only to particles all of one calibre, and with mixed material somewhat different conditions prevail. A bed of sand mixed with gravel may be protected by the latter, and so at times the sand may be left behind whilst some of the pebbles are moved on.

Many authors have used the term *fully-laden* river, but it is very doubtful whether the phrase has any real meaning. The presence of load within the water increases its density and so it might be argued would increase the velocity because of the greater weight moving downhill, but on the other hand not only has the momentum been increased at the expense of the velocity, but also internal and peri-meter friction are both increased and these tend to slow down the water movement.

There is a tendency for the river to differentiate in favour of a small calibre load, and so larger stones are dropped and smaller ones picked up wherever opportunity offers. This leads to the well-known and easily observed selective effects of fluvial transport, so that we commonly find a river bed consisting of pebbles of a certain size and upwards with all the fine fraction washed out.

The grading of fluvial deposits is due to the ejection of pebbles of a certain size as the current velocity falls below a certain figure. It is often more the result of graded deposition than of selective pick-up.

Two terms must be defined in connection with a river's load. The *capacity* of a river is its ability to transport material measured in terms of total quantity. *Competence* is its ability to do so measured in terms of calibre. Thus a slow flowing, very large river would have a low competence but might well have a large capacity.

EROSION

Before a river can move material by means of any of the mechanical processes just described, the rock must be broken up. This is accomplished by *corrasion, attrition* or *cavitation.* When once the material is so broken, it may be moved by *hydraulic erosion,* which is the type already discussed. The solid, as well as the broken material, may also be removed by *corrosion,* that is, by solution, as has already been described.

Corrasion is the process of wearing away the solid rock bed of a stream by the grinding action of the sand and pebbles which the water is already carrying. These act rather like a file on the rock and so wear it away. Various patterns may be produced, but perhaps the most important is the *pothole,* where a whirlpool laden with pebbles results in a mortar and pestle effect. Figure 114 shows such potholes in a portion of the stream bed of the river Ribble, dry during a

Fig. 114. Potholes in dry river bed

drought. Each hole averages about a foot (30 cm) in diameter and 9 inches (23 cm) in depth. The pebbles, which grind away the solid rock when the water is present, may be seen.

A similar action may occur due to turbulent eddies without the formation of actual holes, and this is illustrated in Fig. 115 in the river Wharfe, near Bolton Abbey, Yorkshire. Again this photograph was taken when the river was exceptionally dry and parts of the rock floor were visible. A width of about 8 feet (2·5 metres) is seen in the photograph.

Fig. 115. Eddy grooving in river bed

Fig. 116.
Straight fluting
in river bed

Boulder strewn
stream
Fig. 117.

Fig. 118.
Change of gradient
affecting flow

Figure 116 shows straight fluting of a river bed where grinding is quite powerful but more directional in a less turbulent current. This is a small river, Glenridding Beck, in the English Lake District, again photographed during a dry spell.

Attrition results in the gradual break-up of large boulders which may have fallen down the mountainside into the river and which are beyond its competence to move whilst they remain their original size. Figure 117 shows such circumstances. Pebbles of a size the river can carry bombard the obstructing rocks, and the multiplicity of small blows eventually breaks off a portion and so gradually reduces its size.

Cavitation erosion occurs only when the current is sufficiently fast, about 40 feet (12 metres) per second in normal river water. Raging mountain torrents rarely have an average velocity as much as half this, but with these turbulent streams, there may well be localities where constrictions and obstructions lead to the necessary velocity. In waterfalls with a sheer drop of little more than 50 feet (15 metres) or so, 40 feet (12 metres) per second may well be reached.

At or above this velocity, the water pressure equals the vapour pressure, and there is a spontaneous and sudden change from a liquid to a vapour and back again, with the result that pieces of rock are virtually sucked out from the solid bed of the stream. Under suitable circumstances, this can be very severe, and it occurs without the aid of any load within the water.

This type of erosion is particularly significant in such engineering structures as propellers and pumps, where perfect metal surfaces may become so pitted as to be unfit for further use after as short a time as a single hour, and besides the instances already described, it is probable that sub-glacial tunnels may have streams flowing through them which reach the critical velocity under the influence of the hydrostatic pressure that occurs in such cases (see Chapter 20).

GRADE

Figure 118 shows a stream (Boya river, Sogn, Norway) at a point where the gradient suddenly steepens. From a calm flow the river changes suddenly into a turbulent, although shallower, torrent and small boulders protrude above the water-level. The water is moving faster and both its competence and its capacity are increased. Erosion is accelerated and this particularly occurs at the beginning of the steeper reach before the load has been substantially augmented. Thus for every little eroded from the lower part of this reach, more

Fig. 119. Alluviation in less steep reach

will be removed from the upper part, and the steeper gradient will thus gradually be reduced.

The reverse argument holds when the river moves from a steeper to a less steep reach – in this case the concavity of the long profile tends to be filled up, and Fig. 119 shows *alluviation* occurring in the form of pebble beds in part of a river which enters a less steep reach (above Gudvangen, Sogn, Norway).

Discussions such as this have led to the idea of a *graded river,* where every part of the bed has its slope so nicely adjusted that it can just carry the load which the river brings with it. This condition, however, depends upon so many variable factors, and especially upon the constantly varying one, the quantity of water flowing, that it is virtually impossible to consider any portion of a river ever to be truly graded. To be so, it would require a new profile every few hours, with every change in conditions, and clearly this cannot be.

The actual profile which is observed in any particular case must be thought to be the average grade that is appropriate, taking into consideration the average conditions prevailing in the river and whether or not those conditions have existed over a sufficient number of years to enable the river to adjust itself to accord with them. For example, if a gradual change of climate is occurring, the river may or may not be able to keep pace with these changes and adjust its profile to match.

Some changes, such as change of relative sea-level and others that are described later (see p. 209) may initiate an entirely new profile, and this may well only partially be completed when we examine the river.

Nevertheless, there is a general curve to which many, non-rejuvenated river profiles may approximate (Fig. 120), and this may

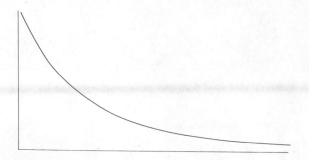

Fig. 120. Profile of a simple 'graded' stream

be considered to be the idealistic shape towards which the river is working; but since every change in water volume, every variation in geological structure and rock, every tectonic change, and so on and so on, modifies this curve, it is exceedingly rare for it to be attained.

TRANSVERSE VALLEY PROFILE

The transverse profile is a rather simpler matter, if merely because it need only be considered at one point of the course at a time. It is axiomatic that the river itself can only erode what it touches, although by oversteepening it may lead to gravitational collapse of the bank. It is thus roughly true that the river alone would cut a gorgelike valley, and it actually does this if it flows through an arid countryside, such as is the case with the Grand Canyon of the Colorado river, U.S.A.

The conversion to the V shape is accomplished by local sheet erosion, the result of local precipitation, and by slope collapse. The rates of these, relative to vertical erosion by the river itself, determine the steepness of the slopes of the V. A canyon is the extreme case where local precipitation and consequently downwash is at a mini-

Fig. 121. The Grand Canyon, Colorado

mum (see Fig. 121), whereas Fig. 122 shows Rigg Beck, a small,
youthful stream cut in easily eroded Skiddaw slate rock west of
Keswick, in a humid climate where a perfect V shape has developed
and already destroyed the valley form resulting from glaciation. The
slow down-cutting as a river nears the sea, often coupled with the
heavy precipitation of coastal regions, generally leads to so wide
open a V that it is often difficult to realise that the river is in a valley
at all.

Every possible intermediate between these extremes is to be found, and some will be specifically described below in connection with particular rivers.

ROUNDING A CORNER

The movement of water along a straight stream bed is by no means simple. Naturally its velocity is lessened by friction in those parts of the water near the bed and banks, and there appears to be a tendency for the two halves of the river's width to rotate in a somewhat spiral form with a downward descent along the middle line of the stream and ascents on either side. This tends to spread the bed load away from the centre line and to move at least some of it nearer to the two banks.

These complications are greatly emphasised when a river rounds a bend. The bend may be initiated by some obstruction which deviates the stream sideways a little. Since the water naturally does not sense the approach to the bend, there is a tendency for each section of it to continue straight on until it meets the curving bank. The movement is not similar to a column of troops rounding a corner where the outermost soldiers must move faster than those on the inner side in order to preserve the ranks. Instead, the water tends to plunge when it reaches the outer bank of the curve, and the whole stream takes up a kind of spiral or transverse rolling movement, the particles which have plunged by the outer bank crossing

Fig. 122. V-shaped valley in easily eroded rock

the bed of the stream and reappearing at the surface on the inner bank. This description is, of course, very much simplified, but it suffices to show that there is a downward and consequently accelerated movement on the outside of a curve, and an upward and consequently decelerated movement on the inside of a curve. There is erosion on the outer bank and deposition on the inner.

This is illustrated in Fig. 123 which shows a bend in the middle course of the river Ribble, northern England. The water is flowing away from the viewpoint, a bank of pebbles has built up on the inner bank in the foreground and erosion is seen on the outer bank in the middle distance, as well as on the left-hand side of the view. The photograph was taken during a dry period, when the deposition banks were visible. The erosion of the far bank is seen to take place by collapse after being undercut by the water itself, and this is further illustrated in Fig. 124, where, in the river Thames at Runnymede, undercutting may be seen in action, with collapsed blocks about to be washed away by the stream of water.

This erosion on the outer curve of a bend and deposition on the inner tends to increase the original curvature and to produce *meanders,* but the development of meander belts with their accompanying flood plains and blufflines will be discussed later in this chapter.

Fig. 123. *Erosion and deposition on a curve*

Fig. 124. River bank erosion in clay

The transverse profile of a river bed on a curve is typically as shown in Fig. 125, and this is a further example of the distribution of erosion and the concentration of most of the flow on the outer side of the bend.

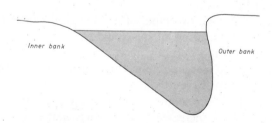

Inner bank

Outer bank

Fig. 125. Transverse profile across bed of curved river

CONFLUENCE

It was an early geomorphologist (John Playfair, 1748–1819, Professor of mathematics and philosophy at the University of Edinburgh), who wrote regarding the way in which two rivers join and drew a contrast with the junction of glaciated valleys. Since that time his statement has been known as Playfair's law and the substance of

Fig. 126. Two rivers join in the Duddon valley, English Lake District

it is that when rivers meet they do so on the same level (Fig. 126), their gradients being adjusted to make them do so, 'a circumstance which would be infinitely improbable if each of their vallies [*sic*] were not the work of the stream which flows in it'. This last part of his account is significant for the lack of *accordant junctions* occurs most often at those places where the rivers have not themselves made their valleys, where, for example, they have been inherited from glaciers. In such instances there is a *discordant junction,* usually accompanied by a waterfall.

The reason for the two types of confluence lies in the different down-cutting mechanisms of rivers and glaciers. A river is some-what like a saw and depends upon speed for its erosive power, whereas a glacier is slow and clumsy and depends mainly upon sheer weight. If one river were to join another at a lower level, the high tributary would be accelerated over the steep link between the two and so would have increased erosive power and would cut down relatively quickly until accordance was attained. The way in which glaciers may, on the contrary, produce discordance will be described on page 307.

RÉGIME

Mention has already been made of the fact that the quantity of water in a river varies almost from moment to moment. In temperate and warmer countries, every rainstorm temporarily increases the water supply, and the length of time for which augmentation lasts depends upon the duration, the amount of the precipitation and the local hydrological conditions.

Perhaps an extreme case is to be found in the *wadis* of the Sahara and similar features of other hot deserts. In such areas, a channel which has been dry for months or even years may become a wide, deep torrent in a matter of minutes after a sudden thunderstorm. The flow may only endure for an hour or two, and there are roads in the Sahara where the sign instructs the motor driver not to cross the wadi if the river is flowing, but to wait until it dries up!

The constancy of river flow is dependent upon the constancy of rainfall, and in such areas as Britain, where the variation from month to month is not very great, the rivers flow with much the same volume for the whole year, variations being from day to day rather than from season to season, and the result of a few rain showers or of brief drought. In Britain variation in evaporation between summer and winter is in fact the main cause of such seasonal variations as do exist.

In areas of glaciers and snowfields, the spring thaw is the main cause of variation within the fluvial régime. In such places, the rivers

Fig. 127. Almost dry river bed in autumn in thaw fed river

are in spate, floods occur and waterfalls are at their most spectacular in the late spring and early summer. During much of the winter and in early spring before the thaws have set in, as well as in the autumn when the thaw is over, these rivers are often dry or almost so, as in the case of the Bow river at Banff, Alberta (Fig. 127). Photographed in August, the stream, cloudy with glacial clay, only occupies a fraction of the width of its full bed when it breaks through the range of steeply dipping Palaeozoic strata in the eastern edge of the Western Cordillera. Conifers grow on esker ridges and on the fan deposits in the foreground, as well as on all the medium height ground above the river-level.

FLOODS

Floods occur when the water-level of the river rises to such an extent that it overflows beyond the limits of its banks and covers part of the surrounding countryside. They are of at least three major kinds. Those which take place annually as a regular feature in the river's régime; those which are entirely irregular, unpredictable (excepting perhaps that a few hour's warning may be given), and are so sudden as very often to be catastrophic; and those which are not directly related to heavy rainfall.

The Nile floods annually in August and September as the result of the seasonal monsoon rains in the more equatorial districts of its catchment area. Such floods are anticipated and often even beneficial from the silt they deposit on agricultural land, and, in the case of Egypt, from the annual watering which they give the land that would otherwise be virtually desert. Modern irrigation schemes are often designed to bring such occurrences under greater control.

In other districts, a sudden heavy rainfall over a particular catchment area will often produce a flood. Flooding in lower reaches especially occurs when the time interval between rainfall and the water reaching the river is such that the relatively minor floods of individual tributaries all reach the main river at the same time and so produce an additive effect.

In many instances, floods are double, the first being caused by the arrival of the surface run-off and the second by the water which has been delayed by percolation through the ground. Floods are less severe in such cases and also when the tributaries are of varied lengths, so that the individual flushes of water reach the principal stream at differing times.

Floods are worsened if a heavy rainstorm follows several days of wet weather. In that case the ground is already waterlogged and the water from the final storm all becomes surface run-off, and thus greatly increases the sudden rise in river-level.

In cooler regions, the high latent heat of melting of ice and the great reflecting (and consequently low absorbing) power of snow and ice to solar radiant heat, both slow down the spring melt and so lessen the severity of floods from these causes.

Catastrophic floods may be of quite a different nature. Large landslides falling into a lake may cause a sudden, temporary, rise in water level, but in such cases the wave produced by the impact normally does the greater harm. Two landslides into Lake Loen in western Norway have occurred within recent times. One in 1905 produced a flood wave which drowned sixty-one persons, and another in 1938 drowned eighty-four. The fallen rock produced permanent islands.

THE SIMPLE RIVER

We may define a *simple river* as one which flows over a rock that is uniform both in lithology and structure, in an area that has experienced no recent tectonic change, where the relative height of land and sea has been unchanged, where the rainfall has considerable reliability from year to year, and where there is no very dry or very wet season. Probably no such river is to be found, but it is useful to consider this as the basic river, which may then be adjusted to accord with any specific natural conditions.

In its upper reaches, the river will be small, but will be continually increasing in size as it progresses downhill because of seepage into it from the banks and by the addition of tributary streams. The gradient is likely to be fairly steep, the stream will soon pick up loose grit from the regolith and so acquire tools with which to promote further erosion. It will be deepening its bed.

Tributaries that join it at frequent intervals (see Fig. 128) increase its volume by a series of sudden increments, and on each occasion the total load that may be carried becomes more than the sum of the individual streams because of the decrease in total bottom friction. The capacity is increased and thus the amount that the river bed is lowered below the profile of the original slope increases downstream. This accounts for the shape of the upper part of the river's profile (see Fig. 120).

The river is, however, tied to a *base level* which it cannot lower. This is most often the sea, but quite frequently it is the bottom of an inland basin or the water-level of a lake that occupies it, such as the Caspian Sea. All lowering of the river bed in the upper part of its course automatically involves a less steep lower course (Fig. 129). It is only because a larger river has so much less perimeter friction that the less steep portion is able to transport the load that is brought to it by the steeper upper portion.

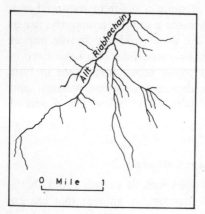

Fig. 128.
Tributaries joining principal stream

This transition from the zone where the mountain height is the dominant factor to the zone where the base level controls events is gradual, and thus the whole profile in fact becomes the curve shown in Fig. 120. In its middle reaches the river is somewhat calmer, it can no longer be called a torrent and few if any rocks protrude above the water-level (see Fig. 123).

Nearer the mouth, the gradient may have become so slight that extensive *meanders* develop. As already described, a river tends to accentuate any curve that already exists by erosion on the outside of the bend (see Fig. 123) and deposition on the inside. So meanders grow, and this is much easier in the wide open valley with gentle lateral slopes such as have developed in the lower reaches of the river.

The meander loops are constantly working to new positions. There is a general tendency to migrate downstream, and so every

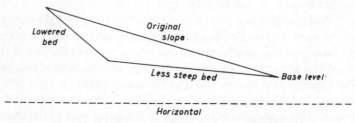

Fig. 129. *Effect of base level on river gradient*

part of the *meander belt,* the lateral width of the swings, is river bed in turn, deposition on the insides of the curves tending to build a level surface, which often floods during periods of high river level. So a *flood plain* is produced with *blufflines* on either side.

Figure 130 shows how extensively such features have been developed in parts of the Jordan valley, although the limits of the flood plain here tend to coincide with two of the many fault lines that have formed the rift valley. As the meanders accentuate themselves, two adjacent bends tend to approach nearer and nearer to one another. This occurs near the right-hand side of Fig. 130 and in the middle of the photograph there are several examples of *cut-offs,* where the narrow *swan's-neck* has been breached. Some of these are older than others, and especially on the left, remnants of such abandoned meanders are seen to be virtually out of contact with the existing river course, and form isolated and often stagnant *oxbow lakes.* Ultimately vegetative growth encourages them to silt up completely and they become little more than elongated, curved grooves on the surface of the flood plain.

Fig. 130. Meanders in the river Jordan

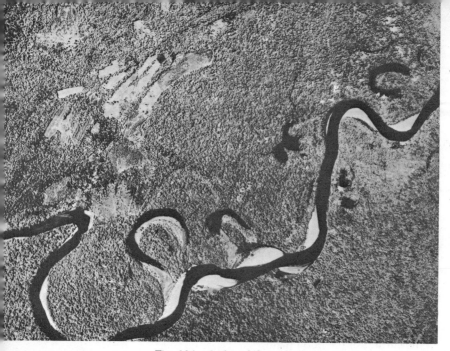

Fig. 131. Oxbow lakes in a Texan river

Figure 131 shows similar features in wooded country in Texas. The black areas are water (river and oxbow lakes), the very white margins to parts of the river indicate the expanded size of the river when in spate. The treeless, grey areas linking two of the oxbow lakes to the river show dry portions of the old course.

Fig. 132. Swan's neck in a New Zealand river

Fig. 133. Meanders on a alluviated glaciated valley

Figure 132 is an oblique view of a fine swan-neck near Lake Manapouri, Otago, New Zealand. Very little further erosion by the steep curve on the left will suffice to break through the neck. When this occurs, probably during a flood, the course will be shortened considerably, so that the gradient at that point will be increased and the whole of the river will very soon take the new, direct course and leave the oxbow section stagnant.

Flat areas that lead to the development of meander belts may be provided in a variety of ways, and one example of such an occurrence amongst hill country is provided by the river Glass in Strathglass, Inverness-shire (Fig. 133, an oblique air photograph looking up-valley from near Struy). In this instance, the U-shaped glaciated valley has been largely infilled by sediments on the floor of a lake formed by a rock barrier farther down-valley. This followed the melting of the glacier, and when eventually the river cut through the dam so as to drain the lake, the river invaded the level, silted floor and meandered upon it.

A more slowly moving river is less turbulent than a fast one, and the tendency to meander is very largely determined by turbulence. The greater the turbulence the longer the wavelength of the meanders, and the narrower the width of the meander belt. If the turbulence is sufficiently great, as it is with a fast, shallow mountain stream, then meandering is practically eliminated and the river flows directly downhill.

Fig. 134. Alluvial fan in large calibre material

Fig. 135. Alluvial fan in small calibre material

ALLUVIAL FANS

Whenever a river is checked by a sudden decrease in gradient, deposition occurs. Often this is merely within the limits of the ordinary banks, but where the decrease is very great and the stream is very heavily laden, a feature develops which seems almost to be midway between a scree slope and a delta.

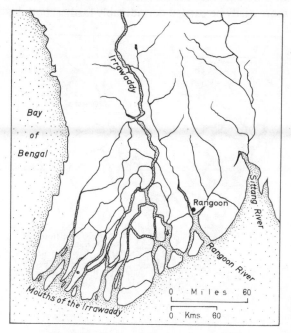

Fig. 136. Delta of the river Irrawaddy

Two varieties of these are shown in Figs. 134 and 135. These are from two areas in Norway and both occur where the river is composed of glacial meltwater, in each case the glacier being less than 2 miles (3 km) away from the points pictured, and where the river has plunged over the lip of a hanging valley. In such circumstances, the water is provided with a plentiful supply of glacial debris and so is fully laden for a steep gradient. The sudden slackening on reaching the main valley, which lies across the picture in both localities, results in deposition to such an extent that the main stream channel becomes blocked, and a whole series of *distributaries* is formed over the fan-shaped deposit. The one in Fig. 134 is active in its central parts where there is consequently little vegetation (the birch-clad slopes on either side are also part of the fan), whilst in Fig. 135, the debris is of smaller calibre and thus spreads farther into the floor of the main valley.

DELTAS

When, however, the river reaches a lake or the sea, conditions are somewhat different since the material is deposited under water and can the more easily be carried considerably farther, both because of

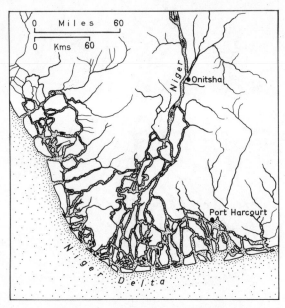

Fig. 137. Delta of the river Niger

the buoyancy effect in water, and also because after deposition it may often be moved on again by tidal currents and the like.

Deltaic deposits are of all sizes from a few yards across at the mouth of a small stream to many miles. Maps of three large ones are shown.

The Irrawaddy delta (Fig. 136) starts about 180 miles (290 km) from the sea and is about the same distance across from the most westerly to the most easterly mouth. For a delta of this size it breaks into fewer distributaries than is most common, but they join and redivide constantly in the usual way.

The Niger delta (Fig. 137) is very complex and has spread so wide that it accumulates the waters of several other rivers, although they are much smaller than the Niger itself. The stretch of coast occupied by the numerous mouths is at least 180 miles across (290 km), but may be much more, depending upon where one considers the Niger delta to end. It starts near Onitsha and covers an area of about 14,000 square miles (36,000 sq km), which is greater even than that of the Nile delta.

The delta of the Volga (Fig. 138) is only half the linear dimensions and consequently about one-quarter the area of the two just des-

Fig. 138. Delta of the river Volga

cribed. The river and its tributaries have drained a vast area of glacial deposits, yet the quantity of sediment brought into the Caspian Sea, although immense, is not so great as it would be were the gradient of the river, and consequently its speed, greater. The material is mostly silt, and this is probably the reason why the delta carries so many distributaries. Entering a tideless inland sea, conditions at its mouth are more static because of this relatively fixed water-level (although it changes with the seasons) and this may favour lack of concentration of the two hundred mouths.

CHAPTER SEVENTEEN

The Development of Single-cycle River Systems

A MAIN river and its tributaries is a system which has a beginning, develops and declines into old age and senility, although the sequence of this life may be interrupted more than once by rejuvenation or other changes. It is initiated whenever an area of the sea bed is raised above sea-level and precipitation falls upon it. It develops from the initial stages to those of youth and maturity, and eventually, if time permits, it passes on into old age when erosion has so far reduced the relief that there is but little gradient either in the long or the transverse profiles of the river. By that time it is a sluggish, meandering stream, the mere shadow of its youthful, vigorous, rapidly eroding, turbulent self.

DRAINAGE ON NEW LAND

As soon as changes in relative level bring new land out from beneath the sea, fluvial conditions begin to prevail, unless, of course, the climate is such that low temperature makes this a glacial area. By the nature of its origin, the new land is normally one of gentle relief, the relief of the old sea bed, and in general there will be a fairly simple slope downwards towards the new coastline. On this a series of parallel rivers will be initiated (see Fig. 139), their spacing being determined principally by the amount of the precipitation. This is

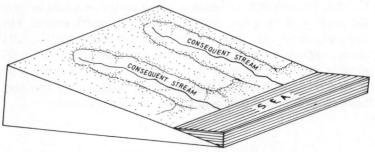

Fig. 139. New rivers on old sea bed

the first, early youthful stage of the drainage pattern, and as uplift continues, so that *absolute relief,* that is, the height above sea-level, increases, the gradient of the rivers may also increase and they will erode their valleys the more vigorously. At the same time they increase their length by headward erosion, as well as by extension across newer new land.

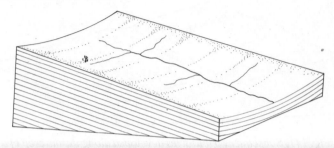

Fig. 140. Tectonically warped new land with trunk and tributary streams all consequents

Any hypothetical area of this type borders the old land on the continental side of the old coastline, and on this a river system will presumably be already developed. The more widely spaced rivers on this older area become extended across the new plain to reach the more remote coastline. These rivers will be somewhat larger than those freshly initiated, but being the lowest parts of existing, and perhaps nicely balanced, river systems, they will probably be able to perform little erosion and may well have little effect on the drainage pattern of the new land, on which all the rivers will flow in a direction down the initial slope. These are known as *consequent* streams.

The main slope may be warped so that it has a gently undulating relief, and thus it is possible to have a main river and a group of tributaries all of which are consequent streams (see Fig. 140). This particularly occurs where gentle tectonic warping of the new coastal plain has produced a plunging syncline during uplift, as is shown in the figure.

SUBSEQUENT STREAMS

Rain falls over the whole area and the water has to find its way to the few streams that exist. Runnels, streamlets and streams are developed everywhere and a whole system of tributaries and subtributaries is produced. Erosion soon removes some of the original surface, and valleys of erosion come into existence. The thickness of material removed in this way is determined, in the different parts of one area, by the relative ease of erosion, and rocks and unconsolidated material which are easy to move are taken away in the greatest quantity. The relative resistance to fluvial erosion will thus lead to the formation of relief features, and valleys will be formed along the more vulnerable lines.

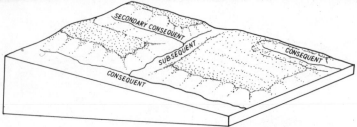

Fig. 141. Subsequent tributaries developed along the outcrop of a low-resistant rock

These may well be the outcrops of less resistant rocks, often clays, as contrasted with sandstones and chalk and limestone, and rivers that are developed for this reason along the strike of the rock, that is, along the bands of outcrop of less resistant rock, are known as *subsequent* streams. This name is used because they generally begin to flow some time after the consequent streams have come into existence. It is commonly the case that they lie at right-angles to the direction of the principal consequents (see Fig. 141).

Secondary consequents develop as tributaries of the subsequent streams flowing down the original slope, and short *obsequents* are initiated down the backward-facing slope produced by the development of subsequent valleys.

SINGLE CAPTURE

In this way the simple idea of a river basin will be developed and by headward lengthening it is highly probable that some of the subsequents will work so far along their clay or similar vales that they eventually reach the neighbouring consequent and capture its water. Figure 142 shows the way in which this gradually occurs. For these events to happen, one of the two consequents must be more vigorous than the other, with the probability that its valley floor will be the lower of the two (left-hand river). If these were A and B, and if CA and CB are the profiles of two of their tributaries on the same clay outcrop, it is likely that the steeper tributary CA will deepen its valley more quickly than will CB. This difference may be increased by a greater precipitation and consequently greater run-off on the left-hand slope.

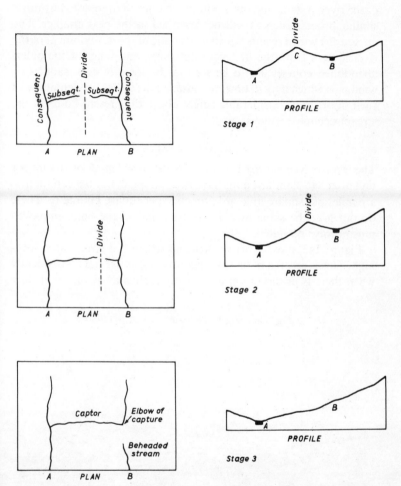

Fig. 142. Migration of a divide leading to river capture

Later positions of the two main valley floors and of the profiles of the two tributaries are as shown in the stage 2 profile. The effect of this is to shift the divide gradually towards the right. Eventually it travels so far in that direction that the headwaters of the left-hand tributary reach the actual bed of the stream B, and at first some, and later all, the water of this stream is captured and turned into the left-hand river system. The three diagrams clearly illustrate the principle of the *migration of divides* and the initiation of *river capture*.

It should be noted that this is a simple result of the development of the river system, and owes nothing to rejuvenation or to any other similar process such as will be described in the next chapter. The *integration* which results is a characteristic of the development of the river system from the first youthful stage, and relics of the older, abandoned courses are to be seen in the form of cols, saddles or windgaps which may in time, because of later valley deepening, have their floors at a considerable height above the present floors of the stream-occupied valleys.

STREAM DENSITY

The term *stream density* is defined as the total length of stream per unit area. No standard units have been adopted, but the commonest are miles per square mile or kilometres per square kilometre. These do not give the same numerical result and so the units employed must always be stated.

Figure 143 shows part of Arizona where the stream density is high. This is an area of few but heavy rain storms, and consequently when there is precipitation it is mostly carried away on the surface

Fig. 143. High stream density in Arizona

and every slope develops its system of gullies and streams. Since they flow for such a small proportion of the time, such an area ages very slowly, and the pattern may be considered to be a very youthful one.

Stream density decreases with the maturity of the area concerned, for streams tend, as has been described, to integrate with one another, but the density depends to a much greater extent upon the nature of the ground – highly permeable chalk, for example, has an exceptionally low surface stream density. It also depends upon the way in which the precipitation falls, whether it be a series of heavy downpours or long periods of light rain.

Figure 144 shows three areas in Britain. One is peat-covered sandstone and shale moorland of Edale, Derbyshire; one a glaciated region in the Scottish Highlands; and the third a region in the English Midlands, where the surface is mostly covered with till (see Fig. 145). Edale has a stream density of 3·02 km per sq km, the Ben Wyvis area gives 0·91 km per sq km, and the lowland area, where the relative relief in the area is of the order of 200 feet, has the low density of 0·62 km per sq km. These are each typical of their types of

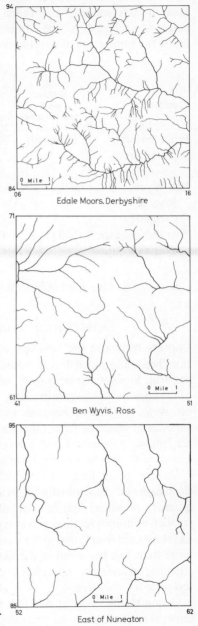

Edale Moors, Derbyshire

Ben Wyvis, Ross

East of Nuneaton

Fig. 144. Streams in three diverse areas of Britain

area. In each case an area of radial drainage outward from a central height was selected. All these three areas may be considered to be in much the same stage of development.

Locality	Highest point feet (metres)	Lowest point feet (metres)	Annual rainfall inches (cm)	Geology
Edale moors, Derbyshire	2,090 (640)	700 (210)	50 (130)	Peat on sand-stone; shale
Ben Wyvis, Ross & Cromarty	3,430 (1,050)	750 (230)	60 (150)	Moine metamorphics
East of Nuneaton, Warwickshire	500 (150)	300 (90)	30 (75)	Lower Lias

Fig. 145.   Data regarding areas mapped in Fig. 144

MISFIT AND UNDERFIT STREAMS

Capture results in the *beheaded* stream losing its headwaters and thus becoming much less in volume. Such a stream is a misfit or underfit. Strictly, the term *misfit* only indicates that a stream is not of the appropriate size for its valley, and it may thus be either *underfit* or *overfit*. If a stream becomes overfit due to acquiring additional supplies of water or from other causes, its erosive powers are correspondingly increased and it very soon enlarges the valley size to accord with its new volume. Overfit streams are thus quite rare.

On the other hand, an underfit stream results from volume shrinkage and consequently lies in a valley which is too large for the quantity of water, and in particular its meander swings become smaller in amplitude and wavelength, especially the latter. Figure 133 shows the river Glass with meanders whose amplitude is scarcely more than half the width of the flat valley floor. This is an underfit stream – underfit because it has been given a glaciated valley that is too wide for the river.

Owing to the rarity of overfit streams, the two terms misfit and underfit are commonly treated as synonymous, although the second term is more exact. Underfitness may be the result of capture, but there are also many other possible causes.

CONSECUTIVE CAPTURE

There are numerous examples of capture in most mountainous districts and very often a sequence of consecutive captures may be found. An illustration from an actual locality is best and Fig. 146 shows a complex sequence of events which have occurred in the mountains of South Wales between Lampeter and Llandovery. The whole pattern has been influenced to some extent by the fact that it has experienced the relatively recent presence of valley glaciers, but we may interpret most of what is shown on the presentday (lowest) sketch map as being the result of a succession of river captures.

In stage 1 (top map), the Gorlech, Melinddwr, upper Marlais (above Llansawel), and the Cothi (above Edwinsford), were all tributaries of the Dulais (which itself flows into the Towy). With a valley floor then much higher than it is today, the Gorlech took the route over the present 610-foot (190 metres) col. The Melinddwr and upper Marlais joined south of Llansawel and flowed together over the present 520-foot (158 metres) col and then, with the Cothi, across what is now the 350-foot (107 metres) col at Talley (then probably about 450 feet (137 metres)) to the Dulais. The upper Cothi was a relatively important river and had already carved out a wide valley for itself.

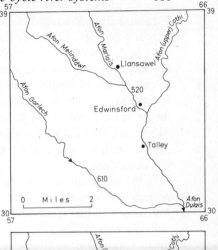

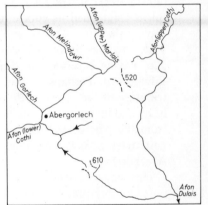

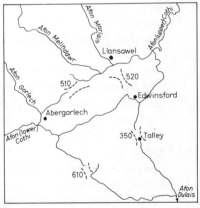

Fig. 146. Three stages in the development of part of the Afon Cothi, South Wales (heights are in feet)

In stage 2 (middle map), the lower Cothi, which lies roughly on the junction between the Silurian and Ordovician and along a plane of weakness, deepened and extended its valley so as to capture the Gorlech at Abergorlech. It then extended its headwaters still farther to capture the Melinddwr and the upper Marlais. It is possible that it extended itself even to capture the upper Cothi, but this is by no means certain and is not marked on the maps. The fact that the 610-foot (190 metres) col is higher than the 520-foot (158 metres) col accords with the idea that the former became dry a little earlier, as just described.

In the meantime, a double tributary of the lower Cothi at Abergorlech had been extending its headwaters southeastwards and eastwards, and so had reversed the drainage northwest of the 610-foot (190 metres) col. The easterly tributary here was even more successful. It lengthened its course along a second plane of weakness to capture the upper Cothi near Edwinsford and so turned the valley at Talley, by then down to 350 feet (107 metres) (stage 3), into a windgap, having reversed the drainage along the half-mile reach at Edwinsford. Perhaps at the same time, a northeasterly flowing tributary of the upper Cothi (see stage 2) was working back at its head, and this eventually stole the upper Marlais and the Melinddwr from the Abergorlech captor and so completed the present river pattern (stage 3) with a windgap at 510 feet (155 metres) northeast of Abergorlech.

This sequence, which is the most probable, although not the only possible, interpretation of the events in this area, illustrates how complex such histories can become, even though this one involves mere development of a simple river system without the necessity of rejuvenation or any other changes in the conditions, such as the introduction of a second cycle.

INFLUENCE OF LITHOLOGY ON VALLEY FORM

The relative vigour of the middle Cothi in this area has already been attributed at least in part to the fact that it lies along a line of geological weakness, and variations in the lithology within the course of a single river regularly lead to variations in the nature of the river valley.

Again a specific example will be considered. The river Vosso, in central western Norway, displays this interrelationship between lithology, structure and valley form. The portion of the river mapped in Fig. 147 lies very close to the line of the major Caledonian thrust

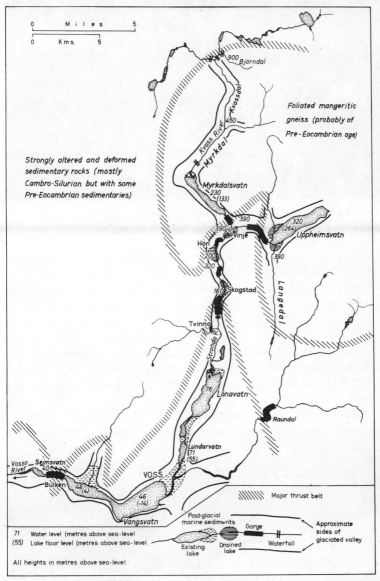

Fig. 147. River Vosso valley, central western Norway

Fig. 148. Foliated rocks in the Caledonian thrust belt. The face shown is about five feet across

belt, and in these particular parts the rocks are so shattered and foliated, as shown in Fig. 148, that rapid down-cutting, and consequent gorge formation, is possible. The illustration is of part of the gorge wall between Uppheimsvatn and Vinje, whereas the relatively undisturbed strata on the north side of Myrkdalsvatn are shown in Fig. 149.

The contrast between these two rocks is as obvious as is the contrast between the resulting river valleys, shown in Figs. 150 and 151. The former of these is in the same gorge below Uppheimsvatn

Fig. 149. Undisturbed sedimentaries near the Caledonian thrust belt

Fig. 150. River gorge in the Caledonian thrust belt

Fig. 151. Open Myrkdal valley in undisturbed strata

Fig. 152. Bulken gorge and bridge at the outflow of Vangsvatn, Norway

as is the shattered rock of Fig. 148, and the latter is the wide open valley just upstream of Myrkdalsvatn. Here the down-cutting has been much slower and there has been more time for valley widening to take place.

This alternation of gorge and wider reaches is repeated each time the major thrust plane is crossed, and a particularly fine example of this is shown in Fig. 152, which looks directly at the downstream end of Vangsvatn, and shows the entry of the outflow into the Bulken gorge, so narrow that it is crossed by very simple single-span bridge. After following the side of the 5-mile (8-km) long lake, which in places is a mile (1·6 km) in width with sloping banks, it is a great contrast suddenly to come to this narrow gorge about ¾ mile (1·2 km) in length, only 20 to 30 yards (18 to 27 metres) wide and several hundred feet (a hundred metres) deep. Beyond it the valley opens out again to Seimsvatn and the river continues on towards the sea.

Clearly the map shows that there are many other interesting features in this valley. It was occupied by a glacier during the ice ages and many parts of it demonstrate valley-within-valley forms, but the features just described are primarily of fluvial origin and have mostly been produced in post-glacial times within the floor of the ice age glacier.

Valleyside form is very largely the result of the relative rates of fluvial incision and slope erosion.

WATERFALLS

Besides affecting the nature of the valleysides, variations in lithology also effect the long profile. Many waterfalls owe their origin to the presence of a belt of rocks that are resistant to fluvial erosion and these occur as the result of fluvial action only. Others are the result of glacial and marine processes and these will be described in the proper places.

A band of more or less horizontal massive limestone over an easily eroded shale has led to the formation of Hardraw Falls in the northern Pennines (Fig. 153). The drop is about 100 feet (30 metres) and because the shale is eroded even by merely being wet by spray from the falls, there is a considerable overhang, and it is possible to walk behind the water. Two people are seen doing this behind another fall in the same district (Fig. 154), and the removal of the lower rock eventually leads to the collapse of the hard upper band and the gradual movement of the lip of the fall up-valley. These are termed *cap-rock falls.*

Fig. 153. *Hardraw Falls, near Hawes, Pennines, England*

Fig. 154. Thornton Force, Ingleton, near Ingleborough, Pennines

Fig. 155. Vöringfoss (600 feet) and Måbödal with Fossli Hotel on the edge of the valley head, Norway

Similar up-valley migration is seen in Fig. 155 which shows the famous Vöringfoss at the head of Måbödal, east of Hardangerfjord in Norway. The road is the Oslo–Bergen main highway. The building at the top of the falls is a hundred-roomed luxury hotel, and this gives some idea of the size of the valley, which is nearly a thousand feet (300 metres) deep, the final leap of the fall being a single jump of 600 feet (180 metres). The general ground surface is part of the Hardangervidda (see p. 216), and the valley is cut like a great scar in this rolling surface.

There is some doubt as to its origin – it may be partly glacial and partly fluvial, or it may be entirely fluvial. It is believed that the line of the valley marks a fault-line and therefore a line of relatively easy erosion, and the view from the end of the gorge from near the hotel is one of the spectacular sights of the world. Notice the extensive screes lining the sides of the gorge, the results of catastrophic collapses. The road climbs from the bottom of the gorge by a series of intricate loops and a number of tunnels, one of which may be seen negotiating the sheer precipice in the right centre of the photograph. The length of the gorge may well illustrate the up-valley creep of the lip of the falls, of which there are now two, the main one on the right and an equally high, but less visible, one on the left.

Fig. 156. Victoria Falls, Zambezi river, Rhodesia

Victoria Falls, Rhodesia, on the Zambezi (Fig. 156) is of a quite different type. Here the river meets a series of fault-lines which intersect the joint planes in the basaltic lava flows which it is traversing. At a point where it is nearly a mile ($1\frac{1}{2}$ km) wide, it plunges into a chasm about 350 feet (105 metres) deep. This crosses the line of the river at right-angles, and the opposite side of the chasm is only between 30 and 80 yards (10 and 24 metres) away. The river finds its exit by a 40-mile (65-km) long zigzag gorge, which has the same origin as the plunge chasm.

ESCARPMENTS

Subsequent rivers in clay or similar vales have already been mentioned, and if these occur in gently inclined strata there is a tendency towards the formation of escarpments. These are typically found in southeastern England, such as the escarpments of the Chiltern hills and of the North and South Downs (see Fig. 101). This type of landform has already been described in Chapter 15, and there is still some doubt whether rivers play any direct part in their formation, other than by the provision of a line of scarp-foot springs (see Fig. 105). It is most probable that they owe their origin very largely to weathering processes, rather than to direct fluvial erosion – it is certainly rare to find a river actually flowing directly in contact with the foot of an escarpment.

Tilted strata does, however, lead to a lateral movement of the river bed if the subsequent river has worked down to a more resistant layer, and in that case the river may be found at the scarp foot, and it may be producing direct erosion. The river in such circumstances tends to wear away the more easily eroded band and so to undermine the more resistant rock until it collapses and thus causes the escarpment to retreat a little. Whether fluvial or weathering processes will dominate in the retreat of any particular scarp face is determined by the relative rates of the two processes in the particular example.

RIVER TERRACES

The general formation of flood plains has already been described in the previous chapter and the existence of such a feature is indicative of a gentle gradient and relatively slow, non-turbulent flow. It also indicates a slow rate of incision, probably because the river is nearing the sea and the level below which it cannot erode. The flood plain is primarily cut in solid rock, but the shift of the meander loops results in the deposition of a few feet of alluvium, which forms the actual surface of the flood plain. In regions of unconsolidated deposits, such as ground moraine left by ice sheets, the flood plain is naturally cut in this material and the bluffs are also composed of moraine.

If the river is still deepening its bed, although but slowly, successive meander swings over the same part of the plain will each be at slightly lower levels, and if they are also of smaller amplitude remnants of

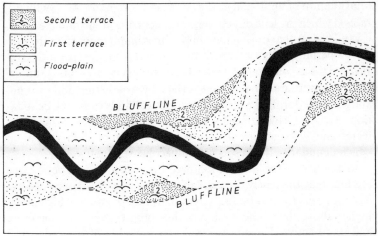

Fig. 157. *Meander migration leaving remnants of the old flood plain as terraces*

older stages in the development of the flood plain may be left as *terraces*. Figure 157 shows how these may occur, as successive meander loops traverse the locality under consideration. These terraces are of successively lower height on alternate sides of the flood plain and are not paired. Terraces of this type are *single-cycle terraces,* produced by one continuous erosion of the flood plain.

Changes in conditions which result in rejuvenation or the reverse initiate new cycles and may lead to a new set of terraces. In these instances, the differences in height of successive terraces are usually greater, and they will be described in the next chapter.

SINGLE-CYCLE FLUVIAL TOPOGRAPHY

In the simplest case a single cycle comprises a period of uplift during and following which fluvial erosion and deposition occur.

It is not easy to calculate the rate at which the whole surface of a drainage basin is being lowered at the present time by the combined efforts of weathering and fluvial erosion, but it is clear that mountainous basins are being eroded much more rapidly than are lowland areas, as one would naturally expect. It seems that figures range from about $\frac{3}{4}$ inch (2 cm) per thousand years for basins like those of the Elbe and Seine, to 2 or even 3 feet (60 to 90 cm) per thousand years for mountainous basins.

Rates of tectonic uplift are apparently much greater than these. Using what facts are known concerning the major orogenies and the total amount of uplift and its duration, and comparing these with the rates at which present-day changes are occurring in earthquake areas, it would seem that during the times of maximum movement the rate was something of the order of 30 or more feet (9 metres) per thousand years. This is very much faster than the likely maximum rate of general lowering of the ground surface by weathering and erosion, and so uplift during the orogenic periods certainly overtook denudation. Areas which had been sea bed would thus be raised out of the water and lifted sufficiently to become high mountain ranges on which denudation processes would become very active.

In a period of rapid uplift followed by a stillstand, the conditions are first that the newly formed land gains in height above sea-level and the rivers formed upon it continually find themselves higher and higher above their base level, and thus progressively become more and more active. Erosion is rapid and probably of the order of 3 feet (1 metre) per thousand years over the whole area – much more in some parts and less in others.

This is a period of rapid down-cutting by the rivers. Valleys are deep, side walls steep, but some parts of the original sea bed on the medial lines of the interfluves scarcely experience any erosion. Slopes will be mainly convex as shown in Fig. 158a.

As time progresses and uplift continues, the valleys continue to be deepened relatively to their flanking hills and plateaux, and the *relative relief* continually increases, whilst at the same time the *absolute relief* (that is, height above sea-level) also increases. This stage is shown in Fig. 158b. With increased relative relief the width of the valleys also increases even though their walls are still steep, and consequently there will eventually come a time when the valley width is approximately equal to the average interfluve width, and the whole surface is occupied by valley hill slopes and no remnant of the original sea bed remains undenuded. This is the stage known as *maturity,* and it is shown in Fig. 158c. At this moment the relative relief is at its maximum.

It may well happen that during the next stage the rate of lowering of the crestlines may equal the rate of valley incision, so that the relative relief may remain constant, all parts of the area being denuded at approximately the same rate. If uplift has now ceased, then absolute relief will have reached its maximum and will be in a decline.

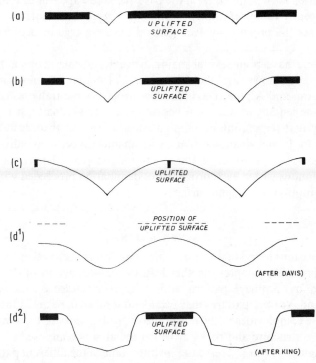

Fig. 158. Valley development in a single cycle

Owing to this decline in height of the valley floor above its base level, the rate of incision by the river decreases progressively, whilst the rate of weathering and mass movement denudation remains unchanged. The lower slopes of the valleyside will now become concave and the whole hillside will be a double curve, convex in the upper part and concave in the lower (Fig. 158d^1).

The hill slope profile may, however, be more complex than this, and may in fact become a pediment with a waxing slope in the upper part, a steep, fairly high free face at middle levels and a pediment forming the lower part of the slope (Fig. 158d^2). The development of various slope profiles has already been discussed in Chapter 14, and need not be repeated here.

G 2

Whatever the precise form taken, the fact remains that the upper levels will almost certainly lose height more rapidly than the valley floors, and thus the relative relief (as well as the absolute) will become reduced. If there is time, and recent calculations indicate that there has often been ample time in the past, the landscape will be reduced to a gently rolling plain, a *peneplain* or a *pediplain*, according as to whether the process involved general mass wastage or pedimentation.

There have been several major orogenies during geologic time. The best known are the Charnian, Caledonian, Armorican or Variscan and Alpine. The individual orogenies naturally lasted for varying lengths of time, and began and ended gradually. It is very likely that the mountain-building parts of each of them lasted for between 10 and 40 million years, with an interval between individual orogenies of the order of 100 to 150 million years. Uplift was discontinuous within each orogeny but denudation proceeded without interruption on all land surfaces.

RIVER BASINS

The various individual factors which have been discussed in this and the preceding chapter together lead to the production of the river basin and drainage pattern, which can be observed on the actual ground. Various patterns may occur and some of these are influenced by the complexities of the recent (geological) history of the area and by the structure and rocks of which the area is composed.

Figures 159 to 162 serve to illustrate some of the different patterns that can be produced. The Mississippi river system is perhaps one of the most regular type, and is known as *dendritic*. In this the whole appearance of the map is similar to the trunk and branches of a tree, where no particular streams dominate over others and there is a general symmetry and uniformity about the whole of the pattern.

Figure 160 gives the plan of the river Thames basin, and here there is obviously a tendency for each major tributary to collect a number of others before it joins the main river. The map gives something of the appearance of a number of treelike patterns (some of them inverted), each anchored to the central mainstream. This is largely due to the geological structures and the nature of the outcrops (chalk for example between the Kennet and the upper Thames and Thame, with an escarpment facing roughly north). This could be termed a *compound dendritic* pattern.

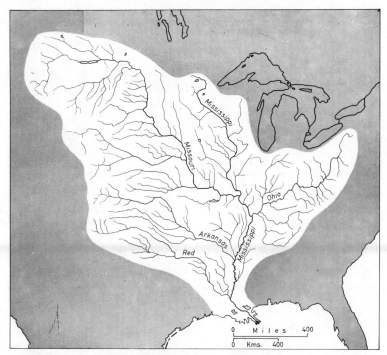

Fig. 159. The Mississippi basin

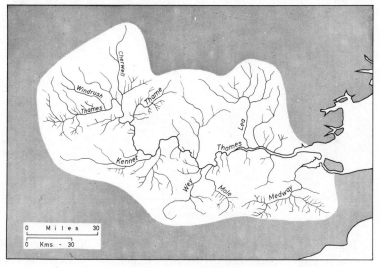

Fig. 160. The Thames basin

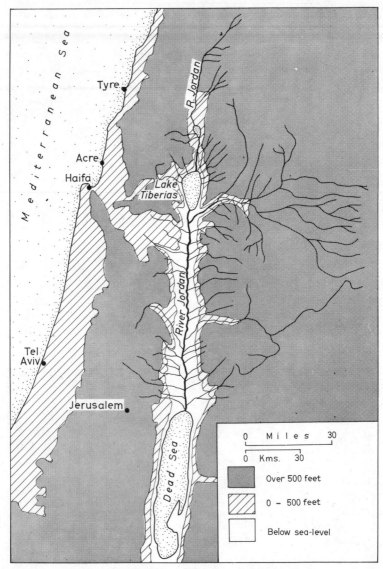

Fig. 161. The Jordan basin

Figure 161 shows a very good example of the *trellis* pattern. The Jordan is largely contained between two major fault-lines and lies in a rift valley. The floor slopes down gently towards the south, and so determines the direction of flow of the main river, whilst the steeply sloping flanks lead to a series of parallel eastward or westward flowing tributaries. This is an area of inland drainage, the water-level of

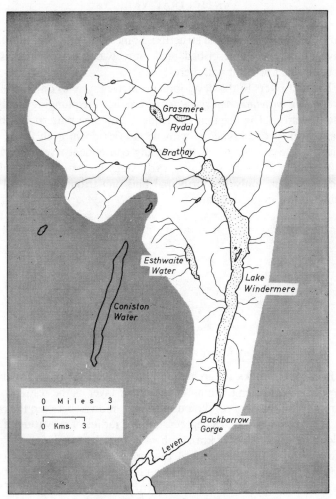

Fig. 162. The Windermere basin

the Dead Sea, which is the world's lowest lake, being 1,300 feet (400 metres) below sea-level. Figure 162 also shows a trellis pattern resulting from different causes. The Windermere basin in the English Lake District was an area of fairly intense valley glaciation, and thus a troughlike system of valleys was produced which have been taken over by the fluvial drainage, leading to the trunk river (and lakes) with short tributaries roughly at right-angles to the main direction.

ANTICLINAL VALLEYS

As many modifications are produced on river patterns as there are variations in rock type and structure. Some of the effects of lithology have already been described, and only two specific patterns of structure will be dealt with here.

The first refers to the development of river systems on an area of *alternating anticlines and synclines* where they are plunging gently in one direction. The original consequent drainage pattern will be a main river in each syncline with tributaries down each flank, the limbs of the anticlines, all these being consequent rivers (see Fig. 140). Figure 163 shows a fairly early stage in the development of such a system, only one principal and one tributary consequent being shown in the diagram.

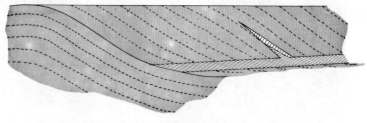

Fig. 163. Erosion of an anticline – stage 1

Because the rocks are arched up to form the crest of an anticline, there has been a lengthening of the upper layer as the result of the curvature. If the angle of dip on the flanks midway between the crest and the trough is, say, 18 degrees, and the radius of curvature of the fold is about 12 miles (18 km), both values similar to what commonly occurs, and if the thickness of the strata is about 2,000 feet (600 metres), then the *lengthening* of the outermost layer will be more than 300 feet (90 metres) as compared with the central stratum of the deposit, and the lowermost layer, 2,000 feet (600 metres) below the surface will have been *compressed* also by more than 300 feet (90 metres). This geometry is illustrated in Fig. 164, which is drawn to scale, and it shows that the expansion of the surface is 300 feet (90 metres) per 20,000-foot (6,100 metres) length or 1½ per cent, and the compression of the innermost is the same amount.

A lengthening of 1½ per cent means that if the rock is already jointed, as it almost certainly will be, being on the surface, then these joints will be opened up a little, and the rock may be said to have been 'slackened'. Weathering and erosion will be able to operate all

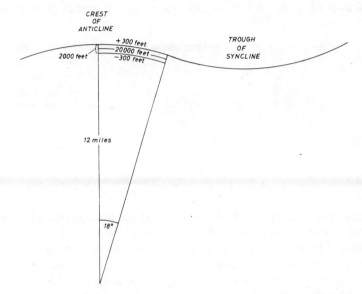

Fig. 164. Lengthening of the upper surface of an anticline

the more easily. The rock on the crest of an anticline is weakened and is relatively vulnerable. Conversely, there is compaction on the outermost surface of a syncline, where with similar dimensions there would be a compression of 1½ per cent. Consequently all existing joints are tightly closed and the rock becomes proportionately durable and difficult to erode.

This has a profound effect on the development of topographical features in this type of country. When the tributary consequents lengthen their courses sufficiently to reach somewhere near to the crest of the anticline, they discover the weakness there, and subsequent streams are formed which develop rapidly along the crest line in either direction, as shown in Fig. 165. Figure 166 shows this kind of valley in the Kuh-i-Bisyair in Iran. This range is a single steeply folded anticline in a region of slight vegetational cover owing to the very occasional nature of the rainfall, which, however, is considerable in quantity when it does occur. The anticline is very young, being of Pliocene age, and thus the erosion is still at an early stage.

In the left-hand part of the ridge, the development of the subsequent valley has begun to lengthen itself along the axis of the ridge, with the deep, narrow consequent valley giving egress on to the foothills which border the anticline itself. This is the beginning of the stage shown in Fig. 165. A little farther away along the same ridge, erosion

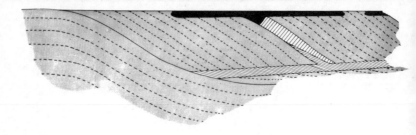

Fig. 165. Erosion of an anticline – stage 2

has developed more rapidly to a later stage, and the anticline has been dissected into a number of valleys parallel to the axis and the level of their floor is almost as low as that of the terrain outside the ridge. This is a rather complex illustration of a stage midway between that shown in Fig. 165 and that shown in Fig. 168.

This more advanced stage in anticlinal erosion is better seen in Fig. 167, which shows the Kuh-i-Pabda range in Iran. The anticline is plunging away from the viewer. The whole of the upper strata have been removed by erosion, excepting on the extreme flanks and in the distance, where the inward-facing escarpments swing round to join one another. A relatively non-resistant belt has resulted in the formation of a deep subsequent valley in the floor of which a river may be seen. This is in fact two rivers flowing in opposite directions and joining about a quarter of the way from the bottom of the photograph. At the junction they turn to the right and plunge in a very deep and narrow ravine through the limb of the anticline. This pattern is very similar in type, although not in magnitude of relief, to the Weald of southeast England. There the gaps in the North and South Downs have been produced by the persistence of the original dip-slope consequent streams, as they have gradually cut their courses deeper and deeper, and acquired subsequent tributaries.

These strike streams deepen their valleys quickly, whereas the principal consequent, lying in the base of the syncline, is on resistant rock. It deepens its valley but slowly in spite of the fact that it has a

Fig. 166. Development of strike valleys along an anticlinal ridge, Kuh-i-Bisyair, Iran

Fig. 167. Further development of the drainage pattern in a pitching anticline, Kuh-i-Pabda, Iran

greater supply of water than have the subsequent strike streams. As time goes on, the more rapid erosion along the anticlinal axis results in that valley becoming lower than the original main valley (Fig. 168), and drainage in the tributary is reversed. The anticlinal valley

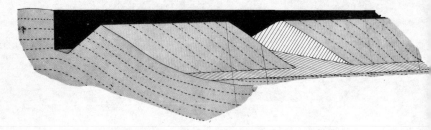

Fig. 168. Erosion of an anticline – stage 3

becomes the main one, and the river in the synclinal valley is captured and diverted to the anticlinal valley. This is so common an occurrence that *anticlinal valleys,* sometimes even with *synclinal ridges,* might often be said to be the typical type of topography in such folded areas.

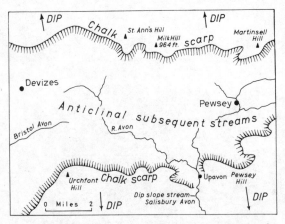

Fig. 169. The Vale of Pewsey, southern England

The anticlinal Vale of Pewsey (Figs. 169 and 170) is an example of such a valley in about the stage illustrated in Fig. 165, where the subsequent streams are still tributaries of the dip-slope consequent, which in this case is the main stream, flowing southwards as the Salisbury Avon to the coast at Christchurch, near Bournemouth.

The chalk had been folded into an asymmetrical anticline, with the steeper dip on the northern limb, and subsequent streams found this material so fractured that erosion was relatively easy. The whole of the chalk has been removed from the crest of the anticline, bringing

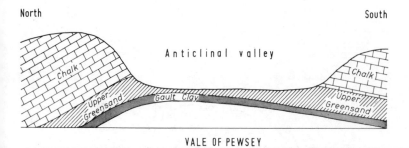

VALE OF PEWSEY

Fig. 170. Section across the Vale of Pewsey anticlinal valley

the older, Upper Greensand rock on to the surface of the vale. In this way, a valley some 4 miles (6 km) in average width and about 20 miles (30 km) long has been produced in the heart of the chalk country. Because of the configuration of the structure to the south, it is unlikely that in this instance the final stage, where the anticlinal stream becomes the master stream as shown in Fig. 168, will ever occur.

DOME AND BASIN PATTERN

The second example is that of the Great Lakes region of North America, where, because of recent glaciation, additional complexities have been added to the evolution of the area. To the north (Fig. 171) lies the Laurentian Shield, one of the very ancient stable blocks of world history. The area south of that is an area of much more recent sedimentary rocks and as such it was raised out of the sea and became a new land. Gentle folding occurred in the form of a series of domes, two of which are marked on the map, the Wisconsin dome and the Algonquin dome. Between them and rather to the south was the Michigan down-warped or basin area. Consequent streams therefore flowed in much the directions shown by the heavy lines, and, as time went on and they deepened their valleys, they cut through some of the upper strata and worked down into a series of less resistant rocks. Along the lines of two of these outcrops especially, subsequent rivers developed as indicated by the heavy broken lines. These produced subsequent valleys and eventually led to the formation of the great Niagara and Onondago escarpments. The Allegheny escarpment was produced in a somewhat similar way.

At this time, the main drainage of the area was into what is now the Missouri–Mississippi basin, but with the coming of ice sheets

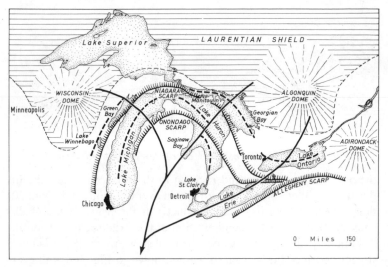

Fig. 171. Development of the Great Lakes, North America

from the north several of the subsequent valleys were over-deepened so that when ultimately the ice melted away for the last time, these hollows became lakes and bays attached to the lakes. The presence of morainic ground to the south, coupled with tilt towards the northeast, largely the result of isostatic depression, led to the way southwards becoming closed and to the opening of the St Lawrence valley route to the Atlantic Ocean. This very much simplified account of the origin of the Great Lakes drainage system serves to illustrate the effect of dip-slopes and alternating bands of resistant and less resistant strata upon the pattern of a drainage system.

Rift valleys, block mountains, domes and all other tectonic features exert their own types of influence, but these examples serve to show the development of fluvial topography on areas which had already been folded. Regions where uplift is still going on, and is therefore affecting pre-existing rivers, will be described in Chapter 18.

CHAPTER EIGHTEEN

Composite and Polycyclic Fluvial Topography

THE general progress of the development of fluvial topography within a single cycle of erosion and deposition was described in the last chapter, and it is now necessary to consider what may happen when there are interruptions in the cycle, and when a fresh cycle commences.

THE TERM 'CYCLE'

The term *cycle* as used in geomorphology is a misnomer. The word truly should refer to a series of events which follow one after the other and when completed automatically repeat. This is what does in fact occur in the case of the well known biological cycles, such as the nitrogen cycle, where the set of processes continue to repeat themselves in due sequence for an indefinite number of repetitions. All kinds of automatic manufacturing processes go through repetitive cycles in exactly the same way. In discussing such cycles it is generally possible to begin consideration of them at any stage – there are no starting or ending points.

The *hydrological* or *water cycle* of the meteorologist is a true cycle. The sun raises water from the oceans into the air, the wind blows the vapour to the mountains, it rains, rivers bring the water back to the oceans, and the cycle continues into a repeat without interruption. One may begin to study this cycle at the ocean, where the rain falls on the mountain, or at any other intermediate point.

The so-called *fluvial cycle* is not, however, of this type. It has a definite beginning, which is when the land area is raised above sea-level, and it has a slow, dying termination, which is when the pene-plain or other type of plain is fully developed. At this point the 'cycle' ends, and there is no continuation unless, and this is entirely by chance, another period of uplift or some similar movement occurs to 'reset' the mechanism and start it off again. *Fluvial sequence* would be a more accurate descriptive term, and when we use the word 'cycle' we must all the time remember that in geomorphology it does not refer to an automatically repetitive series of events.

COMPOSITE TOPOGRAPHY

(a) *Climatic Change*

It often occurs that, before it is completed, a single fluvial sequence may be interrupted either by a change of climate, or by the fact that the river has cut down to a different type of rock, which induces a new fluvial pattern.

The most notable change of climate which has occured within recent geological time is the change from the last cool period of the Pleistocene Ice Ages to the warmer climate of the present day. This is a worldwide change and to this extent all land areas are *composite* in landform.

The most obvious are those areas where actual glaciation occurred. These show all the clear signs of the past presence of ice caps, glaciers, lowland ice sheets and so on, such as will be described in Chapter 23. Figure 133 shows the past presence of ice in at least two ways. First there is the undulating nature of the upland with several small lakes upon it, typical of the terrain abandoned by a plateau ice cap, and second there is the wide, flat-floored valley, the effect of a glacier. This valley has now been adopted by the presentday river. The river is clearly too small for the valley, and as it finds the gradient too gentle it is forced to meander from side to side between the steep rock walls. This then illustrates the change from an ice-produced terrain to one where fluvial, and sheet- and mass-erosion processes endeavour to modify the forms produced by their pre-decessors.

This is a composite topography, the glacial sequence having been cut short by the onset of a warmer climate.

Figure 256 shows the effects of a reverse change of climate – from the warmer climate when fluvial processes were dominant in pre-glacial times to a glacial climate when ice erosion was active. The gently rolling, full-bodied surface of the summit areas of Snowdon is a remnant of the massive mountain of preglacial days. Into this fluvially produced terrain, the valley glaciers by headward erosion cut the deep cwms which almost succeeded in removing the whole mountain.

Figure 245 shows both changes. The full-bodied rounded shapes of some of the mountains are the result of preglacial fluvial processes. The rocks have since been smoothed by ice and the deep glacial valleys were cut during the cold climate. Now the stream, very tiny compared with the size of valley, is bringing the area slowly back to that of a fluvial landscape. This is thus a three-phase composite landscape, and innumerable other examples can be found.

Climatic change is not necessarily one of temperature change. An area may experience an increased or a decreased rainfall, producing rivers of greater or of less volume and completely altering their régime. The passing of permafrost may result in an apparently impermeable rock becoming permeable so that dry river valleys are produced by the water going underground, and a single river may demonstrate what would be the effect of change of climate by passing through several climatic zones along the length of its presentday course. The Nile passes from tropical grassland to hot desert with corresponding changes in valley form. Many of the northward-flowing rivers of Asiatic U.S.S.R. pass from steppe to taiga and thence to tundra, from lands of perennial flow to those of winter freeze. Such rivers show two or more types of topography in different reaches at the same time.

An even more dramatic example of the effects of climatic change is afforded by Fig. 172, which shows part of the Canterbury Plains just southwest of Christchurch, New Zealand. Here the great plain abuts directly against the edge of the rugged mountain massif. The latter owes much of its present form to past glaciation, for the present fluvial epoch has only started its work of bringing the relief back to that characteristic of a warmer climate. The plain consists of outwash sands and gravels which may partially have been deposited almost contemporaneously with the glaciation of the Southern Alps, but which are largely the result of great fluvial transportation of glacial debris from the mountains with deposition immediately on reaching an area of lower gradient.

Fig. 172. *Contrast between mountains and plain in South Island,
New Zealand*

Fig. 173. The superimposed river Avon near Bristol

(b) *Superimposition*

Another way in which composite landforms may be produced is due to a river cutting down through a surface rock to another which has qualities that lead to a different type of valley. This occurred at Bristol, where the limestone that now forms the surface of the Clifton Downs was originally covered by Triassic marl. Across this cover the river Avon flowed downhill to the sea. The limestone ridge lay hidden, and when the river cut down to it, it still maintained its original course and trenched the limestone. This produced the gorge-like valley seen in Fig. 173. The narrow part is about four miles (6 km) in length and has an average depth of about 200 feet (60 metres).

Except for a few isolated patches, the whole of the original Triassic cover has been removed, as well as a great deal of rock which originally filled a hollow to the east of the limestone ridge. The peculiarity of the present topography is that there is now a through valley, not used by any river, southwest of Bristol, and the river Avon ignores this easy route to the sea and plunges straight through the limestone ridge.

This is an example of *superimposed (= superposed) drainage*, since it has been imposed on the present surface rocks from a one-time cover of other rocks on which the pattern was initiated. Similar circumstances often occur when a thick cover of glacial till blankets the original irregularities. A new river system forms on the upper surface of the till and the pattern that is so developed may well be quite inappropriate for the undulations of the hidden rock surface. When these in time become exposed, the rivers find themselves compelled to maintain routes which would never have been used had they started on this lower surface.

Another type occurs when a river system is superimposed on to a permeable deposit below from an impermeable rock above. This often leads to the production of dry valleys, as the drainage goes underground.

POLYCYCLIC TOPOGRAPHY AND DYNAMIC REJUVENATION

Relative change of land- and sea-level, operating during the life history of a river system, breaks off the development at the point which it has reached, and may set a new cycle or sequence in motion.

The change of level may be a rise or fall of land or of sea, and thus may result in a rise or fall in *base level*. It may *age* the processes at work in the area, resulting in very considerable alluviation, or it may lead to *rejuvenation*.

Uplift due to tectonic causes may involve tilt, folding or faulting, and these all give a directional aspect to the rejuvenation. Tilt, for example, may increase the gradient of some slopes, and thus accelerate the rivers flowing down them, and at the same time it may decrease the gradient of others, thus ageing their rivers. This is *directional rejuvenation*.

It is obvious that there is an almost unlimited variety of possibilities, and it must be noted that in the case of inland drainage systems, uplift itself does not affect the base level, since this rises with the remainder of the area, although tilt will still produce directional rejuvenation and ageing.

The most important effect of rejuvenation on a river system is the initiation of a new profile to accord with the new base level. If this is lower than the old, erosion will generally occur in the lower reaches of the river, and this modification of the old profile will gradually creep upstream until, after a long period of time, it reaches the source. The new profile is then complete, and the old destroyed.

In the meantime, further rejuvenation may well have occurred, so that the same process is repeating itself, and it often happens that a single river shows several rejuvenation profiles, each gradually creeping up-valley in a procession. A typical example is shown in Fig. 174.

The rate of up-valley creep is regulated partly by the amount and vigour of the rejuvenation, but also by the ease with which the river-bed lithology permits adjustments to be made. The presence of a resistant band of rock greatly slows down the creep of the *nick-point*, the term given to the limit so far reached by the rejuvenation profile,

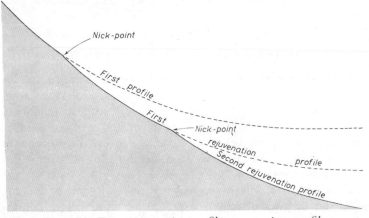

Fig. 174. Two rejuvenation profiles on one river profile

and since this is also a likely site for a waterfall, it very often happens that the two are found together. A nick-point is the site of a steepening in the fluvial gradient, but this is never sufficient to produce an actual waterfall by itself, although naturally an existing waterfall must be destroyed when the nick-point progresses up-valley. The waterfall constitutes a considerable barrier to further creep.

The deepened river course initiates the formation of new valley-sides, and a *valley-within-a-valley* structure is produced. An example is shown in Fig. 175 and where the valley floor is very flat, such as in the flood-plain reaches, *paired river terraces* are produced (Fig. 176).

It should be noted that mere lowering of the base level does not necessarily lead to rejuvenation, for if the exposed sea bed has a less gradient than the lower reaches of the existing river, the extended river, which is across this gentle slope, will then flow so slowly that alluviation, and not rejuvenation, will occur.

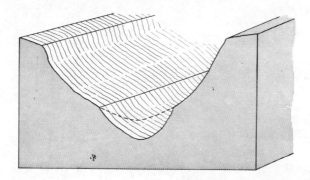

Fig. 175. A valley-within-a-valley

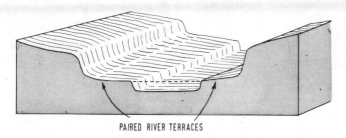

PAIRED RIVER TERRACES

Fig. 176. Paired rejuvenation river terraces

STATIC REJUVENATION

Rejuvenation may also take place without change of base level. This may be termed *static rejuvenation* to distinguish it from *dynamic rejuvenation,* the type already discussed.

Increased precipitation due to climatic change increases the river's volume, but a commoner reason for greater volume is capture. Capture in fact often leads to rejuvenation both above and below the point where it has occurred. The *captor* acquires the additional water, and the *captive* may well gain a shorter route to the sea. This increases the general gradient, and thus promotes revived erosional activity. Valleys are deepened rapidly, so that their lateral slopes become steep and pre-existing meanders may be *incised,* as is shown in Fig. 177. These meanders are up-valley of the *elbow of capture,* where in this instance the distance to the sea was reduced from about fifty-five miles to eleven (90 km to 18 km).

Fig. 177. Meanders incised into the previous wide valley of the river Rheidol, central Wales

One section of a river's course may be rejuvenated when another section up-valley ceases to provide the water with as much load as in the past. This may occur when a river, flowing through glacial gravels, eventually removes them and, by reaching the solid rock, picks up much less material. This means that it has more available capacity to add to its load in lower reaches, and so additional erosion may be set up there.

ANTECEDENCE

Antecedence occurs when a river persists in retaining its existing course even when crustal warping produces a barrier, such as an anticlinal structure, across its path. The river cuts a trench through this barrier as rapidly as it is upwarped and thus maintains its downward path, although often at a considerably less steep gradient than previously, because of the difficulty in keeping pace with the uplift.

During the Pliocene and Pleistocene there has been considerable tectonic activity in many areas. It is reckoned for example that the European Alps and the Pyrenees were uplifted some 6,000 feet (1,800 metres) during the Pliocene; that the Atlas, Caucasus and Andes were all lifted between 3,000 and 5,000 feet (900 and 1,500 metres) in the Pliocene and early Pleistocene; and that at much the same time the Himalayas and the New Zealand Alps were both raised about 10,000 feet (3,000 metres). All these were some of the most recent effects of the Alpine orogeny.

In such circumstances, there seems to be ample opportunity for the occurrence of examples of fluvial antecedence, but in truth the areas are often particularly inaccessible, and most of them have not been surveyed sufficiently accurately to permit scientific measurements to be made. To prove antecedence, it is necessary to discover remnants of the old, pre-uplift valley whose long profile now follows the form of the most recent deformation of the range, through which the river still passes by a deepened valley. This requires both the preservation of the remnants and their accurate measurement.

The river Arun, which traverses the Himalayas by means of a gorge of 10,000 feet (3,000 metres) maximum depth, is the most quoted example, and in Europe, the Austrian river Salzach, a southern tributary of the river Inn, is considered to have cut through a belt of Triassic limestone which was uplifted in post-glacial times. There are a number of rivers in the western American mountains, such as the Columbia river gorge through the Cascades, which are believed to be antecedent, but in other cases there is insufficient evidence to distinguish between superimposition and antecedence.

UPLAND PLAINS

Platforms or *upland plains* often form a prominent and important facet of the topography of a region, and it is fairly true to say that in England any extensive level patch of ground not immediately adjacent to the coast is likely to be very nearly at either 400 or 600 feet (120 or 180 metres) above sea-level. These are two very extensive surfaces in the sense that examples are to be found spread widely over the country, but even so it is by no means certain whether all those at the same height do in fact belong to the same surface. In addition there are other level areas at different heights.

Figure 178 shows the moors on either side of the Ystwyth valley in mid Wales. The skyline is mostly at about 1,700 feet (520 metres) and forms part of the High Peneplain, whilst the foreground is at rather more than 1,300 feet (400 metres) and is a fragment of the Middle Peneplain of Wales.

A third group of platforms occurs at still greater heights in the form of *accordant summit levels* in mountain ranges. Many photo-

Fig. 178. *Upland plains in central Wales*

Fig. 179. *Accordant summit heights in central Norway*

graphs that show a considerable mountain skyline seem to indicate that most of the peaks rise to very nearly the same height, but whether or not there is any real accordance can only be determined by plotting the heights of various peaks and subjecting them to a statistical analysis. This will show if there are in fact particular levels which numerous peaks reach and between which summits are scarce or absent.

When the existence of accordance has been proved it may be considered that the summits indicate the last remnants of a peneplain which may well be of subaerial origin and, of course, belong to an earlier cycle. This is thought to be the explanation of the level skyline produced at 4,800 feet (1,500 metres) by the many peaks north of Dalsnibba in Norway (Fig. 179). This peneplain is reckoned to be of Miocene age.

On the other hand, it may be thought that given even an irregular initial upper surface, the result of fluvial, mass and sheet erosion will be the production of a series of interfluves of approximately the same height as one another. This might be compared by analogy with the fact that an initially irregular coastline is eventually converted into one that is more or less straight, regardless of varying lithology and other factors which might at first be thought to be likely to produce permanent irregularities (see p. 375).

There is at present no certainty which of the above two explanations of accordance is the correct one, and it is probable that in some localities and under some conditions one of them is true, and in other localities the other is correct.

It is fairly generally accepted that the lower surfaces, in Britain those which lie at approximately 200, 400 and 600 feet (60, 120 and 180 metres) above present sea-level, are the result of marine action. Only in exposed localities, where large waves, the result of long lengths of fetch and strong winds, may attack the land, can wave-abrasion platforms be produced, and then, unless with a slowly rising sea-level, their maximum breadth is about a mile.

In spite of this, it regularly occurs that these lower platforms are found in sheltered positions, where wave attack must of necessity have been very weak. In such cases, it is possible that scour by tidal currents may have produced the surface, but the mechanism by which this occurs is not known and there thus remains doubt as to its possibility. For the level surfaces to be cut in solid rock in such localities by marine action, the currents require to be sufficiently fast to move considerable quantities of abrasive material, such as shingle, in order to produce the erosion. Another problem is that these areas are often backed by what appear to be fossil cliffs which could scarcely be produced by tidal action.

It is probable that the surfaces above about 600 feet (180 metres) in Britain have been produced by subaerial erosion, and that they are partially completed peneplains whose formation was interrupted by uplift.

From the above discussion it is clear that here we have reached near to the limit of geomorphological knowledge. The difficulties in interpretation fall into two classes. First, there is so far insufficient field information to make it quite certain precisely what landforms we are trying to explain. It is still not known, for example, whether or not surfaces at the same altitude may be correlated with one another, and until the nature of the features is clear, the production of an explanation is difficult. The second problem lies in our lack of knowledge of the possibilities regarding submarine erosion offshore, and until more is known in that direction one cannot say with any certainty whether or not abrasion platforms in sheltered places may be formed by marine action.

Besides the summit plain, or *fjeld,* at 4,800 feet (1,500 metres) in central and northern Norway to which reference has already been made (see Fig. 179), there is a further, lower, remnant plain in the south. This is the result of Pliocene (as contrasted with Miocene for the fjeld) movements which involved both uplift and a certain amount of tilt. This high plain or *vidda* borders the fjeld on its southern side and consists of a much less dissected upland, since it is of younger, although preglacial, origin. The vidda descends from about 3,600 feet (1,100 metres) in the west to 2,300 feet (700 metres) in the east. Part of this, the Hardangervidda, is seen in Fig. 155. Here the surface is at an average of 3,300 feet (1,000 metres) with low 'hills' gently rising out of it.

Part Four

Ice and Glaciation

CHAPTER NINETEEN

Glaciation and Glaciers

THE meteorologist is concerned with ice whilst it is within the atmosphere in the form of frozen cloud particles, snowflakes or hailstones, and the glaciologist studies it as soon as it lies on land or sea. Such ice includes the great ice caps of the Antarctic and mountain plateaux, the pack ice of the Arctic, frozen rivers and lakes, glaciers, lowland ice sheets and temporarily or permanently frozen ground.

FORMATION OF GLACIAL ICE

Ice is formed by the freezing of water with the onset of colder weather or by the consolidation of snow. Only about one-third of a snowflake is ice, the remainder being air spaces. Whilst it lies on ground sufficiently cold to prevent thaw, snow forms a fluffy, feathery mass, easily blown off mountain tops by the wind and into drifts in sheltered places. This is *powder-snow*. By direct evaporation and reprecipitation without melt, it turns, generally within a few days, into a compacted mass of *firn* or *névé*. This is about half ice and half air, and is distinguished from glacial ice by the fact that it is still porous, most of the air spaces being intercommunicating channels. The original powder-snow falls off a spade as does dry sand, whereas firn holds together and is easy to dig.

A continuation of this same process, generally accompanied by a little thaw and refreeze, leads to the blockage of the air channels, so that the mass becomes non-porous. This is *white ice,* and it still contains air, but in the form of separate bubbles. Compression and more melt and refreeze eventually lead to the expulsion of most of this air, and the substance becomes solid, pure, *blue ice,* having a density of 0·92, which means that an iceberg floats in freshwater with 92 per cent submerged and in sea water with 90 per cent submerged (Fig. 180). Thus only about an eleventh or tenth of the volume of solid ice is seen above water.

Fig. 180. An iceberg in the Barents Sea

ICE CAPS

In a region where the temperature is sufficiently cool for most of the year, not all the snow that falls during the winter will melt in the brief summer. If this continues indefinitely a permanent frozen cap will lie over the area with an outer skin of very recent snow, a layer of firn and, below that, ice. The formation of such an *ice cap* is dependent upon the low mean temperature, and this occurs at low altitudes in high latitudes such as polar regions (for example, the Antarctic polar ice cap), or at higher altitudes in lower latitudes (such as the smaller ice caps in such places as the high plateaux of Switzerland, North America and Scandinavia).

Conditions are more favourable for these accumulations if there is a high precipitation, for in such cases greater thaw is required to dispose of what has been deposited. The largest ice cap in continental Europe is not in the most northerly part, but in western Norway, only a few miles north of the Sognfjord. This Jostedal ice cap extends for about 60 miles (100 km), is more than 10 miles (16 km) wide in many places, and has an ice summit level at about 7,500 feet (2,300 metres), the ice being believed to be up to 2,000 feet (600 metres) thick (Fig. 181). It occurs here because of the high precipitation in this part of Norway.

Recent investigations show that the profile of an ice cap is much the same shape in all cases, and both theory and field evidence sug-

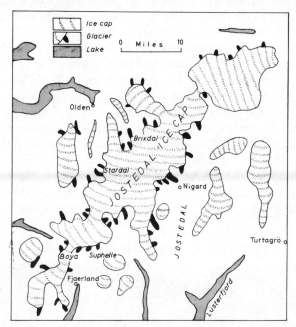

Fig. 181. The largest ice cap in Europe – Jostedal

gest that during the maximum of the last glaciation the Fenno-Scandian ice cap, which covered Norway, all Sweden except the south, the Gulf of Bothnia and most of Finland, had a thickness of more than 8,000 feet (2,400 metres) just east of the Swedish coast. The present Greenland ice cap reaches a height of over 10,800 feet (3,290 metres) and the greatest ice thickness there is 11,600 feet (3,530 metres), the rock bed in the centre of the island being about 800 feet (240 metres) below sea-level in places.

Where an ice cap lies on land and reaches more or less to the coast as in Greenland and Antarctica (Fig. 182), the ice moves slowly outwards from the interior and breaks off in great masses which often float out to sea as *icebergs*. Where, however, the ice cap does not reach the sea, it normally has something of the appearance of cake icing that has been applied too thin and has run over the edge of the cake. This is the fringe of valley glaciers which originate from the cap around its periphery. Figure 183 is a photograph of the edge of the Jostedal ice cap already mentioned, and it shows the Stardal glacier (see Fig. 181), one of the many which tumble over the edge of the plateau. The available fall here is about 3,000 feet (900 metres), but at the present time the ice mostly melts before reaching the bottom. Less than a century ago it formed a substantial glacier on the floor of the valley below. The smooth, domed surface of the ice cap itself forms the horizon, and the acceleration of the ice as it reaches a steeper gradient and eventually the fall itself is demonstrated by the many crevasses with which it is covered.

The ice moves under the influence of gravity, and even if the area is a level one spreads out from its thicker centre. Calculations of the likely thickness of different parts of an ice cap are made from a knowledge of the force required to make the ice move. There is still some doubt as to the kind of substance ice really is, especially at depth in a cap or glacier, where the high pressure, due to the weight of the ice above, alters its properties considerably. At one time it was

Fig. 182. Continental ice cap in Grahamsland

Fig. 183. The edge of the Jostedal ice cap – crevassed ice fall

thought that ice moved by shearing or sliding on itself much as a pack of cards. This is not entirely rejected, but now opinions more differ as to whether it moves in the way that wrought iron does when it is shaped, during which it behaves like a very stiff liquid, or whether the flow is plastic.

In addition, an increase of pressure produces a lowering of the melting temperature, so that the ice melts at high pressure points such as on the up-valley side of an obstruction in the glacier bed. As the material moves over and around the obstruction, pressure is relieved and freeze occurs again. This process is termed *regelation,* and may also occur within the ice mass, where excess pressure causes temporary internal thaw.

ROCHES MOUTONNÉES, GLACIAL PAVEMENTS AND STRIATIONS

Nevertheless, although there may often be a thin film of water between the ice base and the rock over which it is passing, there is sufficient friction to lead to erosion and smoothing. The existence and shape of *roches moutonnées* (see Fig. 184) show both the erosive power of ice and its ability to flex in small radius curves. The rock seen in the figure is a slate, and the apparent joint gaps on the surface are due to later erosion of less resistant bands.

Fig. 184. Roche moutonnée *in Snowdonia*

Figure 185 shows in the background the lee end of a *roche moutonnée* and in the foreground the up-ice end of another. The contrast between the smoothed slope of the latter and the precipitous slope of the former is very clear. The ice moved towards the viewpoint and the broken slope of the lee end is due to the fact that erosion occurred there by plucking, rather than by grinding. Thus *roches moutonnées* serve to determine the direction of ice movement.

At the same time, the ice may well have small stones partially embedded within its base. These act as point erosive tools and cut shallow grooves or scratches in the surface of the rock as they pass

Fig. 185. Stoss and lee ends of roches moutonnées

over it (see Fig. 186). These *striations* are only half an inch or so deep when they are freshly formed, and consequently are fairly soon destroyed by weathering when they are exposed as the ice melts away. They are best found on ice-smoothed rock which has been covered by morainic or other material until very recently.

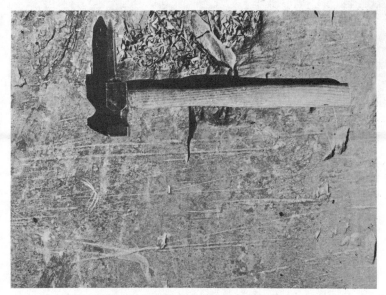

Fig. 186. Striations across a glacial pavement

The general rock surface over which a glacier moves is also smoothed in much the same way as are *roches moutonnées* but without the shaping, and such flat or approximately flat surfaces are known as *glacial pavements*.

CREVASSES

Figures 182 and 183 have already illustrated crevasses from the air, and Fig. 187 shows them on Franz Josef glacier to the west of Mount Cook, South Island, New Zealand. In every case, crevasses are caused by expansion due to acceleration. The extra volume is provided by air spaces.

Crevasses do not normally penetrate deeper than about 120 feet (37 metres), for below that depth ice becomes less brittle, but the opening up of a crevasse takes pressure off the ice beneath and
H 2

*Fig. 187. Much crevassed ice on the Franz Josef Glacier,
New Zealand*

lowers the effective surface of the ice. Consequently, individual
crevasses do penetrate to greater depths. When there are so many
crevasses that the ice becomes a series of pinnacles, the features are
termed *seracs*. Such areas are very difficult to cross, but less intensely
crevassed parts of a glacier or ice cap can usually be traversed with
skill but without much danger. Danger occurs when there has been
a snowfall and some of the crevasses are hidden. It is the crevasse
that one cannot see that is dreaded.

*Fig. 188. Faulted ice covered with ablation moraine – Penck
glacier, Spitsbergen*

The area of Franz Josef glacier shown in Fig. 187 is a confused *icefall,* and the crevasses near the 150-foot (46-metre) ice cliff edges off Grahamsland (Fig. 182) are more regular, being parallel to the edge and transverse to the ice movement and expansion.

Figure 188 illustrates another fracture feature. This is a true fault scarp, but in ice. The grey material is dirty ice and the exposed face is about 60 feet (18 metres) high. This is the slip, and it extended for half a mile. The surface is covered with a continuous layer of rock debris about 10 feet (3 metres) thick, and, since summer thaw in Spitsbergen does not penetrate more than 4 feet (1·2 metres), the ice below the morainic cover does not melt. The exposed scarp face will, of course, now do so.

VALLEY GLACIERS

Not all glaciers have their origin in ice caps. Figure 189 shows part of Spitsbergen, and here the glaciers radiate from a mountain centre

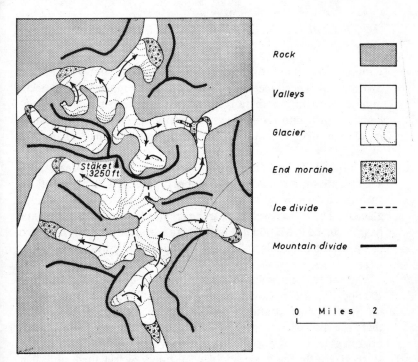

Rock

Valleys

Glacier

End moraine

Ice divide

Mountain divide

0   Miles   2

Fig. 189. Short valley glaciers without an ice cap – West Spitsbergen

Fig. 190. Piz Palū glaciers without an ice cap, Switzerland

with relatively small collecting basins. Figure 190 shows Piz Palū in Switzerland. The slopes are too steep to allow much snow to accumulate on them, for there is no extensive plateau top, and it avalanches down into the hollows to form glaciers. Such a pattern is more typical of a maturely dissected mountain mass than of a plateau.

It sometimes also occurs that a very windy highland area cannot accumulate snow even on gentle slopes because it is all blown off. In such cases there is no ice cap but the area is surrounded by valley glaciers. These may well start in *valley heads* such as may perhaps have occurred in Måbödal (Fig. 155), and as more certainly occurred in the Great Langdale valley of the English Lake District (see Fig. 242).

The pattern occurs at the head of the main glacier (no. 6) in Figs. 191 and 192, which show Monte Rosa (15,230 feet: 4,640 metres) on the Swiss–Italian frontier. From the top right-hand side of the view there is a disorderly tumble of snow and ice, forming a more or less broken glacier, down to the lower level where the full glacier (no. 6) starts. Here the ice is already several hundred feet thick and, if it were to melt away, would reveal a steep-ended valley head of the Langdale type.

GLACIER SYSTEMS AND MORAINES

Glaciers join one another (see Fig. 191) and, being solid, ride side by side without much mixing. *Lateral moraines* are formed along the edges of each glacier, mostly composed of pieces of rock that have been broken off the mountainsides by weathering and have fallen on to the ice below.

As the glaciers meet, the lateral moraines between them become *medial,* and a number of these are shown in Fig. 192. Each of the three glaciers coming in from the right is already a pair (nos. 1 and 2, 3 and 4, and 5 and 6) with a medial moraine; compression is so great in the main valley that glaciers nos. 2 and 4 are pushed beneath other ice and wedged out of view; whilst glacier no. 3 is also overridden by no. 2 at its confluence. Several lateral moraines unite to form a broad composite medial one.

On the left, somewhat similar circumstances prevail. No. 7 is gradually wedged down between nos. 6 and 8, and the latter disappears beneath no. 6, when it meets the intruding buttress of rock.

Thus the composite whole is built up, and one may well imagine the complex of *englacial moraine* contained within the ice from the burial of various medial ones. Englacial moraine is also formed in a more sporadic and casual way by debris falling into crevasses and so becoming engulfed.

Supraglacial moraine comprises stones which fell on to the surface of a glacier, rolled some distance on to the ice, and so failed to be lateral. Such stones feed the crevasse englacial material.

It often occurs that curious isolated patches of moraine appear on the surface. One such 'island' may be seen in Fig. 191 on the bend of glacier no. 3 and numbered 3a in Fig. 192. There are several other patches which may be of the same type. These are *shear-plane moraines* and are produced by bottom ice, containing ground moraine (see below), riding over the ice that lies in front of it and forming what a geologist would term a thrust fault. This brings ground moraine to the surface, and the line of such moraine commonly lies across the direction of glacier movement. It particularly occurs where there is considerable compressional stress, such as at the position shown in glacier no. 3, where there is the sharp turn to negotiate.

There are two other major types: *submerged lateral* and *ground moraine.* Neither of these is visible on the surface of the ice. *Submerged lateral moraine* occurs between the side of the glacier and the valley wall due to lateral erosion by the glacier, which mainly occurs as it is rounding a bend in the valley. *Ground moraine* is composed of material eroded by the glacier and also of englacial moraine that may have worked its way to the bottom of the ice.

Fig. 191. Monte Rosa and its glaciers

When summer thaw melts away the top surface of a glacier, all the debris that was contained in that thickness of ice and which is of too large a calibre to be transported by the meltwater, is concentrated on the top surface of the remaining ice. This is *ablation moraine* and it may form a continuous blanket of powdered stone and boulders covering the whole surface of the ice. If the layer is thin (less than an inch, say), it has the effect of increasing the melt rate, since the stone absorbs solar heat more easily than does ice, so that the thin layer of debris becomes warm and heats the ice beneath it by conduction.

If, however, the blanket is thicker (see Fig. 188), it is sufficient to

Fig. 192. Diagram of the Monte Rosa system of glaciers

prevent solar heat from reaching the ice, and so slows down or even stops further thaw. A block of ice, engulfed in rock material with a thickness greater than that of the active layer above the permafrost will never thaw whilst it remains so covered and whilst the present climate prevails. Such blocks may thus survive for thousands of years although stagnant and long broken from their parent glacier. (They lead to kettle-holes when they eventually melt, see p. 250.)

Fig. 193. Tributary cirque glacier on Aletsch glacier, Switzerland

CIRQUE GLACIERS

Figure 193 is the view across the Aletsch glacier near the Jungfrau, and it not only shows again some features similar to those in Fig. 191, but also shows a very fine *cirque tributary glacier*. This has a semicircular collecting area of steep-walled mountains so that the single glacier, which falls down on to the Aletsch, is actually a collection of numerous quite small ones. The floor of the cirque quite clearly is at a much higher level than the floor of the main glacier, several hundred feet below the ice level.

This is an example of the fact that most cirques have been produced mainly by short tributary glaciers, although, as is the case in Fig. 194, when the climate becomes a little warmer, they may so shrink that the two become detached, and a true *cirque glacier* is formed. The one shown in this illustration is on the northern slope of Fannaråki (6,788 feet: 2,069 metres) on Sygnefjell, Norway. The snout of the glacier just reaches to the lip of the cirque, where it forms an ice precipice from which pieces break off to produce the ice scree at the foot.

Cirques are known as *corries* in Scotland, and as *cwms* in Wales.

The form of the rock back and floor of a cirque will be discussed in Chapter 23, and the chief features to note here are that the short glacier may be a tributary to a main one or may be isolated, and that in either case the cirque floor *hangs* above the main valley bottom.

THE GLACIER BALANCE SHEET

A glacier (and ice cap and ice sheet) experiences accumulation and ablation. *Accumulation* is the volume added to it by snowfall or other precipitation and by windblown or avalanched snow. *Ablation* is what is lost mainly by melting but also by evaporation, and sometimes by wind erosion *(deflation)*. Either of these may be the greater, or they may be equal.

In the up-valley part of a glacier, accumulation is in excess of ablation, and the quantity of ice in the glacier becomes greater. There is a balance on any particular cross-section of the glacier if accumulation equals ablation plus loss by movement of ice down-valley. In such a case that part of the glacier is in *equilibrium,* and it stays the same size.

Below a certain point, whose position will always vary, although only within certain limits, the losses exceed the gains, and the size of the glacier gradually becomes smaller and smaller down-valley. In

Fig. 194. Fannaråki cirque glacier – western Norway

any particular year, the place on the glacier below which all last year's snow has melted away by the end of the summer marks the line where the balance occurs at that moment. This is known as the *firn* or *névé limit*. This corresponds to the *snow-line* on mountainsides. Neither of these is in fact a line, for the micro-climatology is such that transition from one side of it to the other is patchy, and there is a zone where there are isolated areas of firn or snow.

A glacier is bulky because of its slow rate of movement. Speeds that commonly occur lie anywhere between 2 inches (5 cm) a week to 2 feet ($\frac{1}{2}$ metre) an hour, but much slower, and also much faster, rates can be found. Recent measurements indicate that much of the peripheral part of the Antarctic ice cap moves less than a foot a month ($3\frac{1}{2}$ metres a year) – but a glacier is faster.

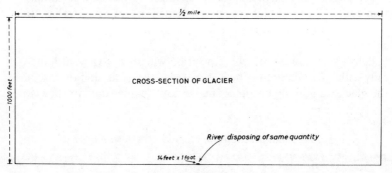

Fig. 195. *The sizes of glaciers and rivers compared*

Perhaps an intermediate value of, say, 10 feet (3 metres) a week is a good average figure for a fairly steeply sloping valley glacier. If it is half a mile (say, 800 metres) wide and 1,000 feet (300 metres) thick, this gives a figure of 26 million cu feet (720,000 cu metres) of ice passing a particular locality each week. This is equivalent to about 24 million cu feet (680,000 cu metres) of water, and for a river flowing at, say, 2 miles (3 km) an hour to dispose of this quantity, it would require a cross-sectional area of only 14 square feet (1·3 sq m). That is to say, a glacier of the dimensions given would only dispose of the same amount of precipitation as would a 14-foot wide stream a foot deep (or, say, 6·5 metres wide and 20 cm deep). With the same precipitation, the same catchment area would be required, and this accounts for the great volume of glaciers and the equally small size of streams that inherit glaciated valleys (see Figs. 195 and 264).

SNOUT

As ablation exceeds accumulation the glacier gradually decreases in size down-valley until eventually it terminates in the *snout*. Figure 196 shows the profile of the snout of Brixdal glacier, one of those which come from the Jostedal ice cap (see Fig. 181). This is exceptionally clean ice, carrying very little moraine with it. The vertical

Fig. 196. Snout of a blue-ice glacier – Brixdal, Jostedal ice cap

edge of the right-hand part of the snout is about 50 feet (15 metres) high and rests in a lake formed by the meltwater held up by an old, abandoned end moraine farther down the valley. The irregular melt is quite typical, and the full colour of blue ice is displayed in the depths of the embayments.

Figure 197 shows the Boya glacier snout, another from the same Jostedal cap, but of a rather different type. Much of the meltwater comes from an *ice tunnel* about 20 feet high and 50 feet wide (6 by 15 metres). The roof of the tunnel is becoming thin and wide, and crevasses are already appearing in it prior to collapse, which occurred in this case about a week after the photograph was taken. A fall of upper ice had occurred on the previous day over the fairly steep front of the snout and had produced the heap of white broken ice.

The position of the snout varies. There has been a general recession up-valley for over two hundred years in most glacial areas where information can be obtained and in addition there are minor

Fig. 197. Ice cave in glacier snout – Boya, Fjaerland, Sogn

short-period and even annual fluctuations. These all indicate long- or short-term changes of climate and the differences between individual winters and summers. A winter with high snowfall and a cloudy, cool summer both encourage a few feet of lengthening.

GLACIAL EROSION AND PROTECTION

It is very ordinary for a glacier to be 1,000 feet (300 metres) thick. Many are much thicker. The pressure on the base of 1,000-foot column is 26 tons per sq foot (30 kgm per sq cm), and even though ice under those conditions has modified physical properties, it is able to erode very effectively. The fact that a glacier does so is clearly demonstrated by the amount of debris contained within it as seen at its snout, and this is normally the case even with those glaciers which have come directly off ice caps without any possibility of weathered rock falling on to them from valley sides. In such cases, everything contained within and under the ice must have come from bottom erosion.

Nevertheless, the erosive rate of the actual ice cap away from its edges is quite slow. Bottom movement is slight and it is this which largely gave rise to the *ice protection* theory, as opposed to *ice erosion*. It is possible that protection because of the ice cover may result under the centre of some ice caps. Normal weathering has been replaced by slow ice erosion, and it is merely a case of which is the greater of the two. Some indication of the results of this, compared with valley glacier erosion, will become apparent when discussing the topography of fossil ice cap areas (in Chapter 23).

PIEDMONT GLACIERS AND LOWLAND ICE SHEETS

It may happen that a valley glacier comes beyond the mountain limit without melting and it thus thrusts out either into the sea or on to a lowland plain. In the latter instance it spreads out to form a *piedmont*

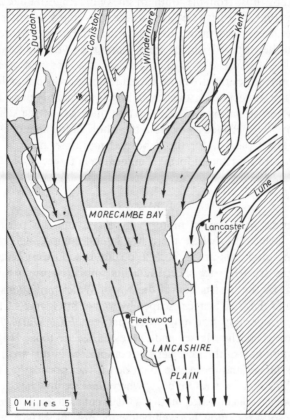

Fig. 198. Valley glaciers forming a lowland ice sheet

glacier. One of the major results of this is that the ice becomes proportionately thinner, and, consequently, with the decrease of pressure upon its base, its power of erosion decreases and it may even begin to deposit some of the ground moraine which it was previously transporting (see p. 241).

When a number of adjacent valley glaciers all become piedmont side by side, they may unite laterally and form a *lowland ice sheet*. This occurred in North America, Europe and Britain during the Ice

Ages and the deposits of such ice sheets are of the utmost importance to all these areas in connection with presentday agriculture. Such deposits will be discussed in the next chapter.

An example of piedmont glaciers uniting to form an ice sheet is afforded by those from the southern side of the English Lake District (see Fig. 198). The Irish Sea at that time was empty of water due to the lower ocean-level throughout the world, and so both Morecambe Bay and the eastern Irish Sea were continuous with the Lancashire Plain. The ice spread over the whole of this area and eventually mostly moved southwards into Cheshire and Shropshire. Although the features associated with such ice sheets are mainly depositional, there are erosional ones also. A certain thickness of the solid rock must have been eroded away from the whole of the area over which the ice sheet passed, for the deposited morainic material always contains a proportion of local or immediately up-ice rock.

ICEWAYS

Some areas were eroded more than others, and this particularly applies to localities where there was lateral compression between adjoining mountain areas. Such a locality is southwest Lancashire where the Irish Sea ice sheet found its southerly progress greatly impeded by the obstruction of the North Wales mountains.

Some of the Irish Sea ice escaped by way of St George's Channel, but a considerable fraction moved between East Wales and the Pennines where the Mersey and Dee estuaries are today (Fig. 199). The eastern half of the ice sheet was compressed in this area, and so became thicker and more able to erode the rocks beneath. This was especially so on the western edge, where the Dee now lies, for there was more ice concentrated on that side. It cut an irregular groove so that the solid rock now lies well below the present surface, which is filled in with glacial and marine deposits. There were three other parallel grooves to the northeast of the first one, as shown on the map. These are *iceways,* hollows eroded in solid rock by the movement of a lowland ice sheet, and in this example they are about 1 to 3 miles ($1\frac{1}{2}$ to 5 km) wide and the deepest parts of their floors are nearly 500 feet (150 metres) lower than the rock ridges that lie between them. One of their characteristics is the irregular long profile, which alternately rises and deepens, as the depth figures on the map indicate, in very much the same way as does the long profile of a glaciated valley.

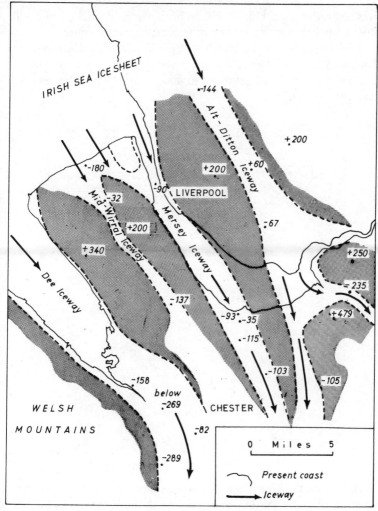

Fig. 199. Iceways eroded by a lowland ice sheet (heights and depths in feet above and below Ordnance Datum)

TIDAL GLACIERS AND SHELF ICE

It may happen that a valley glacier reaches the sea directly from the mountains. If the depth of water is sufficient, the glacier floats without necessarily first breaking up. As with icebergs, 10 per cent of the thickness of the glacier is above sea-water level and the remainder below if the ice is pure. If it contains enclosed air, that is, is white rather than blue, it will be proportionately lighter and will float with a greater fraction of its volume above the water.

This means that a 300-foot (or, say, 100-metre) thick glacier will float with at least 30 feet (10 metres) above water-level and requires 270 feet (90 metres) of sea water to make it do so. Such glaciers are termed *tidal glaciers*.

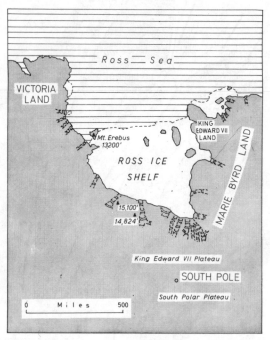

Fig. 200. Ross Ice Shelf, Antarctica

The Antarctic, Greenland and some other ice caps come directly down to the sea without ever passing through the valley-glacier stage. They then behave in exactly the same way, and if the water is sufficiently deep, they float off the bottom and become *shelf ice*. The most famous of all these is the Ross Ice Shelf (Fig. 200), which has an area of about 200,000 square miles (500,000 sq km) (four times that of England) and averages 600 feet (180 metres) in thickness. Not all of it is floating. Naturally, it eventually breaks up and forms icebergs.

CHAPTER TWENTY

Glacial Deposition

As has already been described, a glacier or lowland ice sheet, and to a lesser degree an ice cap, all carry with them a considerable amount of debris of various kinds, known collectively as moraine. As it reaches the end of the glacier or sheet, this debris is deposited as *end moraine*. Some of it is promptly redistributed by meltwater. When eventually the ice melts away, at the termination of the cold period, the whole of it is deposited over a much larger area as *ground moraine*. In addition, active, moving ice often builds up *drumlins* using a part of the subglacial moraine.

DRUMLINS

There is almost invariably a layer of broken rock between the underside of ice and the solid rock. This intermediate detached layer may either be carried along with the ice, or it may tend to stagnate. This alternative action may be demonstrated by placing a thin book on a fairly rough table-top, with a thicker one on top. If you slide the latter gently along without much pressure, the lower book will be left behind; whereas if considerable pressure is applied the probabilities are that the lower book will move along with the upper.

This illustrates the fact that ground moraine (represented by the lower book) is carried along by the ice if the latter is thick and thus

Fig. 201. Drumlins near Millom, northwest England

exerts considerable pressure upon it, whilst it is left behind if the ice is less thick. Deposits of ground moraine of this type thus particularly occur where a glacier enters a wider reach of valley or becomes piedmont. The moraine especially accumulates where there may be obstructions to its movement, such as *roches moutonnées* or the like, and thus stream-lined masses of ground moraine, often with a core of solid rock, are formed beneath the moving ice. These are *drumlins* (Fig. 201).

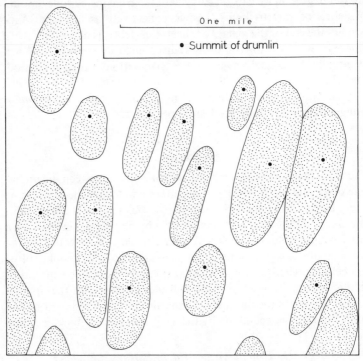

Fig. 202. Drumlins in Furness, Lancashire

They tend to have an oval ground plan (Fig. 202), with the length/width ratio varying greatly, in this instance from 1·6 to 4·0. These drumlins, which are part of a swarm formed by piedmont glaciers of the English Lake District, accurately indicate the direction of movement of the ice which shaped them by the orientation of their long axes.

Fig. 203. Half-drowned composite drumlin in Strangford Lough

It has been said that the stoss end has a somewhat steeper gradient than the down-ice or lee end, but this is very often not the case. Most examples appear to have about the same slope at both ends, although their highest point is usually (but not invariably) near the stoss end. They vary enormously in size from only a few tens of feet (a few metres) to a mile and a half (say, 2 km), but half to three-quarters of a mile ($\frac{3}{4}$ to 1 kilometre) is the commonest range of length, often with a height of about 60 feet (say, 20 metres) above their surroundings.

They show particularly well in areas where they have since been partially drowned by the sea as in Strangford Lough, Northern Ireland (Fig. 203). In this air photograph, drumlins of various shapes are seen and some of them are 'twins'. The warmest post-glacial stage (see Chapter 28) experienced a slightly higher sea-level than today and the resulting cliffing on the right-hand side of several of the drumlins may be seen.

The fact that they particularly occur when the ice suddenly thins due to valley-widening is exemplified in the portion of the Coniston valley immediately south of Coniston Water itself. Here, as is seen in Fig. 204, the valley widens to more than twice its previous breadth,

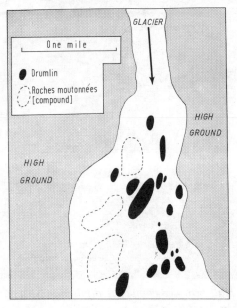

Fig. 204. Occurrence of drumlins coincident with valley-widening

and drumlins are formed in profusion in contrast to the narrower part up-valley where there are none. For the same reason, drumlins are often formed on the plain where a valley glacier becomes piedmont and spreads laterally with a corresponding decrease in thickness.

Drumlins are thus an example of subglacial deposition directly produced by the ice itself, and they most often indicate fairly thin ice (this means ice a hundred or two feet in thickness, as contrasted with ice several hundreds or even a thousand or more feet in thickness).

TERMINAL AND END MORAINES

At the snout of the glacier all the debris contained on, in and under the ice is deposited, although, as already stated, some of it is very often transported or at least sorted and redistributed by the melt-

Fig. 205. Massive end moraine of Blaaisen, Finse, Norway

water. Naturally, material of larger calibre tends to remain where the ice dropped it. If the position of the snout remains unchanged for a number of years, there is a considerable accumulation of such material in the form of a ridge of debris across the valley, or in the case of a lowland ice sheet across the plain.

This is *end moraine*. Figure 205 shows a great heap of end moraine about 100 feet (30 metres) high in front of the fan-shaped, piedmont glacier. *Terminal moraine* is the term employed for the end moraine which marks the greatest advance of the ice during the particular cold period, although the two terms are not always clearly distinguished by all authors.

Figure 206 shows the terminal moraine of the Würm I glaciation across the Vale of York, where it forms a double ridge of gravelly material some hundred feet high and several hundred feet in width. These are known as the York and Escrick moraines. They have modified the drainage pattern to some extent, and north–south rivers make use of natural gaps in the moraine, some of which they have widened by fluvial erosion. East–west roads tend to lie along the summits of the ridges, since these are natural dry routes. The more important of these are marked on the map.

Such end moraines are in general compound in nature, comprising several more or less parallel ridges, some of which may be discon-

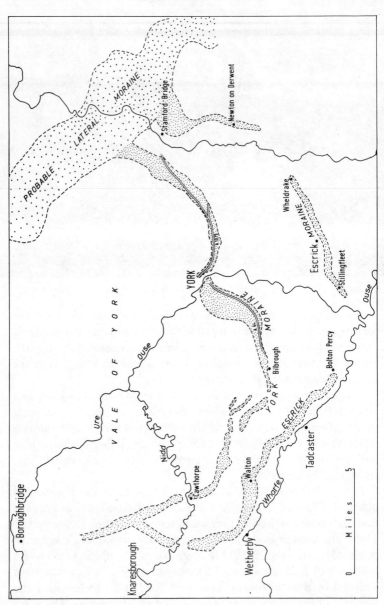

Fig. 206. York and Escrick terminal moraines

tinuous and others of which may coalesce, converge or diverge from one another. Examples of all these characteristics are seen in Fig. 206. Very often the relief form is quite complex.

The terminal moraine of the Daniglacial ice sheet divides Denmark into two by the great change of topography, land use and even culture on either side of it, as is described in Chapter 22.

During the decay stages of an ice sheet, temporarily stable climatic conditions lead to the occurrence of periods of twenty to a hundred years during which the position of the ice margin remains static, and such stillstands are indicated on the ground by minor end moraines. During the Valley glacial (see Fig. 233), the Coniston glacier terminated more or less at what is now the southern end of Coniston Water, but varied in position slightly, so that a group of terminal moraines, or, if one prefers it, a compound terminal moraine, were/was formed. Several of these are shown on the Coniston Water photograph and sketch in Chapter 23.

A glacier snout may be retreating up-valley more or less continuously year by year, and in this case there is insufficient time for a true end moraine ridge to be formed. Each individual year's deposit occurs behind the previous year's, and so there is a more or less continuous, untidy, general spread of debris over a considerable area. This is not ground moraine, but rather is a spread of end moraine.

<h3 style="text-align:center">PUSH AND ANNUAL MORAINES</h3>

It is natural that in most glacial regions little or no melt occurs during the winter months, and the few measurements that have been made show that the ice continues to move during the annual cold period, sometimes even more rapidly than during the summer. The result of this is that the end moraine which has been dropped during the summer, warmer period, is often rammed forward in a bulldozer fashion during the cold period, and may thus be deformed from its original pattern.

Figure 207 shows such a push moraine, seawards of the snout of Penck glacier in Van Keulenfjord, West Spitsbergen. The rolled form of the terrain is very clearly seen, and Fig. 208 shows a section in such rolled material of fairly small calibre at Milton Bridge, Midlothian, where a type of nappe has actually been produced.

When winter re-advance is coupled with a general recession, a series of annual push moraines may be formed in front of the snout of the glacier, and these are shown in Fig. 209 at Blaaisen, Finse, Norway.

Fig. 207.
Push moraine of
Penck glacier,
Spitsbergen

Fig. 208.
Overfold in pushed
glacial sand,
Midlothian

Fig. 209.
Annual moraines
of Blaaisen, Finse

Here the *annual moraines* are about 3 yards high, and are backed by a much larger moraine above 100 feet in height (Fig. 205), which was deposited during a stand when the position of the snout remained more or less stationary for a considerable number of years. In Fig. 209 the glacier is to the left, three or four annual moraines are seen, each having been rammed forward by the winter advance of the glacier, and the large moraine seen in Fig. 205 is off the picture to the right.

A somewhat similar effect was produced on the plains north of Stockholm and Uppsala. At the time of the ice recession, these were covered by the Yoldia Sea which was in contact with the ice edge so that the moraines were laid down under water. The ice retreated rapidly – about 200 yards (180 metres) a year, and it has been thought that each of the moraines indicates a year of retreat. Doubt, however, has been expressed as to whether or not this is a correct explanation, especially since the spacing of the so-called annual moraines does not accord with the much more certain varve chrono-

deposits from icebergs that had calved off the nearby ice front.

Such *washboard moraines* produce a distinctive type of landscape, with level agricultural ground, the old sea bottom, crossed every few hundred yards (metres) by a stony moraine about 5 yards (5 m) in height clad with coniferous trees.

GROUND MORAINE AND TILL (BOULDER CLAY)

An important type of glacial deposit is *ground moraine*. The material of which it is composed is known as *till,* an American term which tends to replace the previous English term of *boulder clay*. Till is a preferable word, since the moraine may be without boulders, some-times is without clay, and sometimes even without both boulders and clay, being in that case a sand, so that the old title becomes something of an odd misnomer.

Till is a more or less continuous cover of morainic material left by the ice, especially by a lowland ice sheet, when it melts away. It represents the debris which lay beneath the ice, together with the material which had become embedded within the ice, or was resting on its upper surface. It is quite commonly stratified to some extent, for the bottom moraine is more closely packed than the upper parts of the deposit, since it had the weight of the ice upon it, and the remainder merely settled down as the ice melted away. The upper, less closely packed part, is known as *ablation moraine*. The division

I

of the deposit into two obvious parts has often misled investigators into thinking that they were looking at the results of two glaciations.

Since a drumlin is formed beneath the ice, it too receives an envelope of ablation moraine when the ice ultimately melts away, and sections in drumlins normally show this distinct upper layer often as much as 2 feet (60 cm) in thickness.

There is a tendency for such till to be smoothed out to some extent by the last movements of the ice sheet, and it produces a gently rolling topography which is induced by the fact that the till is a general blanket covering the undulations of the previously existing fluvial surface modified as it has been by ice abrasion.

If the ice becomes stagnant before it melts away, as happens when the ice is long-distant from its source and loses the motive power which has propelled it forward, it becomes what is termed *dead ice*. As the ground, englacial and ablation moraine then settles down out of this mass, it remains where it falls, and since it was unequally distributed over the ice, it forms a blanket of uneven thickness. This produces *hummocky moraine* with numerous small lakes.

Some of the unequal thickness of this type of moraine results from debris falling down crevasses in the ice and so becoming concentrated in a ridgelike pattern.

KETTLE MORAINE

As ice melts it does so somewhat irregularly, so that isolated blocks often remain during the recession in much the same way as stacks commonly occur on a retreating cliff coast. These ice masses are usually buried amongst the general debris, the surface of which may be more or less flat. When eventually the ice block melts away, the surface of the moraine above it collapses and produces irregular hollows. These are known as *kettle-holes,* and undulating till of this kind is known as *kettle moraine.* The same term is also used when the ice blocks were embedded in an end moraine, which, when they melt, acquires an even more complex form. Small lakes often occur in the hollows so formed.

TILL PLAINS

Very large areas of lowland in regions that have been glaciated, for example, in Canada, northern United States, Britain, West Germany, Poland and U.S.S.R., are today free from ice sheets, but are covered by the layer of till, forming *till plains,* on which most of the agriculture has to be carried on. In the cooler temperate plain lands, the existence of this till is of the very greatest economic importance, for it is on this material that most of the food supply of these areas, and the areas of the world to which they export, is grown.

A detailed knowledge of the variations in composition of these deposits and some understanding of the ways in which they were formed is therefore of the greatest possible importance to those who cultivate these areas.

ERRATICS

Most morainic material has been transported some distance by the ice, and the name *erratic*, or wanderer, is given particularly to boulders which have been deposited by the melting ice on ground which was not their original home. These may be, for example, transported boulders of limestone deposited on other limestone, but the term is most frequently used when it refers to a boulder of one kind of rock that has come to rest on bedrock of a different type.

If the erratic is a rock which has its origin only in a small area, this is particularly helpful, for all stones of that particular material, wherever they are found, will have a known origin. For example, boulders of a particular granite (ribeckite granite), which only occurs on Ailsa Craig in the Firth of Clyde, may be found in the Isle of Man, on the Lancashire plain and even in Cheshire.

Shap granite is another unique rock and *boulder trains* of this may be found which indicate that ice moved from the Shap area across the Pennines into Yorkshire. Figure 210 shows the localities where Shap

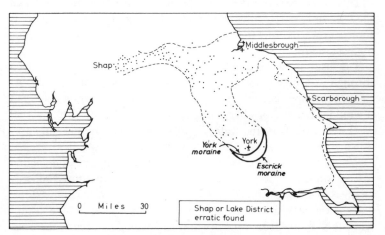

Fig. 210. Train of Lake District erratics into Yorkshire

or Lake District erratics have been found on the eastern side of the Pennines, and the two routes taken by the ice, one along the Vale of York to the York and Escrick moraines, but not beyond, and the other by way of Middlesbrough to the North Sea and just a few miles in on the east coast as far south as the Humber, are very plain to see.

Such *indicator erratics* are particularly important, since they reveal the tracks of the moving ice, and prove that it moved from the source point to the place where they are found.

MELTWATER DEPOSITS

Eskers

Excepting in the coldest climates, there is always a considerable amount of meltwater associated with a glacier, especially during the warmer season. Water has been shown issuing from a tunnel which emerges at the snout in Fig. 197, and waterlain deposits are very often found within these tunnels.

When the water is present in considerable quantity, the flow differs from a river, for if the tunnel is full, the water behaves as though it were in a pipe, and thus is subject to hydrostatic pressure. The static pressure at any particular point in the tunnel is given by the formula

$$P = h \cdot d_w,$$

where P is the pressure, h is the head or height of the point where the tunnel becomes full above the point considered, and d_w is the density of water (see Fig. 211).

This effect does not occur in open channels nor in tunnels when they are only partly filled with water. Piped public water supply is forced upwards into the higher storeys of buildings by this same hydrostatic pressure.

The result in the case of a glacier tunnel is that the water is forced through at a high velocity, depending on the head of water, h. At these higher speeds, the water is able to carry a much larger load than it would otherwise be able to do, both as regards calibre and actual total quantity. Thus the water in a full subglacial tunnel can carry down a very considerable amount of material.

When, in the colder season, the flow of water decreases sufficiently for the tunnel to be no longer full to the roof, the flow suddenly changes to one determined merely by the gradient of the tunnel floor, and the water behaves exactly as in an ordinary river. At the instant when this change from capacity flow to fluvial flow occurs, there is a sudden and substantial change in speed, and thus in load-carrying power. Much of the debris which a moment before had been on the move is deposited on the floor of the tunnel.

Special conditions result if h approaches the value of t, the vertical thickness of the ice, and these will be discussed in the next chapter (see p. 265).

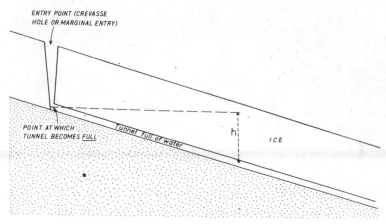

Fig. 211. *Hydrostatic pressure in a subglacial tunnel*

If the glacier itself is in motion, the tunnel moves down-valley with the ice, and thus its position changes. The deposit on its floor is smeared and becomes subglacial moraine. If, however, the glacier is dead, that is, is stagnant, then the tunnel will remain in the one position, and the deposit will do so also. When the ice melts away, the deposit will then be left as a mound snaking across the countryside in the plan of the now vanished tunnel. This is an *esker*.

Figure 212 shows a network of such eskers, now exposed by the melting of the ice, but partly concealed by the waters of a lake. This is in Oviksfjällen, 150 miles (240 km) west of Kramfors, Sweden.

The contents of such a tunnel may of course comprise several layers of deposit, some parts of which may be of larger calibre than others, some of which may even be sand. The section across an esker in Eire is seen in Fig. 213, and it shows coarse stratification of this kind. It is being quarried, as is very often the case, for aggregate for concrete, since here is a deposit of stones without clay.

Since eskers require stagnant ice for their formation, they are to be found in some glaciated areas and not in others. They are in general very rare in England and Wales, for there most of the ice melted

Fig. 212. Esker network in Norrland

Fig. 213. Esker section at Freffans, Eire

away whilst still on the move. On the contrary, they occur in very large numbers and of great size in many of the lower lands of Sweden. Figure 214 shows the large numbers of eskers in the area between Gävle and Nyköping. These are exceptionally long and large (see Fig. 215), both because of the intensity of the glaciation and the long period of dead ice.

There are a number of eskers of moderate size in the central valley of Scotland, and in Strangford Lough, where, besides the half-drowned drumlins already pictured (see Fig. 203), there

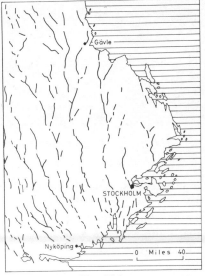

Fig. 214.
Eskers of part of central Sweden

Fig. 215. *The side of the Stockholm esker*

Fig. 216. Half-drowned esker in Strangford Lough

is an esker in similar condition, as seen from the air in Fig. 216. This appears to widen at either end, but part of this may be only apparent as the result of the level of the esker coming somewhat higher so that more is above water-level, or it may be a *beaded esker*, the result of extra accumulation in wider parts of the tunnel.

Kames

The bulbous lobe on the right of the same photograph may well be the point where it emerged from the tunnel at the ice sheet edge, and where a deltaic structure was produced to form a *delta kame*. Again the deposit is waterlain, this time with a much closer stratification.

Other eskerlike ridges may occur as the result of the recession of a glacier snout. The delta kame may be formed at the mouth of a sub-ice tunnel as the position of the ice margin progressively moves up-valley. The mouth of the tunnel naturally moves up-valley also, and thus the kame is elongated. In time a substantial ridge may be formed. This type of *pseudo-esker* or *esker kame* is particularly prone to variations in width along its length, the wider portions being reflections of slower retreat of the ice front or of rapid accumulation of debris from the subglacial stream.

Part of a quarry in a delta kame near Galtrim, Eire, is shown in Fig. 217, and the foreset beds of the front edge of the pebble bank may be seen. The ice and the esker were to the right. Such a kame is an *extraglacial deposit*, that is, it was formed beyond the ice limits.

The word *kame* is one which has come to be used for a variety of water-deposited heaps of glacial debris, and for this reason it is always desirable to preface it with a descriptive adjective of some kind for the sake of clarity. A *crevasse kame* is formed at the foot of a hole in the ice down which a surface melt stream may cascade, taking debris with it. It then often builds up a cone-shaped heap at the bottom. There are also other types of kame in connection with glacial lakes, to be described shortly.

Beyond the snout of a glacier, there is a general outflow of meltwater streams, and since these are in existence at the same time as the end moraine is being formed, it is usual for the latter never to have been made as a complete barrier across the whole width of the snout. It possesses several original gaps breaking it up into sections. These gaps are at the chief points of flow of the meltwater streams. (See Fig. 206 where the gaps have now been adopted by the presentday rivers.)

Outwash Fans or Sandar

The outwash of meltwater from a glacier snout very often spreads over a considerable area of the ground in front of it, with numerous diverging and converging channels. It forms a great expanse of sand and fine gravel in a deltaic fashion, which may occupy the whole width of the valley within which it lies. These are *outwash fans* if fairly small or *sandar* (singular = *sandur*) if large, and they occur particularly where the meltwater brings down considerable debris but where there is little large calibre material with which to form end moraines.

Fig. 217. Foreset beds in the Galtrim kame, Eire

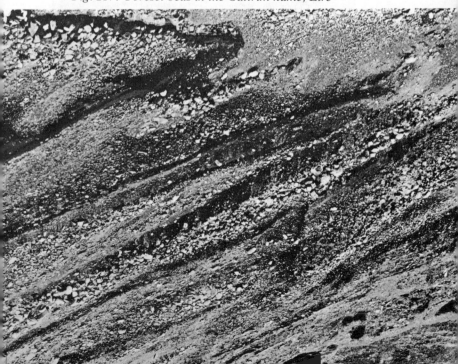

They occur in large size in Iceland, where they especially occupy a considerable proportion of the ground between the Vatnajökull and the ocean. A smaller, fossil one in central Sweden is shown in Fig. 218, where the sandur now lies in a deep glacial trough between two lakes.

Fig. 218. Fossil sandur in north central Sweden

MARGINAL AND LATERAL LAKES AND KAMES

A different type of terrain immediately below the snout is to be found if the glacier is retreating with stillstands, so that a series of end moraines has been formed across the valley at intervals. Some of these may well be sufficiently continuous across the valley floor to act as dams, and so convert the area between the snout and the old end moraine into a lake. A very large number of Scandinavian and Swiss glaciers today have their snouts in contact with such lakes.

These are *marginal* or *ice-contact meltwater lakes.* The water and also the water in the rivers flowing from glacier snouts is normally quite cloudy, due to the amount of clay in suspension.

It is normal for the ice at the side of a glacier to be a little lower than the general ice surface, often by some thirty or forty feet. Since this abuts the steeply rising rock side of the valley, it is very common for ice-bound *lateral lakes* to be formed along these edges. Ice surface streams of meltwater may flow into them, picking up debris from the glacier on the way, and so build small kames, *lateral lake kames.* These kames and the general silt, the bottom deposits in these lakes, are left perched on the valleyside when the lake eventually drains away as the glacier shrinks.

When the lowland ice from Norway and southern Sweden spread across the whole of eastern Denmark, the subglacial meltwater streams found themselves flowing over unconsolidated ground, the till of the previous glaciations. Erosion by these subglacial streams produced grooves in the older till which today, when the ice has long since gone, appear on the surface as *tunnel valleys.*

These are not unique to Denmark, but are particularly common and large there. The valleys, which are the presentday landform resulting from them, are often as much as a mile ($1\frac{1}{2}$ km) in width, although a quarter to a half is commoner. They are usually about 100 feet (30 metres) deep in the general till plain, and the long-profile of their floor may not be continuously downhill.

Since the valley had an ice lid over it when it was being formed, it was then a tunnel, and the water within it, when it filled it, was under hydrostatic pressure and could easily flow uphill. Today these valleys are consequently often bestrewn with lakes in the hollows, and the famous Silkeborg Lake District in northern Jutland (Jylland) is unique amongst scenic, holiday lake districts, in not being surrounded by mountains, but merely by morainic hills.

Owing to the fact that it is very usual for a glacier only a few miles in length to be a thousand or more feet in thickness, the upper surface of the ice often lies at a higher level than the lower parts of the bounding rock ridge. Meltwater from the glacier in such cases very often escapes from its own valley into the neighbouring one by forming an *overflow channel.* Again, because the stream may be linked

*Fig. 219. Fossil glacial overflow channel near Cocksburnpath,
Berwickshire, southern Scotland*

with a temporary lateral lake, it is always possible that the long-
profile may now, with the ice melted away, show uphill sections. An
overflow channel of this type, breaching a low divide in Berwickshire, southern Scotland, is shown in Fig. 219. Note the steep sides
and the dry nature of the floor of the valley which now carries no
drainage. The scale is given by the minor road which makes use of
the easy routeway.

CHAPTER TWENTY-ONE

Deglaciation

A PERIOD of deglaciation is one of particularly intense morphological activity, both as regards erosion and deposition. As amelioration of climatic conditions progresses, the amount of ice covering an
area decreases, and this is a time of periglacial conditions when
freeze-thaw is exceptionally efficacious and there is a very large
amount of running water available for direct fluvial erosion and
debris transportation, with a correspondingly large volume of deposition in the quieter reaches of the streams and in lakes.

THE MELTING ICE CAP

In the case of a substantial mountain massif more or less completely
covered with ice, as, for example, Greenland now is and Scandinavia
was, the crestline of the continuous ice cap is independent of and does
not necessarily coincide with the crestline of the rock beneath, and
may thus differ from the position the watershed will occupy when the
area is freed from ice. The direction of movement of some of the ice
from the maximum ice cap will not therefore be the same as the future
direction of movement of some of the water that will ultimately drain
the massif. This point is illustrated in Fig. 220A, which is a rough
sketch of the conditions that occurred in the latitude of the northern
part of the Gulf of Bothnia. It shows the original iceshed to the east
of the watershed. Whilst these conditions prevailed, some erratics
were moved up the eastern slopes of the mountains and even over the
watershed on to the western slopes.

The division of an ice cap into two with a ridge of rock between is
known as *partition,* and is of fundamental importance, for from that
moment the two basins operate independently of one another and all
major movement must be down the rock gradient. As thaw proceeds,
a temporary lake is likely to develop between the watershed and the
head of ice on the eastern side (Fig. 220B).

GLACIERS, ALIVE OR DEAD

Factors such as aspect, altitude, relative importance of solar and air
mass heat, wind direction, frequency and velocity, and so on, all

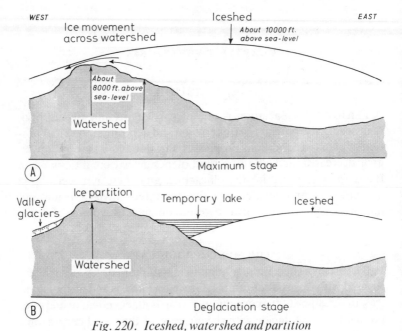

Fig. 220. Iceshed, watershed and partition

determine the relative timing of the melt of ice from the summits and from the valleys. Topographical evidence suggests that for the most part in Britain the valley glaciers largely melted before most of the ice in the mountains, so that they remained *living* whilst they decayed. On the other hand, in Scandinavia it appears that both snout recession and head shrinkage normally occurred simultaneously, with the latter very often the more important, so that stagnant or *dead* glaciers were commonly produced during deglaciation. The ice in these then merely melted away *in situ,* tunnels beneath the ice remained stationary, and eskers and other similar depositional features were formed.

MELTWATER

During deglaciation there is naturally a very considerable amount of meltwater, the quantity being equal to the drainage from the contemporaneous precipitation, together with the amount supplied by excess thaw. At first this water will move over the surface of the ice in streams which have an ice bed and ice banks. They will transport considerable quantities of surface moraine.

As soon as the divide occurs, and the mountain tops and plateaux become at least partially ice free, these meltwater rivers will be supplied with even more debris. The exposed rock surfaces almost certainly possess a great litter of broken rock, freeze-thaw is very active, and, since gradients in general may be fairly steep and there is no protective vegetation, a great proportion of this material is carried away.

Because radiation of black heat[1] from adjacent rock tends to melt the ice margin more rapidly than does direct solar heat in mid-ice areas, water channels tends to occur along these ice margins, and soon the melt is abstracted from the ice-surface rivers and diverted to the ice margin ones. These permanently affect the topography by producing channels with one bank of solid rock and one of ice. When such

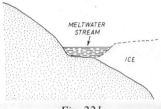

Fig. 221.
One-sided rock channel

features are viewed in fossil form after the ice has gone, they appear as one-sided channels, as is shown in Fig. 221. They are quite common in glaciated hilly or mountainous areas.

SUB-ICE WATER

Having made contact with the margin between rock and ice, there is then a general tendency for the water to leak down the steeper valley slope, rather than to continue along the more gentle gradient of the ice. This *sub-ice water* is supplied from three sources: the melt on the surface of the ice, the current precipitation which drains down the exposed mountainside, and additional water obtained by melt of the base of the glacier as the warmer water melts some of the ice which it touches.

Most of this subglacial drainage is along *sub-ice tunnels*. It is common for these to be full, and thus behave like pipes. As has already been mentioned under eskers (see p. 252), this leads to the development of hydrostatic pressure, to the carrying of very considerable loads, to the ability for the water to move uphill for moderate distances, and to the production of a certain degree of buoyancy to the ice above the tunnel roof.

[1] *Black heat* is heat radiated from a body which is at too low a temperature to emit light also, that is, for example, it is below red heat. Black heat radiation is of a longer wavelength than is radiation from such bodies as the Sun, and this longer wavelength is more easily absorbed by snow and ice than is the shorter wavelength of solar radiation.

This last is a particularly interesting effect, and accounts for the fact that apparently weak arches of ice do not collapse until the water is removed from the tunnel beneath them. They have previously been supported by the upward pressure exerted by the water. This pressure, p_w (see Fig. 222), is the difference between the pressure due to

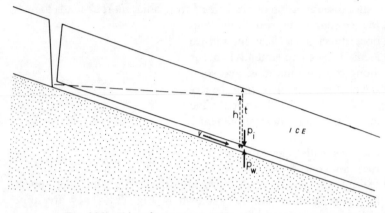

Fig. 222. Tunnel water pressure versus ice pressure

actual head, h, of water and the 'velocity head', h_v, which represents the part of the potential energy that has been transformed into kinetic energy to produce the velocity of the water in the tunnel. Putting this in the form of an equation,

$$p_w = (h - h_v)d_w$$

and employing the usual equation linking potential and kinetic energy, we have

$$h_v = \tfrac{1}{2}v^2/g$$

which gives

$$p_w = (h - \tfrac{1}{2}v^2/g)d_w$$

where d_w is the density of water, v its velocity, and g the acceleration due to gravity.

The pressure, p_i, exerted on the tunnel roof due to the weight of ice above it, is the product of the thickness, t, of the ice and its density, d_i. That is,

$$p_i = t \cdot d_i$$

If p_w exceeds p_i, the upthrust will be greater than the downward pressure, and the ice will actually be lifted off its bed, the water will spread sideways beneath it, and the glacier will ride on a surface of water. In such a case

$$(h - \tfrac{1}{2}v^2/g)d_w > t \cdot d_i$$

and since d_i is approximately $0 \cdot 9d_w$, this becomes

$$h - \tfrac{1}{2}v^2/g > 0 \cdot 9t$$

This shows several interesting points. The ratio between the total head of water, h, and the ice thickness, t, necessary to produce this result depends upon the square of the velocity of the water, and h must be greater for greater velocities. Since the water moves faster in narrower parts of the tunnel, this means that those parts are the less likely to be lifted.

The greater the cross-sectional area of the tunnel, the lower the velocity and the greater the tendency for lift of the ice from its bed.

In one way these various factors all work in a progressive sequence – as the tunnel acquires a greater cross-sectional area, so the ice is already partly losing direct contact with the ground beneath, and at the same time the water velocity is decreasing and thus the likelihood of complete lift is increasing.

These equations ignore the additional head which is required to overcome frictional losses, as well as one or two other relatively minor factors, including the apparent increase in the density of water because of load in suspension. These omissions do not, however, affect the general argument.

The total head, h, of water does not need to exceed the thickness of the ice greatly in order to lift it off the floor. With the resulting spread of water, much of its load is deposited and many wide expanses of sand and even clay material originate in this manner.

They may be distinguished from drained lake floor deposits by the fact that they possess a gradient which is substantially the same as that of the long-profile of the valley. It is clear that, as the ice thins more and more, it tends more and more to be lifted off the valley floor, and it may well be that the majority of valley-spread debris has been deposited by sheet drainage in this way.

EXTRA-ICE WATER

A further stage in the drainage sequence during deglaciation occurs when the ice has decreased so much in quantity that most of the melt is subaerial rather than subglacial and now flows beyond the limits of contact with the actual ice. This is *extra-ice drainage*, and the water behaves as in normal rivers.

The ground already bears a number of glacial landforms, moraines, eskers, kames and the like, which may determine the fluvial pattern very largely and may often lead to the formation of temporary lakes. Besides the accumulation forms acting as lake dams, reversed gradients resulting from rock barriers also lead to the occurrence of lakes, which in this instance are likely to be more permanent than the previous forms, since these are contained by an obstruction that is more difficult to trench, than are those composed of unconsolidated material.

The high erosion rates during deglaciation thus lead to the production of clean rock surfaces and channels, one-sided valleyside channels, channels in moraine and even to gorges. The depositional features associated with this activity are fluvial fans, terraces and flats, all of which may be formed beneath the ice or beyond it, and temporary lake deposits.

DEGLACIATION LAKES AND FLUVIAL DIVERSIONS

The landforms that are produced beyond the ice limits are largely determined by the major as well as the minor relief features which exist in any specific area. The occurrence of large areas of higher ground on the melt side of the ice leads to special effects. Four British examples may well illustrate this point. They are located in northeast Wales, Shropshire, in north Yorkshire and in the Isle of Man.

1. *Wheeler–Alyn Overflow Channel*

North Wales with its mountains often rising to heights exceeding 3,000 feet (900 metres) stood as a great barrier to the southward movement of the Irish Sea ice. The only outlets for this ice were by way of St George's Channel and the Cheshire–Shropshire Plain (reference has already been made to this routeway on p. 238). The mountains themselves proved to be insuperable, and in any case possessed their own ice, some of which moved northwards and opposed the Irish Sea ice.

The Vale of Clwyd (Fig. 223) gave rise to particularly interesting phenomena in this connection, for it offered an apparent routeway southwards for the ice, but was in fact closed at the southern end and possessed a northward-moving glacier. The two sets of ice met midway, and had a kind of push-of-war, the boundary between the two varying in position in accord with changes in relative strength. In general, it was situated near to a valley from which the river Wheeler now issues on to the Vale, and during deglaciation, when the two ice masses eventually parted, the meltwater accumulated in lake form opposite the mouth of this valley.

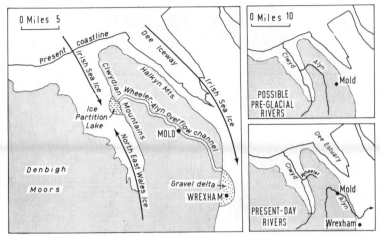

Fig. 223. Deglaciation of northeast Wales

Previous to glaciation, the river Alyn had been a tributary of the river Clwyd (see inset to Fig. 223), and the overflow from the partition lake used the lower part of the Alyn valley and broke through a low watershed to flow alongside the Cheshire lobe of the Irish Sea ice south of Mold.

At this stage, the Cheshire ice terminated somewhere in the latitude of Wrexham, and the meltwater from the Vale of Clwyd built up a considerable gravel delta in this district, as is shown on the map. The sequence of events is complex, and the channel eventually became almost choked with meltwater deposits of various kinds. Now there is a watershed midway along its course, the Alyn turns southeast to Mold and a shortened lower Alyn, now called the Wheeler, flows northwestwards along the overflow channel to the Vale of Clwyd.

2. *Lake Lapworth*

Also on the western side of the Pennines but dating a little earlier than the above events and in the southern part of the Cheshire–Shropshire Plain, a late-glacial lake, Lake Lapworth, occurred as the

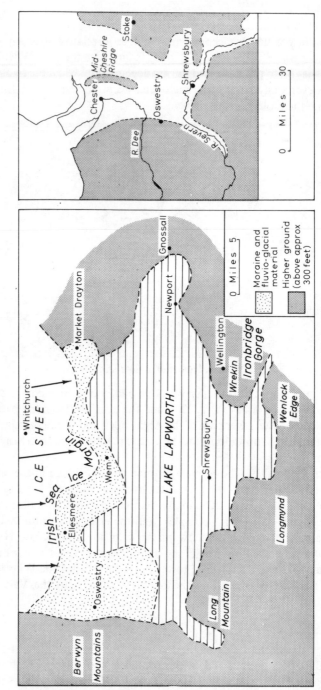

Fig. 224. Lake Lapworth

result of the continued presence of the Irish Sea ice to the north beyond the line of the Ellesmere–Wem moraines and fluvioglacial
deposits. Meltwater from the north and from the upper Severn
glacier came pouring into the rectangle whose three remaining sides
were the Longmynd and associated mountains, the Berwyn mountains and the higher ground to the east. The lake overflowed at an
existing col across the northern end of Wenlock Edge, and cut a deep,
narrow channel now known as the Ironbridge Gorge in the extreme
southeastern corner of the area.

Figure 224 shows the approximate limits of the lake at one stage of
its existence, when the level of the outlet gorge was about the present
300-foot (90-metre) contour (the floor of the gorge today is at about
140 feet (43 metres) O.D.). Old shorelines of the lake at various levels
have been traced and by the time the northern ice melted away, the
floor of the gorge was lower than the moraines and fluvioglacial
deposits to the north. Consequently the restored river Severn, which
in preglacial times had flowed northwards, presumably to the present
Dee estuary, failed to return to its northerly route but remained in
the Ironbridge Gorge. This greatly increased the volume of water in
what is now the lower Severn, which had previously been a much
smaller river. Thus the deglaciation diversion became a permanent
one.

3. *Cleveland Lakes*

In north Yorkshire, the Cleveland Hills – Yorkshire Moors massif
greatly obstructed the southward movement of Scottish and other
ice. There was a clear way on its western side down the Vale of York,
which carried great quantities of ice, and of course the North Sea bed
offered no obstruction on the eastern side. Particularly interesting
features were developed during deglaciation, when the ice had come
out of contact with much of the northern edge of the massif, freed the
upstream parts of the northward-facing valleys, but gave no exit for
their meltwaters (see Fig. 225).

Consequently a whole series of overflow channels and tunnel valleys was developed. These changed their details from time to time,
especially as the ice gradually made less and less contact with the
northern edge of the mountains, and permitted drainage links between the individual lakes at a lower level than at the start. Nevertheless, the ice remained in contact with fairly high ground to the east
for a considerable period, and the meltwater made use of two aligned
pre-existing river valleys by breaching the col between them and

creating a through valley, Newton Dale, which transferred the meltwater to the then Lake, now Vale of, Pickering.

Newton Dale is one of the most spectacular of British meltwater
channels, and a considerable gravel delta was deposited at the entry
to the lake. On part of this the town of Pickering is built, making use
of the dry site. Ice in the North Sea blocked the eastern end of the
Vale of Pickering, and so created that lake and the overflow from it
was to the south by way of the Kirkham Gorge.

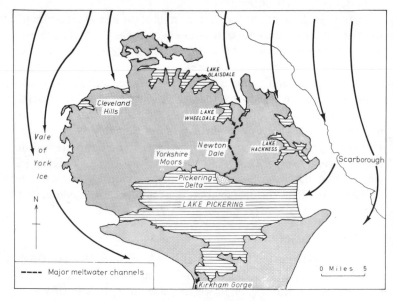

Fig. 225. Newton Dale and lake Pickering

4. *Isle of Man Central Valley*

Finally an overflow of somewhat different type is to be found in the
Isle of Man. On several occasions during the Pleistocene, the island
has been surrounded by a lowland ice sheet occupying the bed of the
Irish Sea. The Isle occupies a somewhat central position in this sea,
and with its mountains rising to more than 2,000 feet (Snaefell is
2,034 feet: 620 metres), it presented a considerable obstruction. The
ice split somewhat earlier than contact with the rather blunt-nosed
preglacial northern coast which ran westward from Ramsey (Fig.
226), and within this gap considerable quantities of morainic and
outwash material derived from Scottish rocks were deposited. (The
Bride Hills across this low area belong to a later glaciation, when the

southern limit of the ice sheet barely reached the Isle of Man, see p. 283.)

It is by no means certain what was the origin of the central valley from Douglas to Peel, but it is very likely indeed that in its original

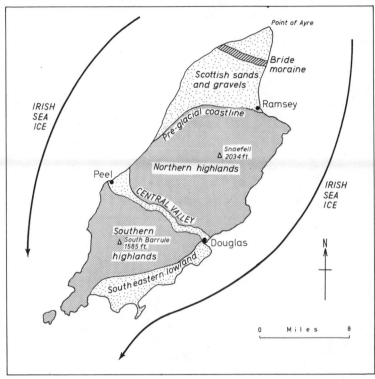

Fig. 226. Central valley of the Isle of Man

form it pre-dated the presence of ice. It is, however, probable that at times the ice on the western side of the Isle was at a higher elevation than that on the eastern, and during melting periods very considerable meltwater would then pass through the central valley and ultimately choke it with thick fluvioglacial deposits. In this instance, as in most cases, the meltwater adopted a pre-existing channel and deepened rather than created it.

THE BALTIC DEGLACIATION

The accounts so far presented all refer to deglaciation primarily on land areas (for the Irish Sea was dry at that period, owing to low sea-

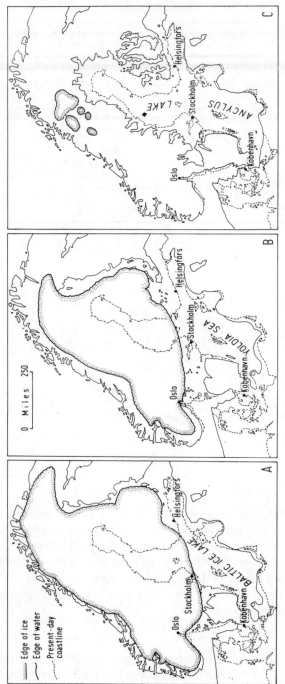

Fig. 227. Baltic deglaciation

Edge of ice
Edge of water
Present-day coastline

Miles
0   250

A

BALTIC ICE LAKE

Oslo
Stockholm
Helsingförs
København

B

YOLDIA SEA

Oslo
Stockholm
Helsingförs
København

C

LAKE
ANCYLUS

Oslo
Stockholm
Helsingförs
København

level), and one of the dominant characteristics of such areas is that beyond the ice limit periglacial processes were particularly active, and that they progressively operated over larger and larger areas as the ice shrank away. Somewhat dissimilar conditions prevailed in those localities where the ice edge lay in contact with the sea or with large masses of water, and this especially led to an interesting series of events in the Baltic area to the east of Sweden.

As will be described in Chapter 22, the Scandinavian ice, which had been the most active in the whole of Europe, had extended not only over the whole of Scandinavia, Finland and northern European U.S.S.R., but also across the Baltic Sea and the German–Polish plain as far south as the Carpathians. During the final deglaciation, as no doubt in the previous ones also, the ice gradually decreased in area until a stage was reached at which it still covered more or less the whole of Norway, but had uncovered Sweden roughly as far north as a line from Stockholm to Oslo. The ice margin passed east-north-east across the bed of the present Baltic to the southern part of Finland (see Fig. 227A).

At this time the sea-level was still low, owing to water shortage (see p. 376), and thus the narrows which now link the Baltic with the North Sea were dry. At about 11,300 B.P.[1] conditions had ameliorated to the extent that the ice margin was still just in contact with land in southern Sweden, and consequently the basin which is now the middle Baltic became a lake, known to glaciologists as the *Baltic Ice Lake.* This lake had come into existence probably about 1,500 years before, and had gradually increased in size, corresponding to the ice recession, until it reached the critical stage shown in Fig. 227A.

Further ice shrinkage resulted in a gap occurring between the ice margin and dry land, since Sweden west of Stockholm is lower than the southern part, and consequently the open sea was able to make connection with the Baltic, whose level fell to the then sea-level. It became a saltwater area as is proved by the presence of marine molluscs still to be found in fossil state along its shores, and especially because of a definitive mollusc, *Yoldia arctica,* now only to be found in Arctic marine waters. From this, it is known as the *Yoldia Sea.* This extended over the area shown in Fig. 227B, and it remained so, with two brief interruptions when it returned to lake conditions, from about 11300 B.P. to 9500 B.P., almost two thousand years.

The two brief returns to lake conditions had been induced by the combination of changing sea and land levels, for not only was the

---

[1] B.P. = years before the present.

sea water rising, but the crust was recovering from the isostatic depression (see p. 377) it had suffered as the result of the weight of the ice sheet lying upon it. About 9500 B.P., these combined circumstances, especially the relatively rapid rise in land-level, brought back a rather more permanent return to lake conditions. This is known as the *Ancylus Lake* from the freshwater mollusc *Ancylus fluviatilis,* whose fossil remains are to be found around the old shorelines (see Fig. 227C).

By this time the ice sheet had waned nearly as far north as the Dal river in Sweden, about 70 miles north of Stockholm, and recession continued to be very rapid.

The Ancylus Lake lasted from about 9500 B.P. until 7800 B.P., and during this time its waters, which were somewhat higher than the then sea-level, drained into the North Sea, first by a route through the central Swedish depression (today occupied partly by Lake Väner), and later by a fluvial route through the present Sound between Köbenhavn and Malmö.

World climate experienced a considerable amelioration at about the end of this period, and the total volume of land ice became considerably less than at the present day, so that the world ocean-level was higher even than it is now. This is known as the *Flandrian transgression* in most of continental Europe, although it has the name of *Tapes stage* in Scandinavia (from *Tapes decussatus*).

The rise in sea-level was sufficient to permit a marine breakthrough between Denmark and southern Sweden, so that the Baltic area once became a sea, for a time somewhat larger than the present Baltic Sea. This is known as the *Littorina Sea,* so named from the periwinkle *Littorina littorea,* found on its shores. It came into existence about 7800 B.P. and gradually merged into the presentday Baltic Sea, perhaps about 4000 B.P. At the same time, the crustal recovery in the Lake Väner region lifted this part of Sweden above sea-water level, and it has remained land since that time.

The earlier Baltic is known as the *Limnaea phase,* and the later the *Mya phase* (Mya is a clam). This change in typical fauna indicates the fact that the water in the Baltic is progressively becoming less and less salt, the mean value being now only 0·8 per cent, as compared with the average of 3·5 per cent for the open sea.

CHAPTER TWENTY-TWO

Glacial Chronology

T HE conditions which prevailed during the various ice ages were not so severe as is sometimes imagined. The whole of the Earth's surface is considered to have been on the average probably no more than 6°C (11°F) cooler than it is today. It is likely that the change may have been a little less at the equator and rather more at the Poles. The presentday glaciers on Kilimanjaro, the 19,000-foot (5,800-metre) mountain only 3° of latitude from the equator, descend its flanks to 15,000 feet (4,600 metres) on the southwestern slope, whereas during the Ice Ages evidence shows that they came down a further 4,000 feet (1,200 metres) to 11,000 feet (3,400 metres) above sea-level.

Because of differences in annual temperature range and other climatic factors, it is not possible to make true comparisons by saying that the climate at the equator then was really similar to what it is at some other place today, but the following table shows a series of localities at which the mean annual temperature, but not necessarily the mean summer or winter temperatures, of each is 6°C (about 11°F) cooler than those on the line below.

Approximate mean annual temperature		Localities
°C	°F	
− 10	14	Barrow (n. coast of Alaska), Spitsbergen
− 4	25	Nome (Alaska), Bear Is. (Barents Sea)
2	36	North Cape (Norway)
8	46	Edinburgh, Bergen, København, Warsaw
14	57	San Francisco, Marseilles, Tokyo, Wellington (N.Z.)
20	68	New Orleans, Parana, Brisbane
26	79	Equator, Georgetown, Lagos, Colombo, Singapore

Fig. 228. Mean annual temperatures

With some approximation, taking the year as a whole, one may thus say that the equator during the Ice Ages may have been about as cool as New Orleans now is; that Marseilles would then be about as cool as Edinburgh today, and so on.

275

Thus each part of the world became what might be termed one stage cooler. Each one of the climatic zones which is traversed from the equator to the Pole was reached at a slightly lower latitude than today, and there was some compression of the zones as the polar area expanded.

There is considerable doubt whether the higher mountains of Britain and the Americas were completely covered with more than winter snow, and the summer conditions on the Grampians must have appeared very like those shown in Fig. 229, which is a June photograph of the Jotunheim in central Norway. Rock outcrops would be frequent, although with a complete snow-cover during the winter, excepting at the steepest points from which it would slip off immediately.

Periglacial conditions would prevail in England south of the Thames during the maximum glaciation and also in a belt across Europe just south of the ice front.

RATE OF ONSET OF GLACIAL CONDITIONS

The advent of each cold period would be very slow. The general rate of cooling was probably not more rapid than the rate at which mean temperature in Europe has risen during the past hundred years. It is so slow that, without measurements, anyone dwelling in the area would scarcely notice any change during a whole lifetime. Supposing that the temperature had fallen sufficiently for ice to have reached a particular area, it would be advancing only at about the same rate as it has recently been retreating in most world glaciers and ice sheets.

Fluctuations are still going on at a rate which is quite as rapid as at the maximum retreat or advance stages of the major glaciations, when the annual retreat on the mid-Swedish Baltic slopes was at the rate of about 200 yards (180 metres) a year, although this was particularly rapid.

For several centuries prior to 1700, the glaciers in Scandinavia were smaller than they are today. Then, between 1700 and 1745, there were several particularly cold years, and they increased in size to a maximum. Since 1745, there has been a decreased snowfall and increased ablation, and the Nigard glacier on the eastern side of the Jostedal ice cap for example, shrank about 3 miles (5 km) in the two hundred years from 1750 to 1950. The mean regression in the Jotunheim was 1,600 feet (500 metres) in the forty years 1898 to 1938, which is at the rate of 40 feet (12 metres) a year. All this shrinkage is due to a rise in temperature, which, although shown on the meteoro-

Fig. 229. Early summer conditions in the Jotunheim today

logists' instruments, has been too slow for direct human detection.

There was some doubt about 1960 as to whether or not the decay had ceased, but since then it has been resumed at apparently an even more rapid rate.

CAUSES

Many suggestions have been made as to the cause of an Ice Age. The first assumption is that it is in fact produced by a general lowering of temperature, although there have been theories which have suggested even that a rise in temperature might so increase cloudiness and precipitation that snowfall in the winter would exceed summer melt.

A lowering of temperature can be obtained for particular parts of the Earth's surface by land elevation, by a shift of the position of the Poles, or by continental drift, but in the last two of these some parts of the surface become warmer at the same time as others are cooled. This does not appear to be what actually happened, for the snow on Kilimanjaro, as already described, extended farther down the sides of the mountain. The cooling would appear to be a universal effect.

There are three principal ways in which the heat received from the Sun could be varied. These are (1) by increasing the radius of the Earth's orbit so that the Sun was farther away (astronomers say this is very unlikely), (2) by decreasing the Sun's rate of heat production, that is, 'by damping the fire down', or (3) by the intervention of a partial screen between the Sun and Earth.

The rate of heat production by the Sun does vary frequently, but measurements have not been made over a long enough period of years to know yet whether it could vary in the way required to produce the Ice Ages.

It is possible that the solar system passed through a cloud of cosmic dust at the times of the Ice Ages. Space contains many fragments of rock, some of which enter the Earth's atmosphere, become incandescent with the friction produced and are commonly called shooting stars. These are meteorites if they succeed in reaching the ground before they are completely burnt up. If at the time of the Ice Ages the part of space through which the solar system was then passing possessed a particularly large amount of such dust, then this would act as a partial screen and so reduce the amount of solar heat reaching the Earth.

The cloud of dust would have had to vary in density to produce the various phases of the Ice Ages, and if we have now passed out of the cloud, then it will never be possible for astronomers to look back whence we have come, and actually detect the cloud. If this is the reason for the Ice Ages, the best we can hope ever to know is that if another ice age should occur, then we would be aware of the dust cloud we were travelling through, and know it to be the cause. Dark nights would afford a brilliant display of shooting stars, and we would then be able to say that probably the past Ice Ages had had the same cause.

There have been many other theories, and even suggestions that ice sheets and glaciers are self-generating without the necessity for much change in the external conditions, but no single explanation so far offered satisfies all the known facts. It is most probable that there were a variety of circumstances which, coinciding with one another, combined together to produce the result. It may well be that it is because of the necessity for a number of separate factors to coincide in this way that Ice Ages have been so rare during geologic time.

The last half million years have seen four or possibly five major Ice Ages, each one of them almost certainly compound, and only one other, during the Permo-Carboniferous, is definitely known to have taken place during the whole of the last five or six hundred million years.

It should be noted that snow fields and ice caps tend to remain in existence when once they have been formed. They are in a sense stable features. A soil or rock surface absorbs a considerable proportion of the solar heat which is incident upon it, and so is warmed to that extent. On the other hand, snow and ice absorb a very small fraction of such heat and reflect the remainder. Thus when the ice is once frozen it requires a considerable amount of sunshine to 'pump' calories into it again. In addition its high latent heat of fusion means that ice requires almost as much heat to melt it as is needed to boil water which has come cold from the tap.

It is for these reasons that mountain snows melt fairly slowly in the spring and consequently meltwater floods are not worse than they are. It is also because of this that there is such an apparent difference in climate on the two sides of the snout of the glacier. The ice may not be melting at all, whilst at the same time a few hundred yards away cows may be happily basking in warm sunshine on the summer pasture.

PLEISTOCENE CHRONOLOGY

The story of the events of the different sections of the Ice Ages of the Pleistocene period is only partially known, and consequently we find that different authors often give accounts which vary from one another in their details. The descriptions which follow and the maps which illustrate them give the results of the most recent research, and so are correct to the best of present knowledge. There is little doubt about the main facts, and future studies are only likely to suggest revisions of the smaller points.

It is now well established that the Pleistocene Ice Ages date from about 600,000 years ago, and that there have been four major cold periods since that time. These were first distinguished in the Alpine region, principally in southern Germany, and were there named *Günz, Mindel, Riss* and *Würm,* from particular rivers or lakes where the evidence was either best displayed or first studied. In this area, it was often possible to link fluvial terraces along present valleysides with morainic deposits farther up-valley and so interpret a sequence. More recently very extensive work has been done, and is still being continued, in Britain, in northern Europe (especially in Poland and Sweden), and in North America, both in the States and Canada, and more and more of the intricacies of the events are being deciphered.

There has recently been some suggestion that there may have been

Years before present	Alpine	North European	British	Irish	American
0		P o s t - g l a c i a l			
100000	**Würm**	**Weichsel**	**Newer**	**Midland General**	**Wisconsin**
	R/W igl	Eem igl	Ipswichian igl	Ardcavan igl	Sangamon igl
200000	**Riss**	**Saale**	**Gipping**	**Eastern General** (incl Brittas Mt gl)	**Illinoian**
300000	G R E A T I N T E R G L A C I A L				
	M/R igl	Holstein igl	Hoxnian igl	Kilbeg igl	Yarmouth igl
400000					
500000	**Mindel**	**Elster**	**Lowestoft**	?	**Kansan**
	G/M igl	?	Cromerian warm	?	Aftonian igl
600000	**Günz**	?	**Weybourne crag**	?	**Nebraskan**

Fig. 230. Chronology of the Pleistocene
(Simplified and provisional: compiled from various sources)

one more cold period, the *Danau* (or Danubian) glacial, prior to the Günz, but the evidence for this is still somewhat inconclusive, and it has been omitted from the table in Fig. 230.

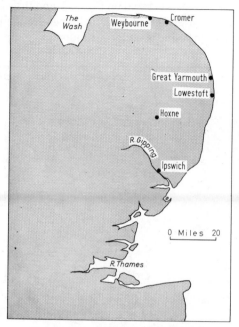

Fig. 231. Localities in East Anglia

On this table, horizontal lines mark the medial stage in the change from cold to warm period, or the reverse, as accurately as the small scale of the table permits, and from this it will be seen that the total length of the warm periods or *interglacials* is rather longer than the total length of the cold periods or *glacials*. The change from one to the other, as has already been described, is, of course, not sudden and the horizontal lines should in fact be transitional bands.

IN BRITAIN

In Britain, the *Weybourne Crag* of eastern Norfolk is a marine deposit of sand, pebbles and clay, and this appears to be of the same date as the Alpine Günz glacial. The various deposits of the whole of the Pleistocene have been most closely studied in their sequence in East Anglia, and most of the names used to designate the different sections are of places in that part of England (Fig. 231). The Cromer Forest Bed of the *Cromerian Warm* period is certainly a deposit

K

derived from vegetation living in a warm climate, and this was followed by the *Lowestoft glacial*. In East Anglia, the ice moved in from
the northwest. There are no end moraines along the whole of the
limits of this glaciation as marked on Fig. 232, and the southern edge
of the ice at its most advanced stage is known by the line beyond
which the ground moraine is no longer found.

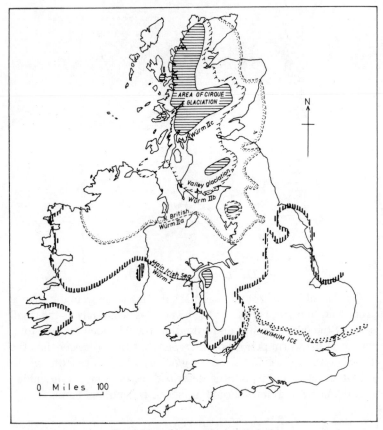

Fig. 232. The Ice Ages in Britain

The *Gipping glacial* seems to have come to East Anglia from the
north, and its till is mainly distinguished from that of the Lowestoft
both by the direction of the long axes of the stones found in it and by
the fact that in places warm climate deposits, belonging to the *Hoxnian interglacial*, may be found between the two tills. Only one very
short end-moraine associated with this glacial is known, and in most

places the limits of the till are not clearly distinguishable from those of the Lowestoft glacial. For this reason, only one line, marked 'maximum ice', is indicated on the map.

Warm climate deposits, representing the *Ipswichian interglacial,* have been found from Trafalgar Square, London, to Cambridge and Ipswich itself, and the more recent tills of the last glacial period, generally known as the *Newer glacial* in Britain, and corresponding to the Alpine *Würm,* are much more clearly developed, so that a more detailed and confident account may be given.

Figure 233 gives the names that have been used for the four stages of this glacial, together with the corresponding Alpine nomenclature. There are a number of alternative names for some of these, and the *Kirkham glacial* is often known as the *North British glacial* or the *Scottish re-advance;* whilst the *Valley glacial* is equivalent to the *Highland re-advance.*

There is still some doubt as to whether these four stages represent successive phases in the decay of an extensive ice sheet, marked by purely local re-advances, such as might be termed the final kicks of a dying ice age, or whether they are separate cold periods with a more or less complete disappearance of ice cover between each stage. The former appears to be the more likely, which is the reason why the final stage of the Würm is here described as *Würm IIc*, whereas it is sometimes given the title of *Würm III*.

The *Main Irish Sea glacial* was no more extensive in the name area than the previous glaciations, but it is the one about which most is known. Its southern limit is marked by moraines at many localities in Wales, in Staffordshire and in the well known York and Escrick moraines. There is still some slight doubt as to the date of the Hunstanton till of the north Norfolk coast, although it is highly probable that it represents deposits of the same Main Irish Sea glacial period. The ice in this case, having left the present land area in north Yorkshire, moved by an arcuate route on the now North Sea floor to come 'ashore' again in south Holderness and Lincolnshire, and just on to Norfolk, where it deposited till containing erratics from the Cheviots.

This was the last extensive ice sheet in Britain, and the subsequent history is one of progressively decreasing size. The *Kirkham glacial* scarcely seems to have entered England on the eastern side of the Pennines, although on the western side it reached as far south as Blackpool and Kirkham (Lancashire) to form the *Kirkham moraine.* This same moraine is picked up again in the Bride Hills of the northern part of the Isle of Man, and in the Carlingford, Kells, Wexford moraine of Ireland. It corresponds in date to the Würm IIa.

This was virtually the last occasion on which British glaciers became piedmont, and in the next phase, the *Valley glacial,* the glaciers in almost every instance melted before they reached the lower ends of their valleys. Examples of this glaciation are afforded by the terminal moraines at the south end of Coniston Water and of Windermere in the Lake District. There were valley glaciers in Scotland and in Wales, and the lines marked on the map (Fig. 232) indicate the approximate limits of these glaciers and do not signify that the areas within the lines were covered by a continuous ice sheet. There is now some doubt as to the reality of the invasion of the extreme northeastern corner of Ireland by Scottish ice during the Valley glacial. If it did do so, it took the form of a lobe of ice which came along the deep Sound of Jura, between Kintyre and Islay. This is Wurm IIb.

Finally, the *Cirque glacial* is confined, as the name indicates, to small cirque glaciers isolated from one another on the upper, colder slopes of the higher mountains. Again the lines marked on Fig. 232 indicate the areas within which such cirques are to be found, and one must imagine a series of small areas of ice, perhaps averaging half a mile or less in diameter, scattered over these highest areas. This is Würm IIc.

IN IRELAND

In Ireland in the earlier glaciations, the whole of the island, apart from a few isolated monadnocks, seems to have been covered by ice during the *Eastern General glacial* (Riss) (Fig. 230), most of the ice being Irish ice, although Scottish erratics are found in northeastern Ireland and along the whole of the east coast. The *Midland General glacial* (Würm I) was almost entirely composed of ice of Irish origin with outward movements from the main centres in Tyrone, Roscommon, southwest Kerry and west Cork.

IN EUROPE AND ASIA

Similar glaciations and interglacials occurred in Europe and North America and tables in Figs. 230 and 233 give the correlations between them so far as they are known. Figure 234 shows the limits reached in Europe by the different ice sheets, together with the names of some of the end-moraines. Little comment need be made excepting again to repeat that clearly, because the clues are fresher, more information is known regarding the progressively more recent glaciations.

Approximate years before the present	Alpine	Northern European	English and Welsh	Scottish	Irish
0					
	P o s t g l a c i a l				
8,500					
	Würm IIc	Finiglacial	C i r q u e		
10,000					
	Würm IIb	Götiglacial	Valley	Perth	Antrim Coast
14,000					
	Würm IIa	Daniglacial	Kirkham	Lammermuir	Kells
27,000					
	Würm I	Warthe	Main Irish Sea	York	Midland General
120,000					

The general name for the Last Glacial in Northern Europe is
WEICHSEL and in Britain NEWER.

Fig. 233. Chronology of the last glaciation (simplified and provisional)

In the Netherlands, only the northern part was covered by ice, and this only once, during the Riss (= Saale). Coarse sands and gravels, preglacial deposits of early Pleistocene rivers, were rammed up by the push of the approaching ice sheet to form some of the rather higher ground to the south of IJsselmeer, as is shown on Fig. 235. The map marks the present surface exposure of this pushed material, but it is probable that it was originally continuous and more extensive so that it reached to the ice front. Most of the areas between the exposures marked are surfaced by later periglacial and wind-blown deposits, and in the Rhine flood plain the pushed alluvium has either been eroded by the river or covered by more recent alluvium.

During the presence of the northerly ice, the Rhine could find no outlet into the present North Sea, which in any case, because of the low ocean-level, was dry, and so it turned westwards through the Straits of Dover to enter the ocean between Land's End and Cape Finisterre, having picked up the Thames, Seine and other rivers on the way.

Denmark is divided by a line which lies roughly north–south along the centre of Jutland as is shown on Fig. 234. To the west of this line, which marks the main termination of the *Daniglacial* (corresponding to the less intense Kirkham glacial in Britain), the land, with a base of ground moraine from the earlier glaciations, is now largely covered with outwash spreads of sands and gravels, which make for a very dry soil and lead to the development of heath vegetation.

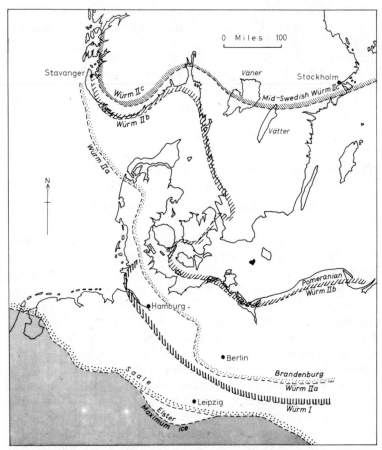

Fig. 234. The Ice Ages in parts of Europe (end moraines named)

It is only during the last hundred years or so that much of this heathland has been reclaimed for agriculture, using the most modern methods to combat its inherent disabilities. To the north and east of this line, the surface is mostly composed of till of Daniglacial age, and this has always been the most important agricultural part of Denmark. This line is the fundamental geographical boundary within Denmark, and on either side there are cultural landscapes of very different character.

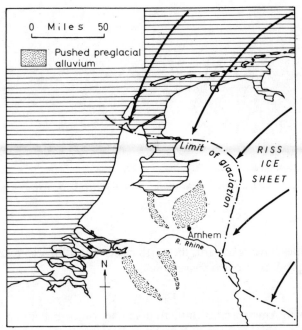

Fig. 235. *Glaciological map of the Netherlands*

Because of its continental climate, with warm summers and consequent considerable melt of ice, the ice sheets did not extend so far south in Asiatic U.S.S.R. as they did in Europe itself, where a lobe of ice between the Don and Volga reached as far south as about latitude 48° N. In Asiatic U.S.S.R., the maximum glaciation line crosses the Irtysh river about half-way between the inflow of the river Tobol and the confluence of the Irtysh with the Ob; crosses the Ob between the mouths of the Vakh and Tym; and the Yenisei near the confluence of the Stony Tunguska. The boundary line then turns northwards to pass just to the south of the Putorana and Verkhoyansk mountains (see Fig. 236).

The rivers of this area mostly drain northwards and freeze during the winter cold. In spring they first thaw in the up-valley parts and

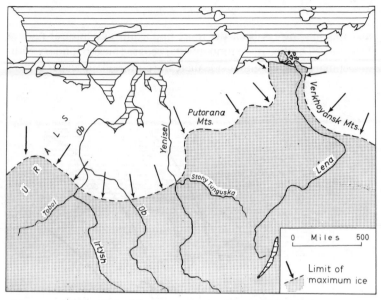

Fig. 236. Maximum ice in Asiatic U.S.S.R.

the water flowing towards the north meets the still-frozen reaches so as to produce very extensive flooding.

IN AMERICA

In North America, the southern boundary of the maximum glaciation runs roughly through New York, Pittsburgh, the Ohio valley or a little north of it to Evansville, then directly west to St Louis, along the Missouri to Kansas City, rather west of the river until it rejoins it near the confluence of the Niobrara, only to leave it again after a few miles and run roughly parallel, mostly about 20 or 30 miles (30 or 50 km) to the southwest of the river.

There were several centres from which the ice spread outwards, the principal parent areas being the Laurentian Plateau, Baffin and the adjacent islands, and southwestern Keewatin, together with relatively short (although important) glaciers from the Rocky and other western mountains.

The various glaciations differed especially as regards their limits, and in particular there are areas in Nebraska, Iowa, Missouri, Illinois and Indiana where the ground moraine of most of the individual glaciations may be studied on the surface, whilst in southwest

Wisconsin there is an area which, although entirely surrounded by ice at various times, was never itself glaciated, or at all events not after the first glaciation, the Nebraskan.

IN THE POLAR REGIONS

From the glacial point of view, the Earth today may be regarded as possessing two major ice covered, circular areas, centred on the Poles. The Antarctic is the more definite of these, since it is largely continental as far as about latitude 70°, and thus affords a solid base on which the ice may rest. The Arctic is almost the reverse, with the Arctic Ocean forming the base as far as latitude 83° (north coasts of Greenland and Ellesmere Island), or about 81° (Spitsbergen, Franz Josef Land and Severnaya Zemlya and some of the Canadian islands). The north coasts of Scandinavia, U.S.S.R. and Alaska average about latitude 72°.

Whilst the Antarctic is covered by a very large ice cap, estimated to have an area of about 5 million square miles (13 million sq km), with nearly 90 per cent of the continent covered by grounded ice, the North Polar ice is entirely floating and thus considerably thinner. At the North Pole area itself, the whole of the sea is generally covered by ice, but there are areas in arctic regions where the ice cover is at times as low as one-tenth the total area.

Little is known in either case regarding conditions during the Ice Ages of the Pleistocene. It is thought that in the Antarctic what differences occurred were mainly the result of changes in ocean-level, for the present limits of the Antarctic ice cap are determined, not so much by climate, as by ocean depth, the ice terminating not far north of the line where it floats off bedrock.

During the cold periods of the various Ice Ages, the ocean-level was low, and thus the Antarctic ice cap could reach farther north before it floated off the sea-bottom.

RADIOACTIVE DATING

Only one method has so far been discovered for determining the actual age of various deposits within the range of years that are involved in the Pleistocene. This is a radioactive method. The element used is carbon. There are several kinds of carbon atoms, all of which behave the same chemically, but which differ physically in respect of their atomic weight.

The commonest variety has an atomic weight of 12, but another has atomic weight 14, and it is this, which is a very small percentage

K 2

of the whole amount of any sample of carbon, that is important for the dating. Being radioactive, it gradually changes and is converted into nitrogen. The proportion of carbon 12 to carbon 14 (C^{12}/C^{14}) in the air is maintained constant by cosmic rays, which penetrate the upper atmosphere, and thus the ratio of the two in the carbon in a carbon compound when it enters into the structure of any living plant or animal is a definite one.

The amount of carbon 14 in any sample halves itself by radio-activity in about 5,560 years, so that by testing any specimen of organic substance to determine the ratio of the two *isotopes,* as they are termed, one may ascertain the number of years back when the plant or animal was alive. This method is useful for ages up to about 30,000 years, after which the residual amount of carbon 14 becomes too little to measure with any hope of accuracy. (Other radioactive substances, with a longer half-life, are used to determine more remote geological times.)

VARVE COUNTING

With changes in the nature of the finer material carried by meltwater during different parts of each twelve months due to variations in amount of flow and so on, it is found that deposits in lakes and seas, such as the ancestors of the Baltic, are laid down in thin layers, each

Fig. 237. Varves in a clay pit near Uppsala, Sweden

of which indicates a period of twelve months. Figure 237 shows a section in a clay pit north of Uppsala in such a *varved* deposit. The layers are known as *varves*.

Varves vary in thickness according to the amount of silt in the meltwater each season. Thus any sequence of varves shows a definite pattern in thicknesses, such as is seen in the illustration, and this pattern is characteristic of the particular period of years. In a neighbouring area, although the actual thickness of the varves may as a whole differ from those to be found on the first site, because the general rate of deposition differs, the same *succession* of rather warm, not so warm, or cool summers will have produced the same, identifiable pattern. It is thus possible to correlate the deposits of one area with another.

At one particular site there may be several hundred varves, indicating a period of several hundred years' deposition, and at another a little distance away it may be possible to extend the series beyond the limits of the first site because at the second one the deposition began earlier or continued later. By so extending the sequence in this way, at a large number of sites in various parts of Sweden, it has been possible to build up a chronology for that area extending over as many as 17,000 years. This is a year by year count, and it has made possible the map in Fig. 238, which shows the position of the receding ice front during the last decay over a period of several thousand years.

POLLEN ANALYSIS

Varve patterns are only useful if there is a deposit which extends over a period of at least, say, fifty years, in order to produce sufficient of the characteristic pattern so that it may be placed in its correct position in the whole sequence. Another method which is much used, especially for unstratified deposits of organic matter such as peat, is that of *pollen analysis*.

Pollen grains resist decay perhaps more than most other organic remains, and because they occur in very large numbers, especially in peat deposits, they are used to study past climates. After they have been isolated from the rest of the material, grains belonging to different genera of plants can readily be identified when viewed through a microscope. The grains are counted. Some species produce more pollen than do others, but when this has been allowed for, the number of grains which are found for each genus is some measure of the prevalence of that group of plants in the past.

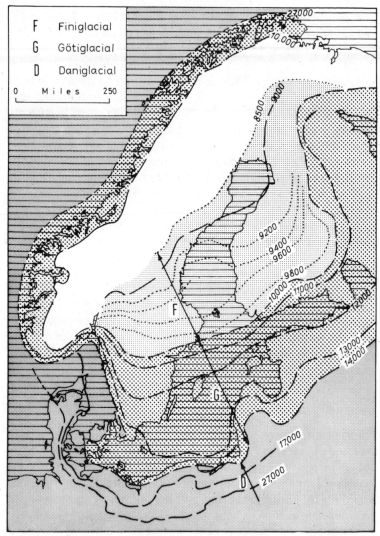

F Finiglacial
G Götiglacial
D Daniglacial

0   Miles   250

Fig. 238. The retreating ice front in Scandinavia (dates mostly determined by varve counts)

Figure 239 shows a typical pollen count diagram which has been produced by taking a number of separate samples of a section of peat from thin layers perhaps 2 or 5 centimetres apart. Such a diagram is produced by counting the number of grains of different genera in proportion to a total tree count usually of 150 grains, and then plotting these results as separate diagrams for each genus in the form of a special type of graph. The broader the black area the more prevalent is that particular genus at that depth of peat, and changes in the width of the black area thus indicate changes in the relative importance of that genus as time has elapsed. The general picture which the

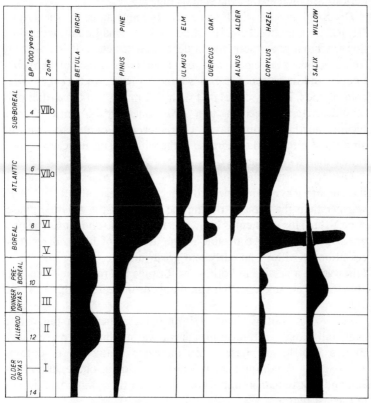

Fig. 239. Generalised and simplified pollen count diagram
(B.P. = *date before the present, in thousands of years*)

various results give at any one level is sufficient to enable an ecologist to deduce the type of climate that must have existed in order to produce such a grouping of plants. It is possible to determine therefore that the climate was cold, cool, mild, warm or hot, and to know something also regarding the total amount of precipitation and its distribution in the seasons of the year, for many plants are tolerant only of certain conditions.

Ecologists interested in this branch of their subject have divided 'historical botany' from the time of the Würm IIb glaciation to the present into eight major divisions or *pollen zones,* which they have numbered I to VIII, zone VII generally being subdivided into VIIa and VIIb. The scale of years as determined by carbon 14 examination, the pollen zone numbers and the names given to the different periods are indicated at the side of Fig. 239.

Dryas octopetala, which has given its genus name to zones I and III, has no common English name, and is a small plant with white flowers, having, as the name indicates, eight petals. It is now only found in the arctic regions and high mountains of the northern continents, and its presence in zones I and III indicates that these were cold periods, in fact, correlated with Würm IIb and the earlier part of Würm IIc. Between the two *dryas* zones is the Alleröd (from a locality north of Köbenhavn), characterised by an increase in the amount of birch, and a decrease in the willow. This indicates a cool, rather than a cold, phase.

During both the Pre-Boreal and the Boreal, zones IV, V and VI, the climate was warming up to reach its hottest, about 2°C (4°F) warmer than the present, during the middle of the Atlantic phase, zone VIIa. This moment is known as the *climatic optimum.* The progressive change saw a decline in the amount of birch, the virtual cessation of willow, an early and great increase in pine and hazel, followed by a decline in both, slow for pine but rapid and considerable for hazel, linked with a simultaneous increase in elm, oak and alder.

Zone VIIb contrasts with VIIa in being rather drier but with a slight fall in temperature, although still warmer than the present day. In this Sub-Boreal phase, hazel increased again, but to nothing approaching the dominance it had in the Boreal phase, and alder, elm and oak remained important, although there was some decline in the last two.

The changes described here are typical of a large number of areas, although naturally every site has its own variations and characteristics. For this reason, the figure is described as being generalised as well as simplified, the latter because in actual examinations one does not obtain smooth curves as are shown in this diagram, but rather rapidly fluctuating ones of which those drawn here give the mean values.

Although pollen analyses give direct evidence of nothing more than the succession of plant groupings and thus of climatic fluctuations, nevertheless, when such examinations have been carried out in many localities and have been linked with other dating methods such as with carbon 14 tests and with varve counts, the climate for different localities during the various stages of the Pleistocene may become known, and further pollen analyses in new localities may well be sufficient, not only to determine the sequence of events in a qualitative way, but also to enable correlations to be made with specific known dates.

DETERMINING THE TEMPERATURE

Ordinary oxygen mostly has an atomic weight of 16, but about one part in five hundred is an isotope oxygen 18. This is not radioactive, but its ratio with oxygen 16 varies with temperature, and thus by examining their ratio in fossil plants or animals, it is possible to discover the temperatures of past ages.

DATING BY RATE OF SEDIMENTATION

Carbon 14 determinations were used in fixing the dates given in Figs. 233 and 239 as far back as 30,000 years, but for dates older than that, the thickness of layers of sediments has been used in areas where there is reason to believe the rate of deposition has not varied through the period. This method is by no means exact, but so far a radioactive isotope which has a suitably longer half-life than carbon 14 has not been discovered.

Attempts have also been made to date the major events of the Pleistocene, that is, to date the onset of glacial or interglacial periods, by a combination of carbon 14 determinations and the rate of sedimentation in deep sea-floor sediments.

A core of organic ooze, perhaps 20 to 30 feet (6 to 9 metres) in length, is drawn up from the ocean bottom, and carbon 14 examination of the upper part of the specimen may perhaps provide the information that the last 30,000 years have there produced a deposition of ooze totalling, say, 70 cm thickness. Farther than this the carbon 14 method cannot go.

It is then assumed that the rate of deposition has been constant throughout the column, and, by extrapolation, the date for any particular layer of the core may be inferred. At the same time, oxygen 18 examination of organic remains within the core at various levels gives the temperatures of the water at those times, and the combined result is to date the various cold periods and to measure the intensity of their cooling. The dates given in Fig. 230 were obtained in this way. Their accuracy is not definitely known, but it is at least very likely that they are of the right order of magnitude.

It is significant to note that dating of the cold and warm periods by this method does produce results which accord with other methods of investigation where these can be used.

Because the causes of Ice Ages are not known, it is quite impossible to tell whether the present warm period is an interglacial or whether it marks the final termination of the Pleistocene group of cold periods. The length of time, of the order of ten to twenty thousand years according to the locality, since the continuous ice cover left an area is still far shorter than most of the known interglacial periods, and the temperature today is still cooler than it was in the long interglacial (see Fig. 230).

This provides an excellent example of the importance of theory. The absence of causal knowledge means that the conditions that must be looked for in order to find indications of the termination or otherwise of the cold periods are not known. Absence of knowledge of the mechanism means that we cannot read the signs, even when it is possible that they may well be displayed clearly in front of us.

We cannot foretell what future climatic changes may be in store.

CHAPTER TWENTY-THREE

Glaciated Landscapes

THE topographical effects of glacial deposition have already been described in Chapter 20, but in Chapter 19, which dealt with glaciers themselves, attention was concentrated upon the ice and the mechanisms by which it was fed and by which it moved from place to place. The present chapter discusses the landforms which become apparent when the ice melts away and which in that sense become *fossil,* attention being paid almost entirely to those that are the result of glacial *erosion.*

Erosion by moving ice occurs in two ways: by *abrasion* and by *plucking.* The full mechanisms by which these occur are still not certainly understood, not the least difficulty being the changed physical properties of ice when it is subject to pressure such as at the sole of a glacier. Nevertheless, it is patently clear that both these two major processes do occur, perhaps accompanied by others of less importance. One only needs to look at striations and glacial pavements to appreciate the fact that abrasion occurs; and at the lee end of a *roche moutonnée* to know that plucking is also a factor of considerable importance (see Figs. 184 and 185).

GLACIAL TROUGHS

Probably the most popularly known result of glaciation is the glacial trough or U-shaped valley. Not all glaciated valleys are now U-shaped, and a great many have experienced modification in post-glacial times. The release of support on the sides of the U when the ice melted away and was replaced by air, often resulted in a more or less immediate partial collapse so as to produce extensive screes, such as occasionally virtually choke at least the narrower glaciated valleys. These might be termed *deglaciation screes,* and they often produce slopes of loose material, which become more or less stable and protect the solid rock faces which they mask from further weathering. Figures 82 and 83 illustrate this.

The trough is most often a modified fluvial valley which the glacier adopted for its own use during the cold period or periods. The slopes above the glacier limits exhibit relic effects of fluvial ero-

Fig. 240. Naerøydal glaciated valley from the valley head. Note the hanging tributary valley on left

sion, and this accounts for the *shoulder,* or sudden change from near vertical to a much less steep slope often at a considerable height above the present valley floor. Such shoulders are markedly visible in Fig. 240, especially on the right-hand side of the valley.

The sides of the trough thus commonly exhibit three facets: (1) the preglacial fluvial upper slope, (2) the side of the glaciated valley, and (3) the deglaciation scree slope. There is often a fourth facet, inasmuch as the floor of the valley may be deeply infilled by post-glacial alluvial deposits associated with immediate post-glacial times or with post-glacial lakes, now drained. Such a flat floor is shown in Figs. 81 and 240.

The steepness of the side of the glaciated valley and its height is well illustrated by Fig. 241, which is an air photograph of Kjösnesfjord, a freshwater branch of Lake Jölster, which is situated about 20 miles (30 km) north of Sognfjord. The almost perpendicular walls here reach nearly to the summits of the mountains and have a height of about 2,500 feet (760 metres) above lake level. They indicate the maximum height of the surface of the ice in the valley glacier.

The deglaciation screes are clearly seen, especially on the right-hand side of the trough. The view is down-valley, and the scale is indicated by the narrow ribbon of the road on either side of the lake. The blunt up-valley end of the lake is the result of the fact that it has shrunk from its original length, and the present transverse boundary is the line along which the alluvial fill becomes exposed, due to lowering of water-level by the deepening of the trench at the lake outlet, some 20 miles (30 km) away.

There are several types of glacial trough which may be distinguished. Some account was given of the Jostedal ice cap in Chapter 19, and there it was mentioned that the cap gives rise to numerous glaciers. They fall over the edge of the plateau in much the same way as sugar icing often trickles over the edge of a cake, and Fig. 183 shows one such glacier. Troughs which have been cut by glaciers originating in an icefall from an ice cap in this way may be termed *ice cap troughs*. They occur commonly in all areas with extensive ice caps, and besides the Norwegian example, there are the numerous ones which today occur in Iceland and in many other localities.

Fig. 241. Glacial trough with deglaciation screes

The second type is the *valley head trough,* and in this case the glacier was surrounded on three sides by mountainous country with sufficiently steep slopes to prevent the accumulation of an ice cap. The fossil valley forms a trough which may be followed far into the mountain mass but which terminates sharply in a wall of rock that precludes further progress except by climbing. Such valley head troughs are common in Britain, an example being the Great Langdale valley of the English Lake District, and they are the normal type to be found in Switzerland. Most Swiss glaciers are today in troughs of this type.

In one sense, the valley head itself may be likened to a cirque, since the glacier was fed by snow falling down the steep slopes from the heights above it, and the ice was first formed in the valley itself. The

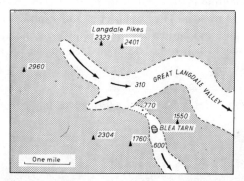

Fig. 242. Blea Tarn ice spillway or diffluence

viewpoint for Fig. 240 was the summit of the back wall at the end of such a trough.

Both the above types of trough have been formed by glaciers which made use of pre-existing fluvial valleys, but occasions arise when the supply of ice is too great for the existing valleys to be able to take the required quantity of material. This difficulty arises chiefly from the fact that a glacier is so much more bulky than the river which transports the same quantity of material, principally owing to the tremendous difference in their velocities.

It often happens that the ice in the glacier thickens until some overflows at a relatively low part of the side wall of the valley. Thus the glacier divides, deepens the col, and produces a *diffluent trough.* Figure 242 shows such a trough which took part of the flow of the Great Langdale glacier into the Blea Tarn route, and Fig. 243 shows a similar occurrence across Red Bank, near Grasmere (both in the English Lake District).

Diffluence may continue to such an extent that the major part of the glacier begins to take the secondary route and perhaps in time that may be the way adopted by the whole of the glacier. Such *transfluence troughs* account for many of the now abandoned through valleys that may be found in most glaciated mountain districts. They are named transfluent, since they switch the glacier from one pre-existing river valley to another and so cross the original interfluve.

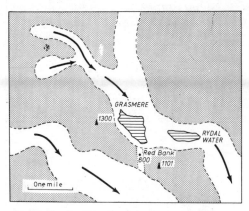

Fig. 243. Red Bank ice spillway or diffluence

A transfluent trough originates as a diffluent one, and the latter becomes the former when the new route takes at least the major part of the total quantity of ice.

A *counter trough* is produced when the original fluvial direction was contrary to the direction of movement which other conditions, such as the presence of great masses of lowland ice, imposed upon the glacier. Dunmail Raise (Fig. 244) is such a trough. Pre- and post-glacially this col has been part of the watershed between northward and southward flowing rivers. During glaciation, the northward-moving glacier in the Derwent valley near Keswick at times found its way blocked by southward-moving Scottish ice on the Carlisle Plain, and so was compelled to find some other outlet. The result was that it turned eastward and then southward at Keswick, and came over the col at Dunmail to join the Easedale glacier at Grasmere, and so assist in the cutting of the great Windermere over-deepened trough (see below).

   Dunmail Raise now stands at 782 feet (238 metres) above sea-level
with mountains rising to more than 2,000 feet (600 metres) on either
side. When eventually the movement of ice stopped, dead ice was
left on the summit and on melting it produced hummocky moraine
typical of such situations. Other associated glacial events led to the
development of the great east–west through trough from Penrith to
Keswick.

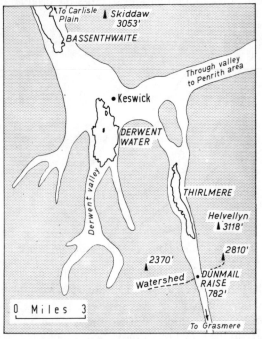

Fig. 244. Dunmail Raise counter trough

   Glacial troughs in Argyllshire, Scotland, seen in Fig. 245, display
a number of features typical of such areas. In the foreground two
large and one smaller (on the right) glaciated valleys converge; there
is a considerable amount of hummocky moraine, choking the left-
hand valley sufficiently to produce two small lakes; the central
trough narrows just before the confluence and it is a through trough
leading to a large lake, which drains away from the viewer, although
the nearer part of the central valley drains towards the bottom edge
of the picture.

Fig. 245. Glaciated valley in Argyllshire, Scotland. Loch Linnhe

OVER-DEEPENING – ROCK BARRIERS

Because ice is a solid and can therefore be thrust uphill at least to some extent by pressure from behind, the long-profile of a glaciated valley differs considerably from a fluvial one. Some of the principal characteristics of such a profile are (1) the general profile tends to be very flat with a steep head, the *trough end* as just described, (2) there is often *over-deepening,* that is, gouging out of *rock hollows,* with the accompaniment of *rock barriers* at their down-valley end; and (3) *rock steps* are common.

Rock barriers between individual hollows are to be observed in most glaciated valleys. Between Grasmere and Rydal Water the rock floor of the valley rises about 300 feet (90 metres) in the space of half a mile (800 metres) to form a rock barrier about a quarter of a mile (400 metres) in breadth across the whole width of the valley between the two lakes. On the lee side, it descends by about the same amount in a further half-mile to Rydal Water. The river linking the two lakes has cut a narrow gorgelike valley through the barrier.

Fig. 246. Kvamsöy rock barrier in Hardangerfjord

Windermere also is divided into two by a rock barrier midway along its length. The highest parts of this barrier protrude out of the water as a series of islands and here the rise is of much the same dimensions as the Grasmere–Rydal one.

Another barrier is to be seen across Hardangerfjord between Norheimsund and Alvik. This is shown in Fig. 246, where the barrier rises nearly to 200 feet (64 metres) above sea-level in the little island of Kvamsöy, whilst the depth in line with the 2,240-foot (683 metre) mountain Samlen on the south side of the fjord is as low as 2,625 feet (800 metres) below sea-level. This gives a rise in rock floor of more than 2,800 feet (860 metres) in the space of 2 miles (3·2 km), and 1½ miles (2·4 km) farther down-fjord (to the right in the photograph), the rock floor is down again, this time to rather more than 2,000 feet (620 metres) below sea-level.

The very dramatic height and steepness of this barrier typifies the intensity of the glaciation in this part of Norway, where so many glaciological features are blatantly displayed.

A *rock step* differs from a rock barrier in having no reversed gradient on its up-valley side. The valley floor after continuing on at its normal almost level gradient suddenly plunges before again settling down to the same steady, exceedingly gentle slope. A rock step is probably a form of trough end inasmuch as it probably marks a stage when its position marked the source of the glacier. When the glacier traversed the rock step it did so in the form of an icefall, with many crevasses. Considerable research still requires to be done on the whole subject of rock steps before one can be quite certain as to their exact mode of origin.

GLACIAL FINGER LAKES

It is only natural that when the glacier melts away, it is replaced in the over-deepened parts of the valley by long narrow lakes known as *finger lakes*. In the Hardangerfjord instance just described, the level is such that the whole length of the valley has been drowned by the incoming sea, although the inner part of the fjord only just misses being a lake, for part of this Kvamsöy barrier is only just submerged.

There are many examples where the barrier was sufficiently high to prevent ingress by the sea completely, and the portion up-valley of the barrier has thus remained a lake instead of becoming a fjord. Hornindal is one example. This is the deepest lake in Europe, with a water-surface at 170 feet (52 metres) above sea-level, and a maximum depth of 1,686 feet (514 metres). It is about 16 miles (26 km) long, and is separated from Nordfjord by a rock barrier about a mile (1½ km) wide, which scarcely rises above the lake-level.

The same kind of feature is developed by some of the lakes in the glaciated valleys of western Scotland. Freshwater lochs Maree, Morar and Shiel are examples of lakes which have only just missed being fjords.

Figure 247 shows Loch Oich in the foreground with Loch Lochy in the middle distance and the sea loch Linnhe in the remote distance. Water-level in Oich is 105 feet (32 metres) above the sea and in Lochy 93 feet (28 metres). The two are separated by the low, flat area seen in the photograph, and besides this there are numerous other indications of the fact that the two lakes have been one. The delta of the earlier route taken by the Garry river, which occupied the valley in the right foreground, is seen just above the mouth of that valley, whilst the present delta is covered with trees in the lowest part of the photograph. Both of these deltas are now above water-level because of a fall in the latter due to the deeper cutting of the trench between Oich and Lochy, and also between the latter and the fjord.

The valley is part of Glen More, and although it owes its origin largely to faulting, it has nevertheless been gouged out by glaciers which have produced the over-deepening, and thus the lakes. Loch

Fig. 247. Lochs Oich and Lochy, Scotland

Ness, at the northern end of Glen More, has a depth of about 700 feet (210 metres) with a rock barrier at its northern end rising to 100 feet (30 metres) above sea-level, giving an over-deeping of about 800 feet (240 metres).

The causes of these over-deepened reaches of glaciated valleys, like rock barriers and rock steps, are not fully understood, but it is very probable that in the main they are due to *convergence*. This may take either of two forms. It may result from the junction of two glaciers into one valley, and a corresponding thickening in the ice so that it becomes heavier on the floor and is able to dig more deeply, or it may result merely from a narrowing in the width of the valley.

A beaded effect is often very apparent in such valleys, narrow reaches alternating with wide open parts. There is, however, rather less accord in such cases with over-deepened parts of the profile, for they do not always coincide with the narrower parts of the valley, as might be expected. One of the difficulties in suggesting a mechanism is that there is a general lack of knowledge of the exact shape of the over-deepened part. It is often either a lake with silt on its bed, or a drained lake floor, and in either case it is not easy to determine the exact form of the rock floor beneath because of the silt cover.

HANGING VALLEYS

A *discordance* is often found in the levels of the rock floors of two glaciated valleys at their junctions. This is contrary to what is found in the case of fluvial valleys (see p. 162). A small tributary glacier is able to cut its valley less deeply than the thicker main glacier, and thus on melting the floor of the tributary is found to *hang* above the floor of the main valley. Such a valley junction is shown in Fig. 248, where a small valley has its floor 250 feet (76 metres) higher than the main valley's floor, in spite of the latter being partly infilled with deltaic material.

There are many examples of *hidden hanging valleys,* where the junctions have been drowned as the valleys have become fjords. Figure 249 shows by spot depths the fact that Fjaerlands, Arna and Finna fjords are in truth hanging valleys above the main Sognfjord valley, and Vetle and Svaera fjords in turn have floors which hang above Fjaerlandsfjord.

The same figure also shows the great actual depth of these valleys in one of the most intensely glaciated localities. The difference in height between Rambera and the adjacent fjord floor is nearly 9,000 feet (2,663 metres). The shoulder is mostly at about 3,600 feet (1,100

Fig. 248. Horpedal hanging valley above dry deltaic flat at head of Fjaerlandsfjord, western Norway

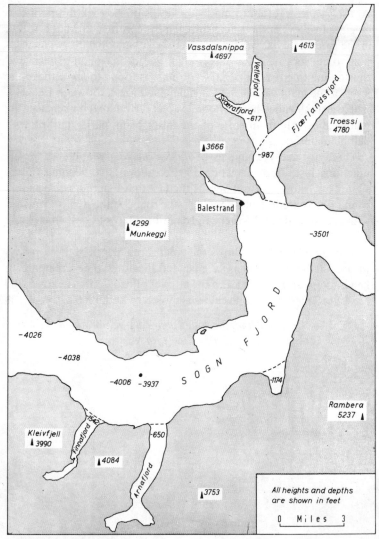

Fig. 249. Sognfjord and hidden hanging valleys

metres) above present sea-level, giving the near-vertical side of the glacial trough a total height of about 7,600 feet or nearly $1\frac{1}{2}$ miles (2,300 metres)!

Figure 250 shows similar hanging valleys by means of contours in an area of Scotland west of lochs Voil and Doine. Here the shoulder

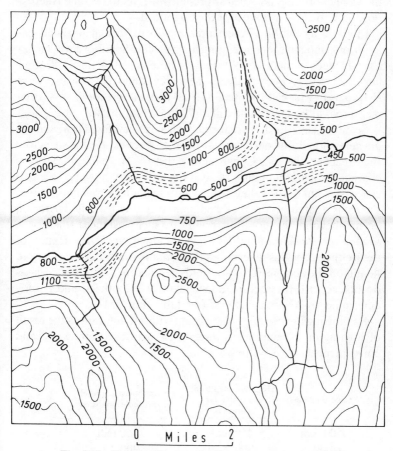

Fig. 250. *Exposed hanging valleys in central Scotland*

is about 1,500 feet (460 metres) above the valley floor, the smaller height being indicative of the less intense glaciation.

FJORDS

A fjord is a glaciated valley whose contours are sufficiently low for its floor to be continuously below the present sea-level. Consequently the sea invades the valley and drowns it so far as the upper reaches. The end of the fjord is not always the end of the glaciated valley, for beyond the limit of submergence, the valley becomes a normal glaciated one. Naeröydal shown in Fig. 240 is pictured from the valley head and not very far beyond the limit of the view shown, the valley bottom passes below present sea-level to become Naeröy-fjord, a branch of a branch of the Sognfjord.

Fjord floors exhibit all the characteristics of normal glaciated valley floors, and have an undulating long-profile. Sognfjord, which has a total length to the head of its longest branch of 114 miles (183 km), has its greatest known depth near Kyrkjebö (just seaward of Hoyanger), where 4,291 feet (1,308 metres) of water has been measured, although still 45 miles (72 km) from the sea.

Scandinavian fjords were formed when sea-level was low, and the glaciers spread out on a coastal plain to become piedmont before they reached the sea. Consequently there is no particular profile characteristic of the mouth of such fjords. When, however, the glacier passes out of the valley directly into sea, it may well happen that the ice is floated off the rock bed, and in that case no floor erosion occurs beyond the flotation point. In such instances, there is a *shallow threshold,* the depth of which is a function of the thickness of the ice there, for this determines the depth of sea water necessary to float it off the bottom. The thresholds of adjacent fjords in such cases do not accord, for each is independent of the others, and is only determined by the ice thickness (see table, Fig. 251).

Shallowing down-valley also occurs without flotation as the result of wasting of the glacier ice, the gradual decrease in thickness and consequently in erosive power.

Ice thickness	Minimum depth of sea water for flotation	Depth (below sea-level) of threshold produced
500 feet	450 feet	450 feet
1,000	900	900
1,500	1,350	1,350
2,000	1,800	1,800
etc.	etc.	etc.
200 metres	180 metres	180 metres
400	360	360
600	540	540
800	720	720
etc.	etc.	etc.

Fig. 251. Ice flotation depths in sea water

Fig. 252. Geirangerfjord from the Eagle's Nest. A typical inner reach of a fjord

The inner reaches of a fjord are often narrow in proportion to the height of the sides which are precipitous (see Fig. 252). In the fjord pictured, Geirangerfjord, the mountains rise almost vertically on either side to a height of about 2,500 feet (760 metres) above sea-level, with summits rather higher, and the width at sea-level is about a mile ($1\frac{1}{2}$ km).

A fjord is, however, often much more open in cross-profile as is shown in Fig. 253, which is a tributary of Nordfjord and seen here at about 60 miles (100 km) from the open sea. Most fjords have profiles of much this shape as they approach the sea, and some, as in this case, maintain it almost to their landward end.

Fjard is a name given to a variety of fjord which has low banks throughout its length. Like a fjord, it is the result of ice-gouging and possesses at least one reach of over-deepening, and in this way differs from a ria, which owes its origin to fluvial action (see p. 383). Fjards occur on the south coast of Norway, on parts of the Baltic coast of Sweden and in some other parts of the world.

The Danish so-called *fjord,* such as Limfjord, which cuts the northern end of Jutland into two, is of different origin entirely, and it is

Fig. 253. Tributary of Nordfjord with sloping sides

very unfortunate that it has the same descriptive name. The Danish fjord is very shallow (often less than 20 feet: 6 metres deep), traverses lowland country and is entirely contained in glacial morainic deposits. The hollow was eroded in these deposits by meltwater streams contained in tunnels beneath the ice. A Danish fjord is thus a drowned tunnel valley, and the drowning is its only affinity with a Norwegian or other fjord.

The drowned glaciated valleys of Scotland are true fjords in the Norwegian sense, and Fig. 254 shows Loch Leven from near its mouth at Ballachulish, which is seen on the nearside of the loch at the narrows on the left. This is a sea loch and the sloping sides of the valley are largely the result of deglaciation scree, the solid rock walls being in general considerably steeper than the present profile. Numerous flat promontories thrust themselves into the loch and are deposits from the various post-glacial rivers entering the loch and building deltas at a time when the sea-level was relatively higher than it is today. The mountains on either side of the loch rise to summit heights of from 2,600 to 3,200 feet (790 to 980 metres). The almost bare rock summit in the right foreground displays the joint pattern very clearly. It is Creag Ghorm and stands 2,372 feet (723 metres) above the sea.

Cirque glaciers have already been described on p. 232, and Fig. 255 shows a fossil cirque in the English Lake District just south-west of Haweswater, the end of which is seen in the foreground of the photograph. This Blea Cirque is on the eastern side of High Street, the snowclad ridge across the centre top of the photograph, and to the right is a full view of Riggindale, a fine example of a short (2 miles: 3 km) glaciated valley with a small cirque perched in its north-west corner (far right).

The tarn in Blea Cirque demonstrates the over-deepening. The lip is solid rock with a terminal moraine about 15 feet (5 metres) thick along it, and the notch cut by the stream draining the tarn today may also be seen.

Fig. 254. Loch Leven and Ballachulish, western Scotland

Fig. 255. Cirque, cirque lake and glaciated valley near Haweswater

BISCUIT-BOARD TOPOGRAPHY

When a number of cirque glaciers cut into a full-bodied mountain mass on various sides, a type of *biscuit-board topography* is produced as is shown in the case of Snowdon (Fig. 256). The actual peak is the far summit a little to the right of centre and rises to 3,560 feet (1,085 metres). The smooth contours of the preglacial mountain are broken by at least four cirques. The present mountain is a mere remnant of what it previously was, and clearly had the cold periods lasted a little longer pyramidal peaks of the *Matterhorn type* would have been formed. Although only four cirques can be seen clearly in this photograph, the whole of Snowdon exhibits the effects of at least fourteen.

FOSSIL ICE CAP TERRAIN

The features so far described have all been those produced by valley glaciers. Plateau areas were often covered by large ice caps during glaciation. Some still in existence have been described in Chapter 19. On the completion of ice decay, the topography beneath the ice cap becomes exposed. It is characterised by the absence of valleys, although these may radiate from its periphery, and the ground is normally gently rolling, perhaps with a few monadnock mountains or mountain groups rising above the general level. The plateau itself often displays the minor, rather than the major, features of other glaciated topography. Drainage is normally rather poor, owing to the undulating nature of the terrain with many enclosed hollows, so that small lakes occur, and since the ice, at least in its later stages, was usually dead, there are often a number of eskers and kames, providing there was sufficient higher ground above the general plateau level to provide the rock debris with which to build these constructional forms.

MULTIPLE GLACIATION TOPOGRAPHY

Most glaciated areas have experienced several glaciations, and the evidence before the fieldworkers is that left by each glaciation superimposed on the previous ones. In most areas, many of the clues left by earlier events were obliterated by the later.

Figures 257, 258 and 259 show an aerial photograph, an interpretive sketch and a morphological map of the Coniston Water district. There is here clear evidence of four glaciations, each of the later ones

Fig. 256. The remnant that is Snowdon

Fig. 257. Coniston Water viewed from the south from the air

of less extent than the earlier, and thus not entirely removing the evidence of former events.

All the fells to left and right of the lake (west and east) have been glaciated to their summits. This is seen on the ground by ice-smoothed rocks, *roches moutonnées* and small amounts of till in the hollows. This more or less flat, glaciated area rises to 1,000 feet (300 metres) on either side with a central level of about 500 feet (150 metres).

It is contrasted with the higher mountains of the core of the Lake District in the left distance. These include Coniston Old Man, rising to 2,635 feet (803 metres). The wide ice cover of the lower heights represents the Main Irish Sea or Würm I glaciation.

Later a glacier coming southwards from Yewdale, fed by several valleys there, had its top surface at something between 450 and 550 feet (140 and 170 metres). This ice divided a little south of Coniston town, part taking the Torver Valley route, now with a rock floor at

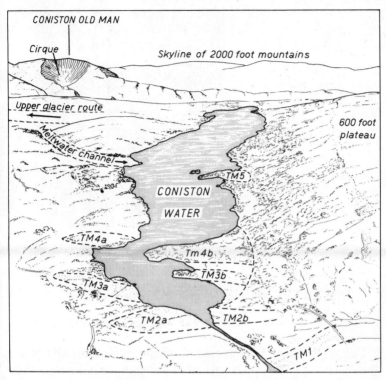

Fig. 258. Sketch interpretation of Fig. 257

about 300 feet (90 metres), and the major part taking the Coniston Water route. Both glaciers passed beyond the limits of the map shown on Fig. 259, became piedmont, and formed part of the lowland ice sheet which terminated in the Kirkham moraine (Kirkham glaciation or Würm IIa).

In the third stage, the ice had a top surface level of between 200 and 300 feet (60 and 90 metres), and as such was unable to enter the Torver valley, being quite weak and finding the easy Coniston Water route. It melted away by the time it reached what is now the southern end of the lake, and it may well be that it lacked the motive power to climb farther out of the over-deepened part of the valley, which had mainly been gouged out by the previous glaciations. This glacier formed the terminal moraine system which is well seen in the photograph and only indicated in a formal manner on the map. There are at least five stages (TMI–5) in the formation of this compound terminal moraine, as are indicated on the interpretive sketch (Fig.

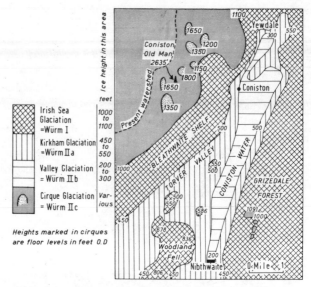

Fig. 259. Morphological map of the Coniston Water area

258). These may be termed the Nibthwaite moraines, and this is the Valley glaciation or Würm IIb.

Finally, there are the cirques on the flanks of Coniston Old Man, the only part of the area shown on Fig. 259 that was sufficiently high to support perennial ice during the last stages, the Cirque glaciation or Würm IIc. As will be seen by the heights of the cirque floors marked on the map, they occur at most levels above 1,150 feet (350 metres).

CONCLUSION

It is important to remember that most landforms in the (today) cool temperate parts of the world have largely been moulded into their present forms by the action of ice, either by erosion or by deposition. The time that has elapsed since the disappearance of permanent ice has been, in terms of landform construction, very short, and events in post-glacial times have only begun to modify what the ice left. Such areas include, for example, most of Britain, the whole of northern continental Europe, the whole of Canada and of the United States north of a line roughly along the Missouri and Ohio rivers. In these, the scenery is one of glaciated mountains, lakes formed by glacial over-deepening and moraine-covered lowlands.

This last, the great spreads of deposited debris, is of the greatest economic significance. It is this general morainic cover that forms many of the great agricultural regions of the northern hemisphere. The soil the farmer must use is the material brought to his area by ice. Its properties are quite different from those of soils of purely weathering or fluvial origin, and vary so much within themselves as to make a detailed study of their nature essential for any successful agricultural usage of the land. It is for this reason that so much stress has been given to the topographical effects of ice, especially of their depositional forms.

The approximate boundaries of the great deglaciation lake Agassiz at its maximum stage are shown in Fig. 260. At that time the

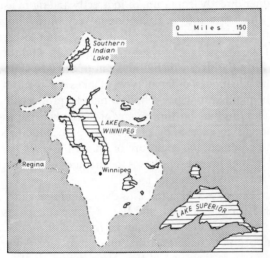

Fig. 260. Lake Agassiz

normal (and presentday) drainage of the area towards the northeast and Hudson Bay was impeded by still-existing ice. Water was impounded by the confused drainage which resulted, and eventually found an outlet into the Mississippi system. Great expanses of clay and silt were deposited over its floor, deltas were built out into it by the inflowing rivers and so produced gravel and sand beds. Now that the lake has long since drained itself, only to leave such relatively small remnants of its former magnitude as Lake Winnipeg, Lake Winnipegosis and the others, the present land use of the area indicates the interdependence of glaciology and agriculture in such areas, for it is as varied as are the variations in soils that have resulted from the episode.

CHAPTER TWENTY-FOUR

Lakes

MANY types of lakes are described in other chapters, but it is useful to make some general remarks here in order to co-ordinate the whole subject.

The feature essential to produce a lake is a hollow. This fills with water, either directly from rain, or indirectly and more usually from streams which flow into it. Excepting in very warm climates where evaporation is rapid, the hollow fills until the water-level reaches the height of the lowest part of the surrounding rim, and there it over-flows to form the river which drains out of the lake (Fig. 261).

Any classification of different types of lakes is in reality a classifica-tion of the manner in which a hollow may be produced on the land surface, and this may be done in any of three principal ways: (1) by subsidence, (2) by excavating a hollow, or (3) by building some form of dam to complete the enclosure of an area already partially sur-rounded by higher land. The last is the method used by man when he makes a *reservoir* or artificial lake.

Most of the lakes which fall into the second and third categories have already been described, and Fig. 263 gives the pages on which reference to the various types may be found.

It is important to remember that many individual lakes owe their existence to more than one of the above causes, or they may have become deeper by deposition of some kind on the rim of an erosional hollow. For example, many finger lakes are made deeper by the presence of moraine at their down-valley end.

Lough Neagh in Northern Ireland and Lake Victoria in East Africa are the two most often quoted examples of lakes which owe their existence to folding. Such lakes are usually fairly shallow and roughly of a circular shape. The fold involved is most often of an inverted dome type.

Rift valley lakes occur because of irregularities in the amount of subsidence of the land surface between the two sets of faults which have created the valley. Very often there are transverse or oblique faults which produce a series of steps or barriers in the general floor of the rift.

Fig. 261. *River draining out of lake Leirvassbu, Jotunheim*

Fig. 262. *Crater lake in Darfur province, Sudan*

Crater lakes are placed under the heading of subsidence lakes for the hollow within which they lie has been produced by the downward movement of the surface of the lava plug, which at the time of the cessation of the last eruption filled the crater to the top. Cooling or other shrinkage has resulted in the present solid lava surface being below the lip of the crater, often by as much as several hundred feet. Crater Lake, Oregon, is a famous lake of this type, and Fig. 262 shows such a lake within the inner crater of one of the extinct volcanic vents in the Darfur province of the Sudan.

The importance of glaciation as a producer of lakes is clear from the classification below where nine of the nineteen types are glacial, and far more than half the lakes of the world owe their origin

SUBSIDENCE LAKES
Synclinal or fold lakes
Rift-valley lakes
Crater lakes
Subsidence lakes resulting from subterranean solution

EROSION (AND WEATHERING) LAKES
Glacial
    Plateau ice cap hollow lakes (p. 315)
    Cirque lakes (p. 313)
    Finger lakes (rock-barrier lakes) (p. 305)
    Tunnel-valley lakes (p. 259)
Oxbow lakes (p. 167)
Deflation-hollow lakes (p. 390)
Limestone-solution lakes

DEPOSITIONAL LAKES
Glacial
    Irregular-till lakes (p. 250)
    Kettle-hole lakes (p. 250)
    Moraine-dam lakes (p. 302)
Landslide-dam lakes
Lava-dam lakes
Coastal lagoons (p. 352)

MORE TEMPORARY LAKES
Proglacial lakes (p. 258)
Deglaciation lakes (p. 266)

Fig. 263. The principal types of lakes

to this single cause. It is significant that Sweden has more than 100,000 lakes in a country with an area of 174,000 square miles (451,000 sq km), so that there is one lake for every $1\frac{3}{4}$ sq miles ($4\frac{1}{2}$ sq km). Most of the lakes are quite small, as must be obvious, but this is typical of an intensely glaciated land, and it is probably right to say that very nearly all of these lakes are of glacial origin.

THE IMPERMANENCE OF LAKES

Mention has already been made of the way in which a single lake may become broken into two (p. 305 and Fig. 247). Lakes are a feature of the youthful stage of any landscape and their life is always short. The number of lakes in the English Lake District, all of which owe their origin to glaciation, is already less than half the number that were present immediately after the ice had completely melted away. This gives a half-life period of about 10,000 years under such conditions.

One of the characteristics of the valley scenery of the Lake District is the presence of flat valley floors between steeply rising, irregular mountainsides. It is this contrast which so greatly enhances the beauty of the scenery and adds to the impressive nature of the slopes. The *valley flats* are the floors of lakes which have drained away (Fig. 264).

Fig. 264. The flat floor of the Great Langdale valley – the bottom of a drained lake

Lakes are destroyed by two processes, both of which are generally operative at the same time. The river flowing out of the lake gradually lowers its bed and so produces a *trench* through the barrier that holds up the water. As the trench is progressively deepened, so the water-level is lowered. In time, the lake could be completely destroyed by this method, excepting in those cases where the lake floor is near or below sea-level. Naturally the outflowing river cannot deepen the trench below the level down to which it can cut, which will be a little above sea-level.

Whilst this is occurring, the rivers which flow into the lake deposit their load on the bottom, for the mass of fairly still water acts as a settling tank and the river flowing out of the lake is without load. The lake is thus gradually filling up with alluvium, and it is at the moment when the bottom of the outflow trench and the surface of the siltation infill reach the same level that the lake disappears.

Part Five

Coasts and the Sea

CHAPTER TWENTY-FIVE

Waves and Currents

THE coastal zone is the triple junction between the three greatest units of the Earth's skin, the atmosphere, the ocean and the land. Or, to put it in more physical terms, the gaseous, the liquid and the solid (see Fig. 265). Where the three meet, naturally there are exceptional opportunities for rapid horizontal or vertical changes. Some of the latter have been described in the appropriate places dealing with meteorology and climatology, and the present chapters are chiefly concerned with the horizontal changes that occur as one passes from the liquid to the solid units, and with the interaction of the two.

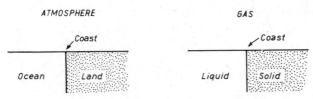

Fig. 265. The coast at a triple boundary

Geographers are particularly concerned with the effects the sea has in building up or removing land, and the principal tool that produces these changes is the *wave*.

WAVES

Waves are the result of interaction between the gaseous and liquid units. Friction between the two at their interface results in turbidity in both the air and the water, and wind continuously playing on their boundary builds up the undulations which we call waves and which are driven across the surface of the water by the wind itself.

The faster the wind the greater the wave it can produce, but whatever its speed, time is necessary to build up a wave of size, and so *duration of wind* is important. Since the wind is causing the wave to travel across the surface, the distance the wave has been moved may alternatively be used to indicate the size of wave that a wind of particular velocity is likely to produce at a given place. This is *length of fetch,* and it is because they have short lengths of fetch that many enclosed or semi-enclosed waters such as the North, Irish, Red and Baltic Seas, do not experience such large waves as do open oceans. It is coasts that face such expanses as the Atlantic and Pacific that receive the great *rollers.*

Waves which are flowing freely across the water surface, having

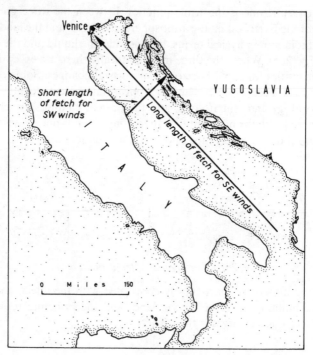

Fig. 266. Fetch in the Adriatic Sea

passed out of the area of the generating wind, are termed *swell,* and these tend to become longer, faster and lower, with a lengthening period.

Elongated areas of water, even though semi-enclosed, may acquire waves of considerable size if the wind generating them happens to blow along their greatest length. Thus in the Adriatic Sea (Fig. 266), waves on the Yugoslav coast produced by southwesterly winds are of much smaller size than those reaching the north coast, such as in the Gulf of Venice, when they have been brought the full length of the sea, perhaps 500 miles (800 km), by a southeasterly wind.

The number of wave crests that pass a particular point per minute is the *frequency*, the distance from crest to crest is the *wave length,* the *velocity* is the speed, measured in any units, with which the waves pass a stationary point, the *amplitude* is the half-height of the wave, the *height* being the vertical distance from crest to trough, the *period* is the time between the passage of two crests.

Several of these features are interconnected mathematically. Both the period and the velocity vary as the square root of the wave length, and thus the velocity and period vary in proportion to one another. The amplitude, as already stated, depends upon the wind velocity and the length of fetch, but it does not increase indefinitely as the latter increases. There is an upper limit to the amplitude of wave that a wind of any given velocity can produce.

BREAKING WAVES

The wave shape and the wave energy are the two factors which move forward. The water on whose surface the wave is formed moves in a circular fashion, individual particles of water each describing vertical circles whose diameter is about equal to the wave height. The water is moving backward in the trough and forward in the crest. The size of these circular orbits decreases rapidly with depth, but it is this vertical movement that causes the wave to 'feel the bottom' when it approaches shallow water. From that point onward, bottom friction tends to retard movement there, whilst the crest continues on at more or less its original speed. The front face of the wave thus steepens as the crest gains slightly on the trough, and in due course the crest is unsupported by water beneath it and the wave breaks.

The movement then changes its nature almost completely, and there is a great rushing forward of water to be followed by a somewhat slower retreat. The movement becomes much more a backward and forward one. This is the familiar *swash* and *backwash* of the water's edge. The surf bather relies on the sudden change from the one kind of wave to the other at the breaking point, beyond which the newly formed *wave of translation* propels him forward so fast and so far.

As the wave plunges in breaking, it produces great turbulence on the sea floor, with the result that sand and pebbles there are tossed into suspension and move with the water.

No wind blows with constant velocity over a large area, and consequently the waves it generates are not all alike. At any given moment, an area of sea is covered with a heterogenous collection of

Fig. 267. Orderly waves approach Braunton Burrows, Devon

wave crests of varying heights and lengths, but in particular circumstances these are restricted within a certain range of sizes and one speaks of a *wave spectrum,* rather than of waves of one particular magnitude. There is a tendency for greater regularity to be produced as waves pass into shallower water, and the ones observed from the water's edge or near-by cliffs are considerably more orderly than those out at sea whence they came (see Fig. 267).

OBLIQUE WAVES

Besides ultimately producing breakers, the shallowing water reduces the wave velocity, and thus may have the effect of swinging the wave crest and producing the effect known as *wave refraction.* This is illustrated in Fig. 268, which marks successive positions of a single wave crest. Because it is oblique to the depth contours, point A, for example, is in shallower water than point B although on the same crest, and so it moves forward a shorter distance, AA′, than BB′ in the same unit of time. Thus the wave crest changes its orientation and refraction results. With the wave conditions represented in Fig. 268, the waves feel the bottom at a depth of 10 feet (3 metres), and refraction then begins. The total amount of refraction illustrated is about 40° (from 60° obliquity at depth to 20° at the waterline), and the spread of energy is in the ratio 10 to 17.

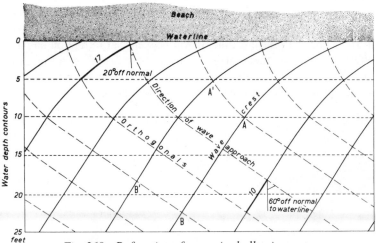

Fig. 268. *Refraction of waves in shallowing water*

Waves that are incident on a waterline at an *oblique* angle (see Fig. 269) are those which are refracted, but the refraction is never so complete as to swing an oblique wave into one approaching directly on to the coast. Borrowing a term from physics, a wave that approaches a coast at right-angles to the waterline is said to approach *normally* or to be *normal* to the waterline.

Fig. 269. *Oblique waves incident on a pebble beach*

In order to evaluate the relative power of wave attack on different parts of a coast, it is usual to draw *orthogonals*. These have been inserted in Fig. 268. They are placed an arbitrary but constant distance apart at the start, in fairly deep water, and then are maintained at right-angles to the crestline. It will be seen that refraction has the effect of spreading them farther apart in the case shown in Fig. 268, and this signifies that the wave energy is likewise spread, and the vigour of the wave approach is lessened by that amount.

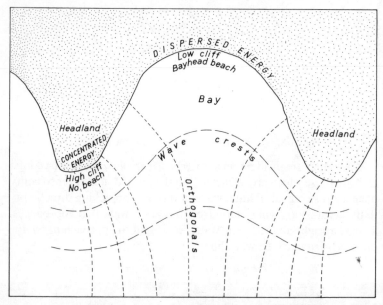

Fig. 270. Wave energy distribution on headland and bay

Figure 270 illustrates by means of orthogonals the effect that a headland and a bay have upon the strength of wave attack. The orthogonals, and consequently the energy, are concentrated on the headland and spread out in the bay. This is one of the reasons why headlands usually have more or less beachless coastlines with upstanding cliffs, in contrast to bayheads, which most often possess sandy or shingle beaches.

These characteristics of headlands and bays result from the obliquity of wave approach on a curved coast: Figure 270 was drawn with the assumption that the wave approach was normal to the general direction of the coast. On the sides of the headland and bay the waves become oblique.

When oblique waves break, even on a straight coast, the *swash* moves upbeach in a similarly oblique direction (see Fig. 271), and sand and pebbles move with it. The water movement then swings round as shown in the figure, to descend the beach also obliquely as

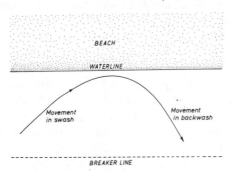

Fig. 271. *Water and beach movement in swash and backwash*

the *backwash*. The sand grains or pebbles may well have been deposited by the water before the backwash is complete, but they will certainly have been transported several feet along the coast. In the case of the coast shown in Fig. 270, this means movement is away from the headland and towards the bay. Thus loose material collects in the bay and forms a *bayhead beach*. Such a contrast between headland and bay is seen well in Fig. 272, which shows Porthcurno Bay

Fig. 272. *Headland and bayhead beach*

with Treen Point in the foreground, four miles southeast of Land's End.

Erosion therefore is greatest at the headland (concentration of orthogonals) with the consequent production of considerable quantities of broken material, and longshore movement of this, by means of obliquely incident waves, rids the headland of the beach it would otherwise acquire, and moves it towards the neighbouring bay.

TIDES AND PSEUDO-TIDES

Tides are a feature of most coasts and are entirely independent of waves, for they are generated by the action of the Moon and Sun and not by wind. The tide *ebbs* and *flows* without any assistance from moving air, and the waves which one watches approaching the water-line as the tide comes in have no connection whatever with the latter. In fact the tide rises and falls even on a completely calm sea.

Tides are described fully in Chapter 31. Different coasts have *tidal ranges* of varying amplitudes, and in the Mediterranean and Baltic Seas there is scarcely any tide at all. A special effect occurs in the latter which is, however, not connected with tides, although giving something of that appearance. It might be termed a *pseudo-tide*. When a steady westerly wind blows along the Baltic for several days, it builds up the water-level at the eastern end of the Sea, and lowers it around the Danish islands and the West German Baltic coast by as much as 10 or even more feet (3 metres +). This often causes considerable inconvenience to shipping in the very shallow water of this area.

The sea-level in the western Baltic is then lower than in the North Sea outside, and so a considerable flow of water from the latter takes place in order to make good the apparent deficit. Then, when the wind ceases, the Baltic water returns from the east again and there is a temporary abnormally high level at the western end, until the surplus escapes back to the North Sea.

COASTAL TERMS

The effect of the tide on beach morphology is to bring the breaker line to different levels twice a day, instead of its remaining more or less fixed along one line as is the case where the sea-level is nearly constant. The depositional and erosive effects of wave incidence are thus spread over a belt which may be termed the *tidal zone* of the beach, but is more usually called the *foreshore* (see Fig. 273). This is the area between low and high water lines, and since these differ according to whether it is a neap or a spring tide, the definition is rendered more precise by considering that the limits of the foreshore are the positions of low and high water during a *mean tide,* sometimes called an *ordinary tide.* On a shore where accumulation is occurring, especially where the coast is one of marshland or sand dunes, only exceptionally high tides, occurring perhaps two or three times a year, reach the actual *coastline,* which is the extreme tidal

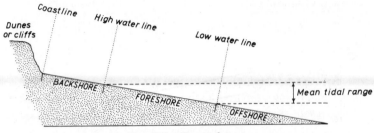

Fig. 273. *Coastal terms*

limit in any area, and then the belt between the mean high water line and the coastline is known as the *backshore.*

The foreshore and backshore together constitute the *shore.* The word *beach* refers to the loose material such as shingle, sand or silt, which may cover the surface of the shore. *Beach* is not used in connection with rock shores.

The sea bottom below low water mark, but where the water is quite shallow, is known as *offshore.*

SHORE MECHANISMS

In a tidal area the gradient of the shore as one walks from the coastline to low water mark is dependent upon the material of which it is composed, whether it be solid rock, shingle, sand or mud, and upon the vigour of the wave attack. There is a particular gradient which matches any given set of conditions, and thus shores are of all varieties of breadth, from zero at the foot of some cliffs which have their feet permanently in water, to several miles in a bank-choked estuary or bay.

In detail the effect of each individual wave, when it is incident normally to the waterline, is illustrated in Figs. 274 and 275. The sequence is usually as follows. The breaking wave plunges and tosses some of the bottom material into suspension. This is carried forward up-beach by the swash. As the latter comes to a halt as it mounts the gentle incline, all but the finest calibre material settles on the beach. The backwash, which follows, combs down some of this material, but this is usually less in quantity than what was brought up-beach by the swash, and thus there is a net gain or *accretion*.

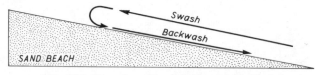

Fig. 274. *Swash and backwash on a sand beach*

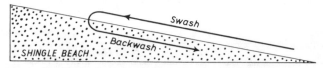

Fig. 275. *Swash and backwash on a pebble beach*

There is less down-combing in the case of shingle beaches (Fig. 275), since most of the backwash returns by way of the spaces between the pebbles rather than on the surface. Nevertheless, if the quantity of backwash is considerable, the buoyancy effect of this moving water

Fig. 276. *Separate zones of shingle and sand on the beach at Borth, Cardiganshire*

within the beach itself sometimes results in very considerable down-beach movement of pebbles. It is this difference in the backwash that produces the steeper gradient of shingle beaches as compared with sandy shores and *mud flats* (see Fig. 276).

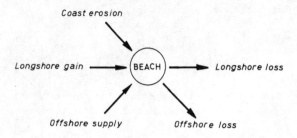

Fig. 277. The beach balance sheet

When the wave approaches obliquely, there is also a longshore component to the movement as already described and a resultant longshore movement of the beach material. Whether or not a beach exists in a particular locality depends upon the combined effect of the supply of material from local coastline erosion, the supply of material from neighbouring beaches, in certain circumstances the supply of material from offshore, the loss of material by longshore movement to neighbouring beaches, and the loss of material by down-combing to the offshore zone. These various movements are symbolised in Fig. 277.

Figure 278 shows an upright, straight cliff of easily eroded, Jurassic rocks at West Bay, Dorset. The photograph was taken at low water and the beach of moderate breadth is fully exposed. The movement of material along the beach is locally towards the west, as is shown by the accumulation on the near side of the solid pier which acts as a *groyne*. The narrower beach on the far side of this pier shows the effect of starvation which the groyne produces. There is no backshore, and the supply of beach material comes almost entirely from cliff erosion. A small cliff fall has produced a heap of debris just in front of the cloud shadow on the beach.

INSHORE CURRENTS

Oceanic circulatory currents move at too slow a speed to effect transport of anything other than floating material, and in any case they have little effect upon coastal morphology.

Fig. 278. Straight, upright cliff in horizontal Jurassic strata at West Bay, Dorset

Inshore currents are those which move over the *offshore zone* and these include *tidal currents*, as well as *longshore currents* which usually are the result of oblique wave incidence.

Tidal currents are generated, especially in seas with narrows, as the result of the additional water that is periodically required in specific areas in order to produce the tide. They are described on p. 424, and they are rarely sufficiently powerful to pick up material from the sea bed.

Narrow straits may produce tidal currents of significant velocity when the two ends of the strait open on to seas which may, at certain states of the tide, be at different levels. For example, the Menai Straits, which separate Anglesey from the North Wales mainland, have a length of 13 miles (21 km) and high water at the northeastern end is about an hour later than at the southwestern end, so that at spring tides there is, for short periods, a water-level difference of 5 feet (1·5 m) at the two ends. This produces, at the critical times, a current right through the straits with a velocity in the central narrows as great as 8 knots (15 km/h). This is sufficient to sweep the channel bottom clear of all loose debris, and prevents the straits from shallowing due to siltation.

Harbours and estuaries with narrow entrances and large basins require a considerable volume of water to fill and empty them twice a day, and this involves relatively high-speed currents at the mouths. This prevents siltation, keeps the channels deep and thus reduces the necessity for dredging. The basin of the middle Mersey at Liverpool is an illustration of such a system (see Fig. 199). Thirty square miles (78 sq km) of inner estuary are filled and emptied twice a day through an entrance at Liverpool which is only $\frac{3}{4}$ mile (1·2 km) wide, and here the water flows at a rate of 4 knots (7·5 km/h) during the ebb. Dredging in this area is almost entirely unnecessary.

Currents of such velocity as these are powerful factors in the morphology of more or less narrow coastal channels, but the tidal current is of no great importance on open coasts other than as a general drift of water in one direction during the flow of the tide and usually in the reverse direction during the ebb. This mass of slowly moving water will naturally take with it whatever mud or sand is put into suspension by wave action, but the forward and the reverse movements have a tendency to subtract out the work done by one another, and the total effectiveness is slight.

CHAPTER TWENTY-SIX

Beaches

THE general principles of the movement of beach material up and down beach by the swash and backswash of individual waves have been described in the last chapter, and in the present chapter two other aspects of beach morphology will be discussed. First, the development of the beach profile, and second, the forms resulting from the longshore movement of beach material. In this chapter we are concerned only with beaches, that is, the loose material which lies on the solid rock beneath. The next chapter deals with rock abrasion platforms and similar features.

THE BEACH PROFILE

It is a matter of general knowledge that the level of a sand or shingle beach varies from time to time in accordance with the immediate past weather. A storm very often results in a great down-combing of the material so that the beach may be lowered as much as four or even more feet (a metre) during a few hours. The quantity of material removed to below the low-water line in this way is very large indeed. For example, if a foreshore a quarter of a mile (400 metres) wide is lowered by an average of only 2 feet (60 cm), this means that more than half a million cubic yards (400,000 cu metres) or approximately half a million tons of material has been removed for each mile (1·6 km) of coast. This can easily happen in a single moderately severe storm. A week or two of calmer weather will restore the beach to its former height.

These great movements are brought about by the waves coupled with the powerful undertow which exists especially during storms. There is still some doubt as to the real differences in wave conditions which are necessary to produce down-combing on some occasions and upbuilding on others. It has been suggested that wave frequency is the controlling factor, and that a large number of waves per minute, of the order of twelve or so, results in the backwash of preceding waves partially destroying the force of the swash of the succeeding ones, but this is by no means certain.

Again, a powerful onshore wind may actually promote an onshore surface current which would produce a significant seaward *undertow* that might well lead to substantial down-combing.

For the moment it may be sufficient to realise that large waves of considerable height compared with their wave length, that is, steep waves, such as occur during storms, coupled with a considerable amount of disorderly turbulence, are conducive to down-combing, whereas calmer weather waves of long wave length, that is, flatter waves, such as occur when there is a substantial swell, tend to build up the beach.

TIDAL BEACHES

The position of the waterline is more or less constant in a tideless sea, whereas it varies often by considerable horizontal distances on other coasts. The effect of this is that in the latter instance a much wider foreshore is produced of a general shelving nature, with a gradient most often of the order of 1 in 120 in the case of sand beaches on open coasts, and approximately 1 in 8 for shingle beaches. This gives a mean fall of about 45 feet per mile (8·5 metres per kilometre) for sand beaches, and the width of the foreshore is thus primarily a function of the tidal range. In both cases, the gradient also depends upon the sand grain or pebble size, and also whether the beach is examined after a constructive or a destructive period.

The slope is most often not a continuous one, but is interrupted by a wavelike profile with a 'wave height' of 4 or 5 feet (1·5 metres) and a 'wave length' of 600 feet (say, 200 metres). These are *fulls* and *lows,* and are shown in profile in Fig. 279 and in plan in Fig. 280.

The *seaward face* and the *crest* of a full are both ripple-free, the former being very compact with a hard surface and the latter exhibiting loose packing of the sand grains so that ordinary walking produces footprints up to 2 inches (5 cm) deep. The *back* is steep and the *low* is generally moist, rippled and of moderate compaction. These features are produced by the incident waves and lie parallel to the wave crests at each point of the beach. A predominance of oblique waves thus produces fulls oblique to the coastline. This is illustrated in Fig. 280, where the curved coastline receives normal waves at the left and oblique ones on the right. On the left, the fulls are parallel to the coastline, but on the right anyone walking along a full in that direction will approach nearer and nearer to the low water line.

The orientation of fulls and lows on a particular coast is of great use as an indication of the *dominant wave direction* on each part of the beach. It should be noted that the wave may have experienced refraction (the wave approach arrows to the right of Fig. 280 are slightly curved for this reason), so that the lie of the fulls may not indicate the dominant wave direction offshore.

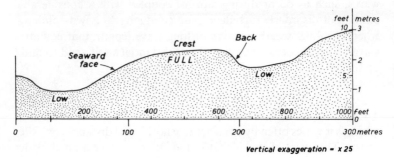

Vertical exaggeration = x 25

Fig. 279. Fulls and lows in profile on a sand beach

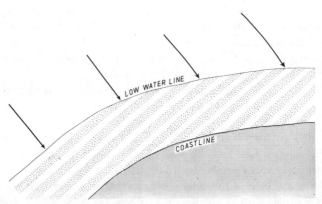

Fig. 280. Fulls and lows in plan on a sand beach

Fulls are not related to offshore bars, which are below-water features, and they are formed in position on the beach during periods of fairly calm weather. They scarcely migrate at all. They are destroyed by storms and are restored generally within a fortnight during more settled weather.

They are better developed on open coasts than in bayhead beaches, although one is to be seen on the bayhead beach at Tudweiliog, North Wales (Fig. 281). This was photographed at low water of a 6-foot tide (1·8 metres). The high water mark may be seen on the

Fig. 281. *Bayhead beach between headlands on the north coast of Lleyn*

extreme left in the upper part of the picture, and the width of the foreshore was 400 feet (120 metres), giving a mean gradient of 1 in 70 approximately. This steeper gradient is common with bayhead beaches. The full is seen, indicated by the drier belt of sand with the shallow captive water in the low on its landward side.

TIDELESS BEACHES

In tideless, or almost tideless, waters, a different beach profile is produced. In such instances the waves are permanently in contact with more or less the same line of beach. During upbuilding periods a *step* is formed at the waterline as is seen in Fig. 282, which is the coast of Algeria, a few miles east of Bougie. The upper limit of the swash coincides with the higher level of the dry beach, and the bottom of the step is marked by the limit of the backwash. The height of the step is thus determined by the rise and fall of the swash and thus by the size of the waves. Each wave deposits a thin layer of sand on the slope of the step, resulting therefore in a gradual seaward progression of its position. The level beach seen beyond the reach of the waves has been formed in this way and is liable to complete removal during storms. In such instances, there is no foreshore, merely a swash-backwash band, but there is a backshore, which constantly widens during calm weather only to be more or less completely wiped out during the next storm.

Fig. 282. Stepped, tideless sand beach in Algeria

SPITS AND BARS

There is considerable confusion in the meaning of the two words *spit* and *bar*. The most accepted usage is to consider that a bar is an elongated ridge of unconsolidated material, generally lying roughly parallel to the coastline and contrasted with a spit inasmuch as the latter is attached to the land at one end, whereas a bar is not. A bar may have its crest exposed at all states of the tide, only at low water, or not at all. These three varieties may be distinguished by terming them *backshore, foreshore* and *offshore bars*. Offshore bars are the commonest, but a full is a type of foreshore bar.

By reason of the definition that a spit is attached to the land at one end, it must at that end at least be above high water level, and is there thus a backshore feature, but at its unattached end the form normally continues at least a little way beyond the point where it is covered at high water, so that this becomes the *foreshore segment* of the spit, and there may even be an *offshore segment*. By contrast, in such cases, the part permanently exposed may then be referred to as the *backshore segment*. These terms are illustrated in Fig. 283.

One of the causes of the confusion between the two terms spit and bar results from spits which lie across the mouths of estuaries. They

L

are very often then considerable barriers to shipping, and consequently tend to acquire the descriptive name of bar. Technically,
they must still be called spits.

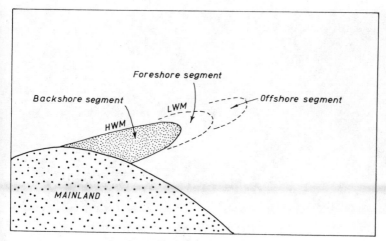

Fig. 283. *Backshore, foreshore and offshore segments of a spit*

SIMPLE, BAYMOUTH SPITS

The commonest locality for the occurrence of a spit is at a point
where the direction of the coastline changes, such as especially at the
entrance to an estuary. Figure 284 shows an aerial view of Spurn
Head, Humber, England, looking almost south, and Fig. 285 is a
map of the same locality. Longshore movement of material eroded
from the cliffs of Yorkshire tends to prolong the lie of this coast
beyond the point where the original line turned landwards to form
the northern coast of the Humber. Many spits are fairly straight in
plan until near their outer end, when a recurved portion is a common
feature. Spurn Head is, however, exceptional in having a smooth,
curved plan almost from the point where it springs from the mainland, and scarcely any recurved tip at all.

Spurn Head is a *simple spit* (rather than *compound,* see below)
largely because it has been more or less completely reformed at least
three times during the last thousand years. Apparently the spit begins
to grow out from the angular point of the mainland, gradually elon-
gates itself to a maximum, which appears to be about the position in
which it exists at the present time, then, being so attenuated, and
because of continued erosion of the mainland coast altering the angle

M

Fig. 284. Spurn Head, a baymouth spit

of contact, it becomes starved in its middle region and eventually waves break through and the whole process begins again. Figure 284 shows how tenuous the mid-portion of the spit has now become in spite of man's attempts to prevent erosion by means of the numerous groynes seen in the photograph and also by sea walling.

The photograph shows the thickened end that is characteristic of this spit, and also two banks, one on either side of the tip. The larger one, Old Den, on the inner side is composed of material which has rounded the end of the spit and become lodged within the inner waters, and the other, Stoney Binks, on the sea side, is composed of sand and pebbles which have been washed seaward from the tip by the outflowing tidal current, which has a considerable velocity here during the ebb as the large area of the Humber drains out.

Fig. 285. The location of Spurn Head

Fig. 286. Recurved spit at Westward Ho!, north Devon

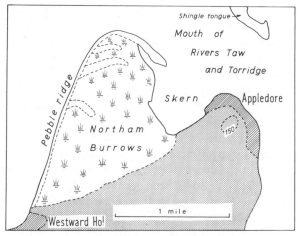

Fig. 287. Map of Westward Ho!

Another example of a *baymouth spit* is seen in Fig. 286. This is Westward Ho!. A single spit, it is about 2 miles (3 km) in length from the town (glimpsed on the extreme right) to the recurve, where the spit turns to extend for a further half-mile into the wide ria of the river Taw. The progressive growth of the recurved end may be deduced from the signs of older recurves to be seen within the present-day one (made clearer in the sketch, Fig. 287).

The important difference between this spit and Spurn Head is the existence of marshland with some sand dunes on its inner side. The old coastline is the margin of the field systems from Westward Ho! to Appledore, and the total area of new land is nearly 2 sq miles (5 sq km).

RECURVED COMPOUND SPITS

Numerous spits are attached to the islands of Denmark and Western Germany in the southwestern corner of the Baltic Sea. An example is at the western end of Lolland (Fig. 288). Albuen spit is nearly 4 miles (6½ km) in length from the point where it springs from the mainland to the tip where it is sharply recurved to extend for a further mile in a southeasterly direction. Like Spurn and many other spits, it is somewhat attenuated along much of its length, with a wider head. Scarcely any of the surface of the spit is higher than 10 feet (3 metres) above sea-level, and the shallow depth of the surrounding water is indicated on the map.

It must always be remembered that what is seen of a spit is usually only a slightly higher part of a wide, flat shallow, that the visible spit is often only a relatively small accumulation of sand or shingle tossed up by storm waves, and that the definite way in which the cartographer normally marks the coastline tends to over-emphasise the subaerial part of the spit. Successive maps of the same spit made at different dates often show considerable changes in position and area, which in truth are of little significance for they represent the movement, accumulation or removal of only very small amounts of the total material. It is only the most elevated part of the very much larger submarine structure that has changed.

Albuen spit is sharply recurved at its tip, and this is partly due to entry into somewhat deeper water, and partly due to the alternative long length of fetch for waves from the north between Langeland and Lolland (see inset map). It is rare for the coastline of a spit, or of any portion of it, to be exactly at right-angles to the direction of dominant wave approach, since before waves reach the line of the spit

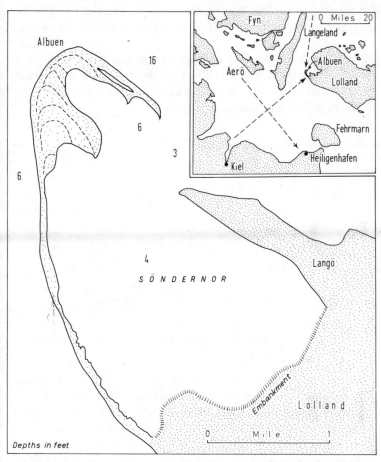

Fig. 288. Albuen compound recurved spit, west Lolland, Denmark

they have been refracted to some extent by the shallowing water. In this instance, for example, the major portion of the main length of Albuen spit faces almost directly west, whereas the dominant waves which formed it came from the southwest. Similarly, the recurved portion faces northeast, whereas its waves have a general direction of approach from almost directly north.

In this spit, the successive recurved ridges marked on the map indicate progressive growth, but all spring from the single main ridge that runs the length of the spit. It is a *prograding recurved spit*.

A SPIT COMPLEX

On the other hand, the Heiligenhafen shingle complex (see Fig. 289 and refer to the inset map on Fig. 288 for location) is a much more advanced structure. Most of the area stippled on this map is glacial morainic material brought by Swedish ice, and the western coast indicated here consists of till cliffs. Longshore movement is towards the east, and about A.D. 1450 the plan of the coast was as shown by the broken line, this being a shingle ridge.

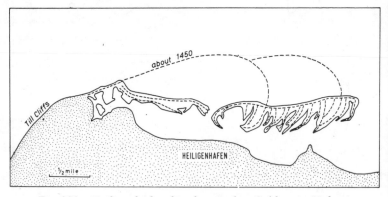

Fig. 289. Heiligenhafen shingle complex, Schleswig-Holstein

This was by no means the first ridge in the area, but merely marked a stage in the development. More and more recurved spits were added, until a change in balance promoted rapid erosion, and converted the whole structure into the pattern which is seen today and indicated on the map. What is now an eastern island is the mere remnant of the much larger mass which existed in the past. Only the tips of the recurved ends now remain, their orientation gradually and progressively (with one or two exceptions) changing from south-southwesterly to southwesterly and even west-southwesterly, as one moves farther and farther eastwards. Now the truncated northerly ends of these tips are linked by a continuous modern west–east shingle ridge, rising about 10 feet (3 metres) above sea-level, and forming the north coast of the island, whilst the recurved tips, no longer receiving fresh supplies of shingle, are largely grass-covered, partly linked by marsh and form a bird sanctuary. The reverse recurved western end of this island is a more recent structure.

Many varieties of spit, mostly with recurved ends, are to be found in the Cape Cod area of Massachusetts. Figure 290 indicates some of these on a small scale.

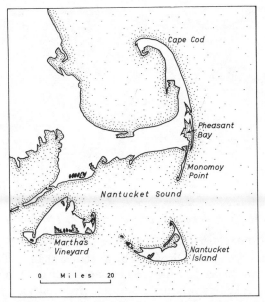

Fig. 290. Cape Cod area of Massachusetts

TOMBOLOS

It occasionally happens that a spit adventitiously grows in such a direction that it joins an island, and in this case it is termed a *tombolo*. Apart from the fact that anchorage at both ends tends to increase stability, there is no genetic difference in the formation of a tombolo from that of an ordinary spit. Chesil Beach, on the south coast of England, is a famous example. It joins the mainland to Portland Island.

BARRIER BARS AND BEACHES

One of the most remarkable coasts occurs along much of the length of the United States from Long Island to Florida. Figure 291 shows two sections of this length. In the case of the Atlantic City area, the *barrier beach* is within 5 or 6 miles (8½ km) of the older coastline, which here is fairly straight. The barrier beach first develops as a *barrier bar,* and is produced when large waves meet a shelving sandy or shingle floor and break some distance from the actual coast. This

352   *Beaches*

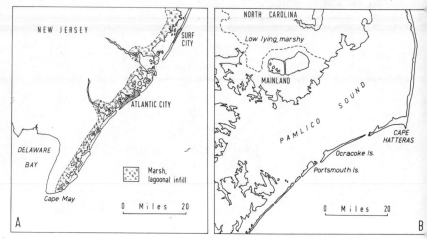

Fig. 291. Barrier beaches off New Jersey and North Carolina

part of the States is a coastal plain of low gradient which has in fairly recent times been partly drowned by a relative change of land and sea level, so as to produce the great estuaries such as Delaware river and Chesapeake Bay, which are drowned river valleys.

The offshore barrier bar was built parallel to the existing coast, and when the last relative movement brought it above water-level to become a *barrier beach,* tidal lagoons were formed on its landward side. These have largely now become silted up and converted into salt marsh, and in some places have even been drained to become agricultural ground. Thus the old coast is flanked on its eastern side by a belt of marshy ground which in turn is bordered on the ocean's edge by a sandy beach that has become a holiday makers' haunt and has given rise to such resorts·as Atlantic City and Surf City.

Farther south the partially drowned coastal plain had an even gentler shelving floor, so that the barrier bar was formed farther from the coastline produced by the submergence (see Fig. 291B). This map is on the same scale as Fig. 291A. The highly indented nature of the submerged coast and its 10-mile (16-km) distance from the barrier beach are both due to the very low gradient. Because of this the unsubmerged part of the coastal plain is very badly drained and is largely swamp ground. This is not lagoonal infill, for very little of that has so far occurred in North Carolina.

The remarkable change in direction of the barrier beach which occurs at Cape Hatteras is due to a change in direction from which the dominant bar-building waves approach, the two sections being constructed by different systems of waves, approaching from the east and from the southeast respectively. In both New Jersey and North Carolina, the barrier is broken at frequent intervals. These openings are kept clear by the in and out flow of tidal water, and by the outflow of river water.

BEACH MOVEMENT AND MAN

Man has sought to make use of beach movement in order to control the level of various beaches, especially with the object of building them up in desired places to prevent cliff erosion. The usual method is to erect groynes of timber, concrete or other material, roughly at right-angles to the coastline, so as to prevent the longshore movement either partially or completely. This usually raises the beach-level where it is desired, but it invariably leads to a decrease of material farther along the coast. This may even be to such an extent that actual starvation results, the beach-level is lowered below the safety level, and erosion of the coast itself is initiated.

This has actually happened in a number of instances, and control of this type should always be undertaken with the welfare of the whole stretch of coast in mind, and not just the desires of one particular locality.

CHAPTER TWENTY-SEVEN

Coastlines

HAVING considered the tools that affect coastal change, and the beach they produce, attention may now turn to the *coastline*, the landward limit of wave action. Although this line may be static, it is more often slowly moving landwards, as the result of marine erosion, or seawards, as the result of some form of accretion. Such coasts are termed *retrograding* or *prograding*.

An area where marine and fluvial actions combine occurs in the locality where a river enters the sea, and it may be convenient to deal first with accumulation resulting from the interaction of these two.

ESTUARINE BANKS

The origin of the funnel or other similar shape of the coastal plan of an estuary will be described in the next chapter, for it is usually connected with changes of relative level of land and sea, but the siltation which occurs in such localities is a process which is continuous and progressive. Most estuaries are virtually choked with banks of sand and mud, which often are a great hindrance to shipping and make it necessary for boats that enter the river to do so by devious routes along the channels remaining between the banks. Regular and considerable dredging is often required to keep the river open to boats at all.

Figure 292 shows the various parts of a delta at Wrightsville, North Carolina. The mainland is seen on the top margin of the photograph, and below that are a number of islands formed by the river dividing, joining and redividing in a large number of *distributaries*. As the ramifications approach the sea, the general level becomes lower, so that at low tide, as when the photograph was taken, there are fairly wide exposed expanses of sand and silt deposit. These are clearly but a continuation of the same deposits that form the delta proper. Where the main river channel reaches the sea, it builds out a fan-shaped shallow whose waterline is becoming arcuate, partly as the result of waves such as those which may be seen breaking against its outer edge. So the delta grows.

Fig. 292. Delta formation at Wrightsville, North Carolina

There is some doubt as to the limit of the meaning of the word *delta*. It is generally restricted to those parts which are more or less permanently above sea-level, and this usually implies that there has been relative elevation of the land. Nevertheless, the banks which are submerged at high tide (the lighter coloured parts shown in Fig. 292) are the outer limits of the true delta formation, although there will be considerable shallowing due to the beginnings of further deposition beneath the low water level. Thus banks in most estuaries may be considered to represent the first stages in visible delta growth.

The river Dee (Fig. 293), on the border between England and Wales, illustrates this. The parallel-sided estuary has silted to such an extent that vegetation has covered the inner banks, and so has resulted in additional accretion at the slack of high water. Further accumulation of humus and the like through the years has made considerable areas into permanent land, and thus an estuarine or *estuary-head delta* has been formed.

The parts which are still submerged at high water, including those beyond low water, are an *incipient delta*. Morecambe Bay is an example with a rather more open plan. Figure 294 shows the areas of this which are covered by water at high tide, the recent marsh areas and also a raised beach which is formed of estuarine deposits linked with a higher sea-level about 6,000 years ago.

There is great variation in the mechanism of siltation within an

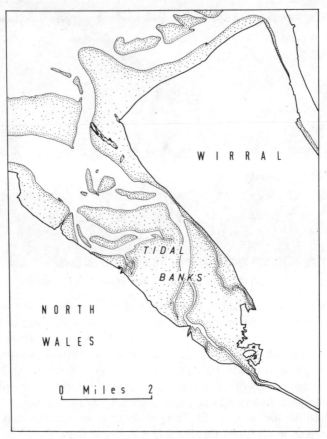

Fig. 293. Siltation in the Dee estuary

estuary. The material in the Humber, Thames, Dee and Mersey estuaries and in Morecambe Bay is mostly material which has been brought in from the adjoining coasts and the offshore seafloor by tidal currents and wave action rather than material which has been deposited by the river itself. On the other hand, the Nile, Mississippi, Niger, Ganges-Brahmaputra, Irrawaddy and many other deltas are at least largely composed of fluvial sediment.

The first bank is formed directly in the path of the major fluvial current, that is, in the centre of the river channel, since this is the locality where the river brings the most material and deposits it when the sea water mass slackens the current. This divides the river current

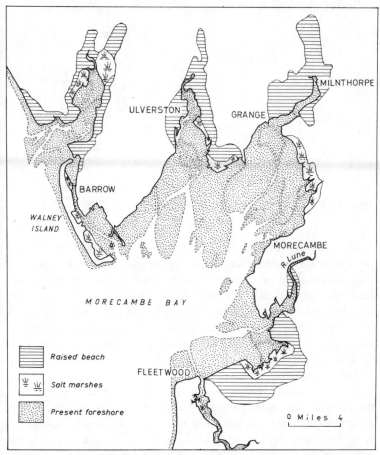

Fig. 294. Morecambe Bay with its tidal banks, salt marshes and raised beaches

into two, and similar banks form in the centres of these two distributaries. There are then four mouths, and the process is repeated with the formation of numerous banks, distributaries and mouths. Direct fluvial deposition can only occur in the various distributaries, and thus there is a tendency for the delta to grow most rapidly where most water flows. This is particularly the case when the deposit is silt rather than sand and is thus impermeable. In the case of sand banks, a considerable amount of water percolates through the sand itself and there is more tendency for massive bank formation rather than for the embankment type of narrow accumulation which is so typical of silt deltas, in which lateral breaks in the banks are frequent.

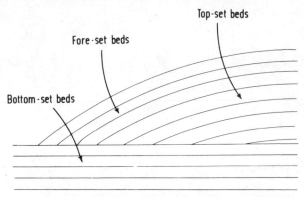

Fig. 295. Deltaic bedding

The deposits which constitute a delta are very often in three layers (Fig. 295). The lowest is the *bottom-set bed* and comprises the general layer of sediment over the whole area prior to actual bank formation. The banks themselves often develop by material being moved over the top surface of the part already existing and sliding down to form an inclined bed on the seaward side. Thus the bank grows seawards by means of a series of *fore-set beds,* whose strata are at a fairly steep angle approximately equal to the angle of repose of the material in water.

When the summit of the bank is sufficiently high to be exposed to the air at all times excepting flood, further deposits only occur during exceptionally high water and these are more or less horizontal *top-set beds.* Fore-set and top-set beds are seen in the quarry face near Fjaerland on a northern tributary of the Sognfjord (Fig. 296) now raised well above sea-level by isostatic land rise (see next chapter).

True deltas are often large. They form low-lying, level plains which are sometimes swamps and at others have been converted into rich agricultural land.

COASTAL LAGOONS

The seaward limit of a delta is commonly reshaped by wave action,

Fig. 296. Top-set and fore-set beds in a marine terrace at Fjaerland,
Sognfjord. The height seen in the photograph is about four feet

so that the coastline may acquire a number of spits and bars (as in
the case of the Nile delta) with the consequent formation of a *lagoon
coast*. This also occurs when offshore barrier beaches are built by
wave action as described in the last chapter (see Fig. 291).

In every case these lagoons tend to silt up. Generally there are gaps
in the barriers so that the water within them is tidal and at least
brackish. Marsh vegetation soon begins to grow, and this greatly
accelerates accumulation. The water shallows and the floor eventually reaches high-water level or even exceptional high-water level.
In time the area changes from the lagoon stage, through marshland
to permanent coastal grassland. The last stage is aided if slow elevation is occurring and very often also it is artificially brought about
by man's taking advantage of the favourable conditions and enclos-
ing considerable areas by means of embankments to keep out the sea.

SALT MARSHES

Salt marshes accumulate in other situations besides those already
described. They are to be found occurring on open coasts, and an
intermediate type is shown in Fig. 297, which is a photograph of
Langenhoe Marsh, just north of Mersea Island, Essex. Mersea Island
is basically a deposit of London Clay capped by patches of glacial
gravels, and the low-lying ground to the northern side of the island
is still partly tidal although now much overgrown by salt marsh. The
photograph looks in a northerly direction, and shows how, as the

Fig. 297. *A salt marsh behind an island fringe on a low-lying coast*

tide flows out, the marsh drains by means of a very intricate pattern of numerous creeks converging on one another. The area shown is approximately a square mile and probably nearly half is covered by water at high tide.

Towards the upper part, an embankment has been constructed in a rectangular shape to protect the land beyond it, so that it may be artificially drained and reclaimed for agriculture. The old meanders of the northerly creek have been cut off by the artificial straight drain (dark line) and show as white, dry loops. The fields in both extreme top corners are already under cultivation. These various features are typical of salt marshes.

The map of Morecambe Bay shown in Fig. 294 has already illustrated the fact that salt marshes may occur at the head and along the sides of bays. Figure 298 shows part of the marsh about 3 miles (5 km) northeast of Morecambe. Erosion still occurs on the near-by cliff formed in a drumlin, and the marsh is composed largely of fine grasses with enclosed hollows filled by water and known as *salt pans*.

Salt pans may be formed in either of two ways. They may be the remains of silted creeks, now forming isolated, elongated hollows, or they may represent points where vegetation initially failed to get a hold. As grasses and other plants act as a kind of filter when the tide covers them during the slack at high water, vegetation greatly increases the rate of silt deposition. Thus the vegetated parts gain height more quickly than do the bare areas. In the case illustrated, the ground-level in the pans is about a foot and a half (50 cm) lower than on the grassed areas.

Marsh coasts have beaches which are mainly composed of silt with little or only a small percentage of sand, and accumulation occurs because of lack of exposure to large waves. The long distance that waves must travel across the shallow sand flats of Morecambe Bay before they can reach the eastern limit means that they have lost most of their energy before they reach the salt marsh area.

Many estuaries, such as the Thames, contain very extensive mud-flats and marshes. This again is because of the lack of exposure, but one must also remember that at the slack of the tide at high water there is a short period, lasting perhaps twenty minutes, when there is little movement. This is ideal for silt deposition, and because of its small grain size, when it has once settled, silt is much more difficult to pick up again than is sand (see Fig. 113).

The extensive marsh which has accumulated on the landward side of Westward Ho! and has already become partly cultivated, was illustrated and described on pp. 347 and 348, and is typical of what often occurs on the landward side of a spit.

Fig. 298. Salt pans in a tidal marsh in Morecambe Bay with cliff erosion on the coastline

Fig. 299. The edge of a mangrove swamp

MANGROVE COASTS

Within the tropics, *mangrove* plays a part that bears some similarity to the part played by salt marsh vegetation in more temperate climates. The mangrove is a tree of which there are several varieties, but all are characterised by the fact that the branches produce aerial roots that not only directly absorb atmospheric gases, but also arch downward and anchor themselves in the mudflat several feet from the parent trunk. These roots then grow their own branches and so the forest spreads to become an ever closer tangle of more or less vertical roots and trunks (Fig. 299). These are clearly ideal conditions for the trapping of silt as the muddy sea water moves amongst the vegetation. Accumulation is rapid.

Mangroves occur especially in tidal estuaries and other sheltered parts of the coast, but they may also be found on straight coasts. In Asia and Africa there are a number of species, each of which normally replaces the other as accumulation progresses and the proportion of the time during which the trees have their feet in the water gradually lessens. This succession is not so well developed in Central and South America, where there are fewer varieties of the plant.

RE-ORIENTATION OF PROGRADING COASTS

Besides the longshore movement of beach material which has already
been described, there is another process which results from the arrival
of large storm waves, which do not by any means always degrade a
beach.

The relatively small waves of mild weather produce most of the
longshore movement, since, being small, they are little affected by
shallowing water, and thus are scarcely refracted at the breaker line
or even in the swash area. Consequently they approach obliquely and
produce longshore drift more easily than do the large waves of
stormy periods, which 'feel the bottom' at a much greater depth and
experience much more complete refraction before they break. The
latter build up *beach ridges* with the material that the smaller waves
have brought.

Large waves thus tend to build up the coast in a line directly across
their line of approach. *Prograding coasts* acquire a waterline that is
normal (= at right-angles) to the dominant large wave approach. A
number of coasts are prograding in such a way as to produce a
re-orientation of their waterline.

Morfa Dyffryn on the west coast of Wales (see Fig. 300) shows an
angle of about 15° between the old coastline and the new, the rotation being in an anticlockwise direction. Morfa Harlech, a similar
dune and marsh foreland immediately north of Morfa Dyffryn,
shows a re-orientation of as much as 55°, also in an anticlockwise
direction. Both these examples are instances where past erosion,
with the production of a cliffline, has reversed to presentday accumulation. The two new coastlines face in slightly different directions,
with an angle of about 8° between them.

Scolt Head Island and Blakeney Point on the north Norfolk coast
show a clockwise tendency in the re-orientation of the coastline.
Both these structures have waterlines which are about 15° from the
previous direction. Sandwich in Kent shows a somewhat similar set
of circumstances, with a clockwise rotation of about 20°.

Changes of this type indicate changes in the direction of dominant
wave approach, and presumably therefore in the wind direction
which generates these waves. No information is available to show
that in fact the wind directions have changed in the localities from
which these examples have been drawn, but there is direct evidence
in the Netherlands that the dominant wind direction there changed
in a clockwise direction by 20° from 1750 to about 1830, and by
about the same amount in an anticlockwise direction from 1830 to
1920.

The actual direction of the waves by the time they reach the coast itself is not the same as in the open sea, for they have been refracted by the shallowing bottom to a considerable extent. Thus the direc-

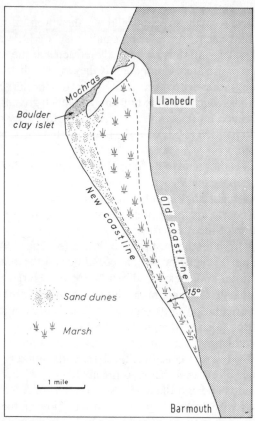

Fig. 300. Re-orientation of the coastline at Morfa Dyffryn, Wales

tion of wave movement at the waterline is also affected by the configuration of the underwater floor offshore. This accounts for the large difference in the degree of re-orientation of Morfa Dyffryn and Morfa Harlech, in spite of the fact that they are so near to one another, and thus must be under the influence of the same large waves.

Morfa Dyffryn, like most other similar features, now consists of a beach which is mostly sand but contains some shingle, backed by a belt of sand dunes behind which there is salt marsh turned into marshland. In this particular instance the northerly end is composed of what was originally an island of glacial morainic material.

CLIFFS

Erosion of the coastline itself occurs if waves reach the actual line frequently. One of the most successful ways of preventing coast erosion is to ensure the presence of a beach sufficiently high to prevent all but exceptional high seas from reaching the landward edge. In other words, the presence of a substantial backshore is a preventive of erosion.

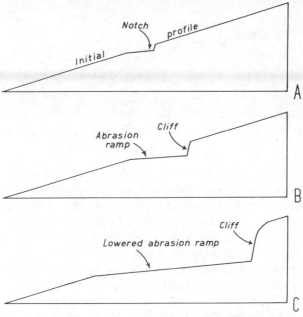

Fig. 301. Stages of cliff formation

The beach may be lowered in level either by powerful longshore movement, by starvation of fresh supplies of material, or by strong down-combing. Any of these permits breakers to reach farther towards the coast and perhaps to reach the line itself.

If one supposes the initial profile to have been a smooth slope rising landwards, erosion's first effect is to notch this (Fig. 301A) and as time goes on this notch recedes and becomes larger until one is justified in terming it a *cliff* (Fig. 301B). The portion of this notch across which the waves break is an *abrasion ramp* or *bench*. This

Fig. 302. Simple fall in a bevelled cliff on the Cardiganshire coast of Wales near Borth

bench is gently inclined seaward in a tidal area, and as the notch recedes landwards so does the incline, successive layers of rock being progressively trimmed from its surface as illustrated in Fig. 301C. The fact that the ramp is sloping greatly facilitates the landward progress of the attack, although of course the depth to which the seaward edge can be eroded is limited by the size of the waves.

This profile differs from that of a tideless sea, where the abrasion bench is virtually horizontal and its maximum width is more quickly reached. The lower parts of the tidal ramp are trimmed at low water, and its slope has the effect of still permitting breakers to proceed to the cliff edge at high water. Cliffs in tidal seas are thus eroded farther back before a balance is reached, and thus are often of much greater height than are those in tideless waters.

The sea is only able to erode that part of the cliff with which it comes into contact. The wave impacts on the cliff face most violently if it is just breaking when it makes contact, and there is an optimum water depth at the foot of the cliff for each size of incident wave. The actual breakdown of the cliff material is chiefly a matter of corrasion (direct attack by bombardment with pebbles and sand), and of hydraulic action, by which the pressure exerted by the wave impact acts as a hammer-blow, or, and this is much more effective, the imprisonment of air in joint lines and any other fissures by closure of the opening by the arrival of the wave crest, followed by a considerable increase of air pressure within the gap as its volume is reduced by the entry of water. This often produces sufficient pressure to force the crack a little wider and the block of rock a little outwards from the cliff face. Eventually it is displaced and erosion has occurred.

Erosion of this type results in undercutting of the cliff and must inevitably finally lead to cliff collapse. The same processes occur as have already been described in Chapter 13 in connection with slip, and Fig. 302 shows the scar of a slip in the upper part of a cliff near Borth, Cardiganshire, which has resulted from over-steepening of the cliff face. Figure 303 shows the result of rotational slope collapse at Egmont Point, Dorset. Here the almost horizontally bedded Portland Stone and Portland Sand may be seen at the top of the cliff, and again lower down, at about mid-height where it has slipped. Hidden behind this slip are weaker shales and marls of the Kimmeridge Rocks.

The moraine cliffs southeast of Cromer on the Norfolk coast reach a height of over 100 feet (30 metres), and, being composed of unconsolidated material, collapse very frequently, a section that is upstanding to the summit being quite rare. In Fig. 304, the rapidity of erosion is obvious. The presence of debris that has fallen to the foot temporarily prevents further direct attack on the cliff itself. It must await the removal of the debris by longshore or downshore movement. For this to occur, considerable atrition may be necessary to reduce the fallen blocks to manageable sizes.

Wave splash may reach to considerable heights up the cliff-face and this may result in chemical weathering (corrosion) or other

Fig. 303. *Rotational slope collapse at Egmont Point, Dorset*

Fig. 304. Cliffs in glacial material near Cromer, Norfolk

Fig. 305. Solution benching at Elgol, Skye

rotting of the rock and so produce a certain amount of recession or weaken the rock so that collapse occurs sooner.

Solution benching occurs on the shore in front of a cliff if the rock is of suitable composition. This is shown in Jurassic strata in Fig. 305 on the foreshore at Elgol, Skye, where the abrasion ramp is very difficult to traverse because of the uneven surface produced by this irregular solution.

CLIFF PROFILES

Two types of *cliff profile* have already been illustrated in Figs. 303 and 304. Both of these were *collapsed cliffs*. *Vertical cliffs* in solid rocks commonly occur, as in the chalk cliffs of the Danish Baltic island of Mön, Fig. 306, whose upright face rises to a height of 420 feet (130 metres). This cliff faces directly east and waves reaching it have a long length of fetch – the whole of the southern part of the Baltic Sea. A fairly narrow abrasion ramp is seen at the foot of the cliff and there is a small amount of scree. The photograph was taken at the end of the summer. Had it been the end of the winter this scree would have been absent and solid chalk would have been visible to the ramp level. Vertical chalk cliffs with the sea in contact are also seen in Fig. 308.

Fig. 306.
Chalk cliffs rising to
420 feet (130 metres)
on Mön, Denmark

Fig. 307. Flat-topped, stepped cliffs in basalt at Giant's Causeway, Northern Ireland

There are various types of cliff top, but as these are normally the result of land processes, they are of relatively little importance to the technical study of cliffs. Figures 307 and 308 show flat tops, whereas Fig. 302 has a bevelled top to its cliff. This is a fairly common form of cliff profile. It is sometimes called a *slope-and-step cliff,* the lower, step portion being, of course, the result of presentday erosion. There has been considerable discussion as to the origin of the bevel or slope, but it is now generally accepted that it is a degraded older cliff and an indication that the sea has produced a cliff in this area in the past, perhaps in the case of the Welsh cliff shown in Fig. 302 during an interglacial period. Then followed a stage when the sea no longer reached the area and normal subaerial slope-producing agents rendered the profile less steep, until finally the present sea is attacking the area again and reproducing the older cliff.

Figure 307 shows a stepped profile at Giant's Causeway (not itself seen in the photograph), Northern Ireland. Successive sheets of basalt constitute the step portions of the cliff, and between these hard bands there is the relatively soft, lateritic weathered basalt of a brilliant red colour, contrasting sharply with the black of the basalt and the green of the grass which clothes some of the slopes and the summit. The uppermost part of the cliff on the near headland shows some residual pinnacles in the columnar basalt, this formation having, of course, nothing to do with marine erosion. The whole of the recession landwards with height is the result of slope collapse and subaerial weathering and screes may be seen in the foreground.

Not only does the lithology of the cliff affect its profile, but so also does its structure. Whilst horizontally bedded strata produce fairly steep cliff-faces, landward-dipping strata lead to self-packing even of loosened blocks of rock and thus to high vertical cliffs of considerable height. Seaward-dipping strata discharge all loosened blocks at once and often produce slopes of such low gradient that they may scarcely justify the name of cliff. Joints, faults and other structural features likewise influence the cliff pattern, and lead to an infinite variety of forms.

Chalk is very often a more or less jointless amorphous mass and this gives upright cliffs. One example has already been seen in Fig. 306, and Fig. 308 shows the fine crenulated vertical cliff 5 miles (8 km) west of Margate at Birchington. Solution of fallen chalk very often precludes the formation of foreshore in such cases and the small indentations are the result of minor differences in the compactness of the chalk from point to point.

Fig. 308. Crenulated cliffs in chalk at Birchington, Kent

CLIFFS IN PLAN

The photograph of Birchington just described draws attention to the fact that cliffs have plan as well as profile. Very small differences in resistance to erosion will produce the pattern seen in Fig. 308 and the nature of the sides of the individual promontories, each at right-angles to the headland faces and to the bayhead cliffs, suggests that erosion has in fact proceeded here along the joint planes. Note the rounded nature of each corner of each rectangular promontory. In instances such as this in a rock of the chemical nature of chalk there is a considerable amount of solution by sea water splash in addition to direct wave erosion.

Similar differential erosion has produced the embayments seen in Fig. 307, whereas the jointless till of similar strength along its whole length has produced the straight cliff southeast of Cromer (Fig. 304).

The initial stage therefore in the development of a cliff is the production of numerous small headlands and bays, known as *coves* in the southwest of England, and Fig. 309 shows how wave erosion picks out planes of weakness. The presence of a fault across a small headland has resulted in a complete breakthrough by the sea.

Fig. 309. *Fault-line etching by waves on the coast of North Wales*

Fig. 310. Stack in process of formation at Anglesey

This is one way in which *stacks* occur, although the more usual process is seen in Fig. 310, which shows a stack in process of formation very near to South Stack Lighthouse on Anglesey. Two faults traversing the headland have permitted the rock between them to slip and so become more or less shattered. Erosion will remove this slipped portion more quickly than the seaward rock, and in time the latter will be left standing as an isolated rock about 150 feet (45 metres) high. Several other small stacks are also seen in the same photograph and Fig. 311 shows a very fine stack in horizontally-bedded Old Red Sandstone. This is the Old Man of Hoy on the largest of the Orkney Islands, and it rises to 450 feet (140 metres) above sea-level. Little erosion of the main cliffs is now occurring, the sea being only in contact with the solid rock for a small height on the part seen to the left of the stack. Above this is a considerable slope of scree, clearly resting on a ledge of rock above the present cliff. This ledge may represent a raised beach, of the kind described in the next chapter.

Figure 312 demonstrates the interrelationship between lithology and coastal plan, for the headland, terminating in the Needles at the western end of the Isle of Wight, comprises the full width of the Chalk

Fig. 311. 450-foot (140-metre) Old Man of Hoy stack, Orkneys

Fig. 312. Differential erosion of various rocks at The Needles, Isle of Wight

Fig. 313. Miniature stacks in an eroded salt marsh, Walney Island, northwest England

outcrop. The strata are almost vertical, and the Needles are the more resistant Upper Chalk. The coastline of the Eocene sands and clays is stepped back approximately a mile (1·6 km) on the left, whilst the Gault Clay and Wealden Beds, older rocks than the Chalk, form quite low cliffs 5 or more miles (8 km) away on the right-hand side of the view. The more rapid erosion of the less resistant beds on either side of the Chalk is thus clearly seen.

Crenulation, with stack formation, even occurs during the erosion of a salt marsh coast as is seen in Fig. 313 on the eastern side of Walney Island, northwest England. These cliffs and stacks are only about 2 feet (say, ½ metre) in height, but they afford examples of every kind of embayment, headland and residual stack, and many lessons may be learned from them.

As time goes on, the fact that the headlands receive the brunt of the wave attack overcomes their resistant nature, and they are worn back more rapidly than the embayments. The coastline thus tends to become smoothed out and eventually, in the mature form, the cliff is either a straight line or a smooth sweeping curve, most often concave to the sea.

CHAPTER TWENTY-EIGHT

Relative Changes of Land and Sea Level

THERE are two ways of altering the level of water in a container such as a bucket. One is by adding or removing some of the water, and the other may be effected by dropping in a few stones so that the water-level rises. Both these types of change have occurred in the case of the oceans, and the second type forms one of the important factors in major and older changes of sea-level such as are discussed in Chapter 18.

EUSTATIC CHANGE OF LEVEL

During the Pleistocene Ice Ages and since, the quantity of water in the oceans has fluctuated considerably, for during the maximum of a cold period a significant fraction of oceanic water is locked on land as great ice sheets. Changes of sea-level which are due to variations in the amount of water are known as *eustatic changes,* and many calculations have been made in order to determine the amount of this change. The most recent suggest that during the maximum ice, the ocean-level of the whole world was lowered by very nearly 500 feet (150 metres). This is a rather larger figure than had been considered likely a few years ago, but it is based on the most recent information regarding the probable volume of the various ice sheets, glaciers and ice caps.

A characteristic of an eustatic change is that it is worldwide. A sea-level 500 feet (150 metres) lower than now must have drained the whole of the North Sea, the English Channel, the Irish Sea and St George's Channel. Parts of these sea floors were covered by ice. The rise of sea-level during deglaciation has masked most of the features that may have been developed at these lower levels during the cold periods, but some of the effects extended into areas which are still land, and such features as rias owe their origin to these low sea-levels (see p. 383).

In reverse, there have been periods of greater warmth than today. For example. botanical and other evidence suggests that during both the Great Interglacial (= Mindel-Riss interglacial) and also during the Flandrian transgression (the warmest period of the post-glacial), temperatures in most of Europe were about two or three degrees centigrade higher than they are today. This resulted in an eustatic rise in sea-level, and during the Great Interglacial ocean-level was nearly 100 feet (30 metres) above present level, although the rise during the Flandrian transgression was considerably less than this.

ISOSTATIC CHANGES OF LEVEL

The mere weight of the ice in the intensely glaciated areas resulted in a depression of those parts of the crust. In the north Baltic Sea, where the maximum ice thickness is reckoned to have been as much as 8,000 feet (2,400 metres), the depression due to this weight was more than 1,000 feet (300 metres), and so far the recovery has been about 500 feet (150 metres) in the Stockholm area, where the beaches belonging to the Yoldia Sea are now at that height above the present sea-level. Farther north, in the Swedish district around Umeå, the beaches of the Ancylus lake are now 650 feet (200 metres) above sea-level. This, however, is only the amount of rise since the time of the Ancylus lake (about 8,500 years before the present), and it is considered that during the preceding 1,000 years the crust there had risen an additional 300 feet (90 metres). In other words, the Umea area has risen a total of 950 feet (290 metres) since the ice decreased from its maximum.

Unlike eustatic changes, which occur simultaneously with the total increase or decrease in world ice, isostatic recovery is slow, and it is still continuing in most glaciated parts. It is particularly fast in the north Baltic, where it is still as much as a centimetre a year, or a metre ($= 3\frac{1}{4}$ feet) a century. The fact that the crust is still recovering at this rapid rate indicates clearly that it has not as yet in any way approached the level it possessed before the Pleistocene depression.

The depression, and consequently the recovery, was dependent upon the weight of ice in a given area, and there appears to have been scarcely any change in land-levels along the southern coast of the Baltic. As a result of this, the individual beaches, which must have been horizontal when formed, are now sloping. The Littorina Sea beaches, only 6,500 years old, are now 30 feet (9 metres) above present sea-level at Kristianstad, south Sweden; 170 feet (50 metres) at Stockholm; and 400 feet (120 metres) at Sundsvall. The gradient of this beach as one proceeds along it at the present time is not constant. It rises about 4 inches a mile in the south, about 9 inches a mile

N

in the Stockholm district, and as much as 14 inches a mile near Gavle (1 cm in 160, 70 and 45 metres respectively).

In Britain the eustatic changes were the same as anywhere else, but the isostatic changes were considerably less than in the Baltic, since the glaciation was so much weaker, and the thickness and weight of the ice proportionately less. As an example comparable with the Littorina beach just described, the Flandrian or Hillhouse beach of northern England, which becomes the so-called 25-foot (8-metre) beach of western Scotland, has its back at 15 feet (4·5 metres) O.D. in Lancashire, about 20 feet (6 metres) in Solway Firth, and nearly 35 feet (10·5 metres) near Oban. The present isostatic rise of different parts of Britain is only vaguely known, but it is thought to be about 2 inches (5 cm) a century near Liverpool and 7 inches (17 cm) a century at Oban.

THE RESULTANT RELATIVE CHANGES OF LEVEL OF LAND AND SEA

For much of the Pleistocene, and especially during the period since the last glaciation, both eustatic and isostatic changes have been taking place simultaneously, and what is observed in the field is of course the combination of the two. A rise in sea-level coinciding with a rise in land-level at the same rate would produce an apparently constant sea-level at the locality concerned, and for the net apparent result to be a rise in land-level, the isostatic rise must be at a greater rate than the eustatic rise, which at the presentday is thought to be about $4\frac{1}{2}$ inches (11 cm) a century throughout the world.

Subtracting this from the present believed isostatic rises at Liverpool and Oban, there is a net relative rise of sea-level of $2\frac{1}{2}$ inches (6 cm) a century at the former place, and $2\frac{1}{2}$ inches (6 cm) fall of sea-level a century at Oban.

Other factors must be borne in mind which may affect the net apparent change. Additional sedimentation in coastal regions or erosion in others must be allowed for, and compaction or decompaction of sediments must also be taken into consideration. It is usual to endeavour to take measurements in places where these additional complications are considered to be slight or non-existent, for they are exceptionally difficult to estimate quantitatively.

EMERGENT COASTS

A number of coastal features result from these various changes of

Fig. 314. Raised bench at Larne, Northern Ireland

relative land and sea level, and the most important will now be considered.

Although the marine-worked shelves, situated at higher levels than presentday coastal agents can produce them, are generally described as *raised beaches,* this is more often than not a misnomer, since it is rare to find any contemporary loose material, that is, actual beach, in the form of sand, shingle or silt, resting upon their surfaces. It would be much more accurate to name such features *raised benches*. These are rock abrasion platforms. When raised beaches are in unconsolidated material, it is most often the case that they are either post-glacial and cut in till or other glacial deposits, or that they are true raised deltas, perhaps with their seaward face stepped by later, lower, seas.

Fig. 315. Garrylucus raised bench, co. Cork, Eire

Figure 314 shows a modern coastline with the sea touching it and a shelf at about 30 feet (9 metres) above the present abrasion level, backed by a good fossil cliff, all in glacial deposits. Figure 315 shows a raised bench on the south coast of Ireland near Kinsale on which glacial meltwater deposits were placed subsequent to the bench formation, for the latter passes beneath the former without change of level, and the rock cliff backing the bench is buried by the glacial material. The bench is sufficiently low for storm waves (this coast faces the open Atlantic) to reach the glacial material, and although the rock bench is fossil the glacial cliff is presentday. This affords an example of the care that is necessary in interpreting features of this kind.

Figure 316 shows a raised bench backed by a fossil rock cliff south of Oban. The fossil cliff is now somewhat degraded and partly masked by scree. There is some loose shingle on the bench, but it is impossible to determine whether this is original beach or modern storm-tossed pebbles – it is more likely to be the latter.

There has been much discussion in recent years as to the truth of the statement that the three principal raised beaches in Scotland and northern England are at 25, 50 and 100 feet (8, 15 and 30 metres) above presentday sea-level. Very recent work in the Forth estuary shows that there they lie at three constant levels from Stirling seawards at 25 to 30 feet, 42 to 50 feet and 120 to 135 feet respectively (7·6 to 9·1, 12·8 to 15·2, 36·6 to 41·1 metres), without benches at intermediate levels. The bench shown in Fig. 316 is at about 25 feet

Fig. 316. Raised bench at Seil, Argyllshire, Scotland

(8 metres), and there is some indication of the '100-foot' (30-metre) bench on the skyline.

The heights of the various raised beaches of Scotland do not vary much as one moves east–west, since the intensity of glaciation in such a direction did not vary much in areas where beaches occur, but as one moves northwards from North Wales or southern Ireland to about mid-latitude Scotland, there is a fairly regular increase in heights due to the greater intensity of the glaciation at the more northerly points and the consequent greater isostatic recovery.

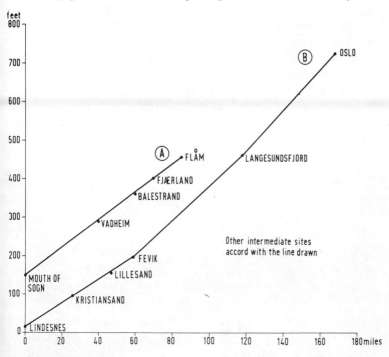

Fig. 317. The magnitude of relative rise in land level as shown by the uppermost marine terraces along Sognfjord (graph A), and by the uppermost marine limit along the south coast of Norway (graph B)

The so-called *marine terraces* of Norway, which are actually fjord-side fluvial deltas, terraced by erosion since their emergence, provide good evidence that the intensity of glaciation increased as one moved eastwards across the Scandinavian peninsula.

Sognfjord provides nearly a 100-mile (160-km) section west–east across mid-Norway. At its mouth the surface of these raised deltas is 150 feet (45 metres) above present sea-level. At Vadheim, 40 miles (65 km) from the coast, it is 290 feet (88 metres), at Balestrand, 60 miles (100 km) inland, it is 360 feet (110 metres), and at Flåm, 85 miles (140 km) inland (measured straight), it is 455 feet (138 metres) (Fig. 317). This gives a constant rise of about $3\frac{1}{2}$ feet a mile (65 cm/km) as one moves eastwards along that line.

The south coast of Norway provides a southwest–northeast profile from Lindesnes to near Oslo, a distance of about 170 miles (270 km). Figure 317 graphs the heights of the *upper marine limit* in post-glacial times along this coast, and from this it will be seen that there is an almost constant rise of about $3\frac{3}{4}$ feet a mile (70 cm/km) along the whole length, slightly less at the western end and slightly more towards Oslo. When it was the actual coast, this upper marine limit was horizontal, and the inclination, which it now has, is the result of isostatic tilt, the consequence of previous greater depression at the northeasterly end of the line, where the glaciation was more intense.

Fig. 318. A drowned lower river valley now infilled with sand and silt and seen at low tide

SUBMERGENT COASTS

Because of isostatic recovery it is true to say that most coasts in glaciated areas are today emergent coasts, exhibiting the various features just described, and equally because of glacial changes in sea-level all other coasts, unless rapid tectonic uplift is occurring at the present time, are *coasts of submergence*, since the last change has been the rise of sea-level consequent on the melting of so much of the ice. As already described, during the coldest parts of the ice ages, the English Channel and the southern (exposed) part of the North Sea were land. At that time not only were the Thames, Rhine and Seine tributaries of one another, but other rivers of northern France and southern England likewise joined the extended Rhine in the middle. These rivers deepened their valleys to attempt to grade themselves to the lower base-level, and the latest consequence of this is that, with the rising sea-level, not only has the English Channel been flooded again, but with it the lower parts of the tributary river valleys.

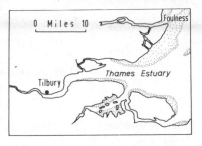

According to the form of valley which has been produced, the result has been the formation of an *estuary* or a *ria*. In general an estuary is a funnel-shaped river mouth and is clearly the drowned lower part of its valley. Figure 318 shows the estuary of the Welsh river Mawddach with Barmouth railway bridge crossing it. The photograph was taken at low tide and emphasises

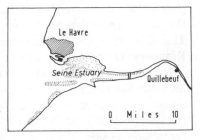

Fig. 319. The funnel shaped estuaries of the Thames and Seine

the fact that such inlets often become heavily silted up with sand or mud banks. Almost the whole of this estuary is now choked, and the low, flat area seen at the right-hand edge of the photograph, with one or two *roches moutonnées* rising out of it, is land which has already been naturally or artificially reclaimed. Figure 319 shows the *funnel estuaries* of the Thames and Seine, but the rivers

Fig. 320. Dart ria, Devonshire, southern England

farther west on both the English and French coasts have mouths of a different type. These were mostly shorter rivers and they deepened their valleys more actively and thus more steeply and narrowly than the larger ones to the east. Figure 320 shows such a drowned valley. This is the river Dart at Dartmouth (left-hand side of river) with Kingswear facing. It is a *ria*.

The characteristic differences between an estuary and a ria are that the latter has much steeper banks and lacks the funnel shape of an estuary as it approaches the sea. Rias result from rivers which have virtually incised their courses as compared with the wide-open, gently sloping sides of the valley which becomes an estuary. Nevertheless, the distinction is more one of convention than of reality, and, for example, the drowned, comparatively narrow, but not incised estuaries of Essex are intermediate between the two.

A second type of ria is to be found especially in southwest Ireland. Here, Bantry Bay, Kenmare River and Dingle Bay are generally known as rias, but they are not flooded river valleys. Instead, they result from the geological structure, being a series of synclines which have been invaded by the sea. They could more properly be termed *structural rias* as contrasted with *fluvial rias*.

THE NORWEGIAN STRANDFLAT

As an example of a coast which owes its origin to a series of differing agencies, the *strandflat* may be mentioned. It extends along much of the Norwegian coast and consists of a more or less level area, often rising to about 150 feet (45 metres) above sea-level, backed by the steep clifflike edge of the main mountain massif, which may rise to 3,000 feet (900 metres) or even higher (Fig. 321). This strandflat is

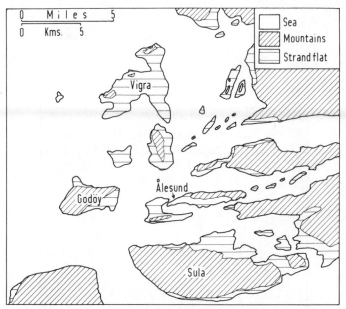

Fig. 321. *The Norwegian strandflat near Alesund (adapted from H. Holtedahl)*

not very smooth, and whilst in places it is undoubtedly a raised bench, either pre- or inter-glacial in age, in others it is a level platform planed off by a series of cirquelike glaciers that existed along its length when the snowline was down to the present sea-level or thereabouts. This explains the fact that in many places there are precipices which cannot be interpreted as fossil cliffs, since they front sheltered water where the waves, that would be necessary to have cut them, could not have existed. Freeze-thaw and chemical weathering just above the waterline have also been very important.

Glaciers from the mountains cut the valleys across the area before the general production of the shelf, for piedmont glaciers would

N2

have spread out laterally and not cut such grooves across a low-lying area of this type.

PRESENT-DAY CHANGES OF LEVEL

There are three types of change of level all of which continue in various parts of the world to a greater or lesser degree and in a positive or negative sense. These are (1) *eustatic changes,* (2) *isostatic recovery* from glacial depression, and (3) *tectonic changes.*

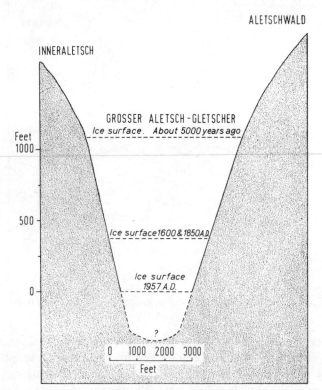

Fig. 322. The Aletsch glacier in 1600, 1850 and 1957. Transverse profile a little way above the snout

It is known that the various ice sheets and glaciers throughout the world have been shrinking for some years, and that they are now all very much smaller in volume (as well as in area) than they were especially about 1600 and 1850, when the Swiss glaciers appear to have reached recent maxima. Figure 322 shows a profile of the

Aletsch glacier in Switzerland as it was in those years and is at present. The volume has shrunk dramatically.

Calculations have been made of the decrease in world volume of ice, and from that it is possible to calculate the anticipated rise in sea-level due to the additional water. In some countries it has been possible to compare precise coastal surveys of some years ago with conditions at the present time and thus to determine directly changes in the apparent sea-level, and it may also be calculated from detailed analysis of tidal records. Such methods naturally give the relative change of level, and not necessarily the actual, for if a particular land mass is rising at the same rate as is the adjoining sea, there will be no apparent change. What is observed is the algebraic sum of the two changes that are occurring individually, but since the eustatic change should be constant for the whole world, it is possible to deduce the magnitude of this component, and so differentiate the two.

The present rate of eustatic rise of sea-level due to increase of water in the oceans seems to be about $4\frac{1}{2}$ inches a century (a millimetre a year) as has already been mentioned (p. 378). Reference has already been made to the resultant net changes at present occurring at two localities on the west coast of Britain. At Pembroke and in northeast Yorkshire, the crust appears to be just about keeping pace with the eustatic rise, so that there is no apparent change occurring at these places. In the London area, the crust seems to be sinking at about a millimetre a year. This added to the 1 mm a year sea-level rise, makes a net loss of 2 mm a year or about 8 inches a century. Precise measurements to give this information have been made at only a very few places, and not over a long period of time, so that at the moment no exact reliance can be placed on the above figures. They merely indicate the trends so far as they are known.

The sinking in southeast England cannot satisfactorily be attributed to any glacial cause, and thus it must be regarded as due to tectonic movements going on at the present time.

CLASSIFICATION OF COASTS

Any attempt to classify coasts on a genetic basis immediately meets the problem of change of level. In a sense every coast is one of submergence, since the last major change that has occurred is the rise of sea-level by some 500 feet (150 metres) at the end of the Ice Ages. Every coast, unless the land has risen at least by an equal amount, is thus partly drowned. Only a few thousand years have elapsed since this rise in sea-level, and consequently there has been no time to develop wide abrasion benches, and all coasts are thus in one sense in the youthful stage. Only a few low-lying coasts in unconsolidated materials have had time to adjust themselves to the new conditions and become mature.

Thus any attempt at coast classification is complex since the genetic processes shaping each stretch have changed probably several times in the relatively recent past. For that reason no schemes so far proposed have proved of any great value when applied to actual coasts, and no scheme is suggested here.

It is of course possible to classify coasts in other, non-genetic ways, such as by a descriptive landform classification. Some types would be: cliffed coasts, dune coasts, straight coasts, bayed coasts, headlands and so on. Such classification is of cataloguing value, but cannot be truly scientific.

CHAPTER TWENTY-NINE

Aeolian Erosion and Deposition

WIND as a geomorphic agent of erosion and deposition is most important in the more arid areas, and of considerable, although not dominant, significance in most other parts also. It is powerless to effect erosion without a tool of some sort, and thus it is particularly effective in those areas where the ground is covered with broken material of suitable calibre for the wind to move and not held by the presence of much vegetation. The wind is never sufficiently powerful to move pebbles (although it may do so indirectly by removing smaller material from beneath them and thus causing them to topple); silt is rarely sufficiently dry for wind to move although under suitable circumstances great dust storms may occur. The most favourable material for transportation by wind is *sand*.

Sand is a very common residual of rock break-up for it is composed of one of the minerals most resistant to chemical action. It is particularly concentrated in two very different environments, namely, the hot deserts and certain coastal area.

MOVEMENT OF SAND

Unaided, moving air can transport loose sand and dry dust along the ground. A minimum wind velocity is required, dependent upon the size of grain, and when once a rolling movement has been initiated there is a tendency for a certain amount of jumping to occur. This is progressive, and soon great numbers of grains are apparently in suspension in the air, quite moderate winds on dry sandy areas producing a continuous cloud of particles up to 2 feet ($\frac{1}{2}$ metre) high, and so filling the air that the ground may not be visible through the 'fog'.

Each individual grain is falling through the air, and thus reaches the ground again quite soon. There it spurts up two or three other grains, which in their turn are caught by the wind and blown along. Turbulence in the lowest layers of the air greatly aids this relay-race type of successive leaps. Such transportation is known as a *saltation movement*:

Where local relief promotes strong upward air currents, the sand may be blown to considerable heights, desert and coastal dunes up to 80 or more feet (25 metres) in height being not uncommon.

The term *competency* is employed to indicate the ability of the wind to transport sand grains. The greater the velocity, the greater is the competency. Some sorting of grain sizes occurs, since smaller grains of sand are tossed into the air whilst the larger grains may only be rolled along. When the movement is up a slope, the small grains shoot beyond the crestline, but the larger grains, rolling up, fall over on to the lee-side and there form the bulk of the material.

Another term used is *capacity*. This indicates the quantity of sand which the wind may transport. It is normally less than water at low velocities since sand settles much more rapidly in air, because of the lower density, and thus the individual leaps of each saltation movement are shorter than in water. Nevertheless, because wind velocities become so much greater than water velocities, and also because they operate over greater areas, the total amount moved by wind is much more than by water. It has been estimated that 1,000 million tons of dust are carried an average distance greater than 1,000 miles (1,600 km) per year in the air over the Mississippi valley. In the last hundred years, Europe has received nearly 6 inches (15 cm) of dust from the Sahara, and the Nile delta has lost 8 feet (2·4 metres) by deflation in 2,500 years.

Sand is moved less spectacular distances since it is rare for its saltation hops to be longer than about 30 feet (say, 10 metres) and consequently any belt of water, such as a river, which is wider than this virtually stops all further movement.

AEOLIAN EROSION

The simplest type of erosion by wind results from the removal of sand and other already loose material so as to produce a *deflation hollow*. This very often occurs amongst coastal sand dunes where an area has become partially or wholly devoid of vegetation for some reason. Consequently dunes, which had previously been built up by extraction from the wind and had accumulated around grasses and other vegetation, are blown away until the floor of the hollow reaches the level of the water-table. Below that the wind cannot remove further sand, for the grains are wet, too heavy to be picked up and to some extent adherent to one another. Such level floored hollows amongst sand-dune massifs are termed *slacks* (Fig. 323). Deflation continues to the low summer level of the water-table, and so in winter the slacks become flooded to a depth of a foot or so. Because no

Fig. 323. Slacks occupying deflation hollows amongst sand dunes in south Lancashire, England

further removal of sand occurs and the area is moist, vegetation soon returns to cover the whole of the floor. The ecology of such areas is completely different from that of the drier dunes themselves.

Similar deflation hollows also occur in desert regions and the Qattara depression (7,500 sq miles (19,400 sq km) in area) of western Egypt is an extreme case. It is nearly 190 miles long by 90 miles (300 × 140 km) at its widest. Its lowest point is 440 feet (134 metres) below sea-level, and its eastern end is 125 miles (200 km) west of Cairo.

Figure 324 shows a rock formation in the east Pennines at Brimham near Pateley Bridge, which has been attributed by some to chemical weathering, but which almost certainly owes at least a part of its sculpturing to the abrasive effect of wind-blown sand. Concentration of faster moving air current at various levels, coupled with greater load of sand grains, linked also with less well-cemented strata in the rock itself, produce greater erosion at particular heights, and the unusual forms such as are seen in the photograph. The pattern on these features is typically horizontal and should be contrasted with the vertical shaping of chemically rotted rock seen in Figs. 72

and 93. Such features as these are sometimes termed *zeugen*, especially when they have been eroded in such a pattern that a massive upper portion stands on a relatively narrow pedestal.

A minor feature resulting from wind erosion but often of considerable interpretive importance is known as a *ventifact*. This is a

Fig. 324. Eroded and weathered sandstone rocks in the eastern Pennines

pebble which has become polished and faceted by the passage of sand grains borne by the wind, and it often happens that the orientation of numerous such pebbles in the same area is in the same direction. This then serves as a guide to the wind direction at the time the pebbles were shaped and has even enabled this to be determined in some deposits of geologic age. When the pebbles acquire three facets, the usual term given to them is *dreikanter*.

COASTAL SAND DUNES

On coasts with wide sandy beaches which may be largely dried out during ebb tide, on-shore winds blow considerable quantities of sand as far as and beyond the coastline, and so lead to the formation of sand dunes (Fig. 325). Not being in an arid climate, these soon acquire a cover of vegetation, sea couch grass (*Agropyrum junceum*), sea lyme (*Elymus arenarius*) and marram grass (*Ammophila* or *Psamma arenaria*) most often being the first colonisers. The last named is capable of quick growth through additional covers of sand, and the total length of root and stalk of this grass often reaches as much as 30 feet (say, 10 metres). The resulting tangle of vegetation forms a great mesh through the dune and acts as a kind of reinforcement of the whole mass of sand and greatly aids stabilisation.

Coastal dunes only persist in areas where marine erosion is not occurring, for they have almost zero strength with which to resist wave attack, and consequently they are generally associated not only with sand beaches, which can provide the material, but also with coasts with backshores of some width.

They often develop on the crestlines of barrier beaches and backshore bars, and are one of the major factors in determining the sites of coastal holiday resorts. They occur extensively along the shores of the Bay of Biscay; on the North Sea coasts of Denmark, Western Germany and parts of the Netherlands; on the south side of Moray Firth, Scotland; in Lancashire, England; on many stretches of the Atlantic coast of United States; as well as in many other parts of the world. A dune massif of moderate size is seen on the Devonshire coast at Braunton Sand (Fig. 267).

The landward side of such a dune belt is often flanked by a considerable spread of level sand not built up into irregular mounds. Such an area, which at times may reach more than a mile in width, is known as *links sand,* and it owes its level nature primarily to an insufficient quantity of material with which to build dunes.

Fig. 325. Coastal sand dunes, Formby Point, England

HOT DESERTS

The location of the hot desert areas, which are primarily the result of aridity and the consequent lack of vegetation, has been described in Chapter 8. The common feature of the surface of these areas is that they are almost entirely devoid of vegetation and consequently both the rock surface and the regolith are particularly vulnerable to attack by various erosive and weathering agents.

Although these areas are invariably arid, the occasional rainstorm, which may occur only once a year or even less frequently, has a powerful erosive effect, even though short-lived. Many of the features of a desert landscape are the result of sporadic, but intense, fluvial or sheet-wash activity.

These areas are, however, particularly favourable to wind action, since the dry surface makes the movement of small calibre regolith relatively easy. It is usual to divide the desert surface into three types. These are generally known, especially in the Sahara, as the *hamada,* the rock desert tracts; the *reg* or stony desert; and the *erg* or sandy desert. Small valleys, along which torrential streams flow for a few hours a year, are known as *wadis*. An *oasis* is generally a deflation

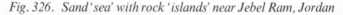

Fig. 326. Sand 'sea' with rock 'islands' near Jebel Ram, Jordan

Fig. 327. Sand desert in California

hollow where the water-table is fairly near the surface thus enabling vegetation to survive and permitting habitation.

Figure 326 shows the type of landscape that is produced when a great quantity of blown sand infills hollows between individual hills or mountains. This is in the desert just north of Aqaba at the northern end of the Red Sea, and such a landscape is often described as a *sand sea* with rock 'islands'. The latter are also sometimes called *inselbergs,* but an inselberg is more correctly an isolated, residual mountain on a plain. Those shown in the photograph are merely the summits of a generally hilly terrain.

A sand sea uninterrupted by rock outcrops is shown in Fig. 327. This is a great mass of sand dunes in Death Valley, California, although the area is not absolutely devoid of all vegetation. The sharp-crested ridges mark recent movement of sand by wind. In the case of the central ridge especially, it is clear that the most recent movement has been from the left. The sand has moved up the long slope which is in deep shadow, and has fallen over the brightly lit steeper right-hand slope of the ridge. This slope is at the angle of rest of the sand and a slightly darker pediment of earlier deposition is seen at the foot of the slope.

Fig. 328. Desert dunes near Delta, Utah

The pattern of dunes in Sevier Desert, Utah, is remarkably shown in Fig. 328. The wind has been moving from the left, and each of the individual dune ridges is of a pattern similar to the one described in Fig. 327. This aerial photograph gives a general view and the similarity to a succession of great rollers moving across the ocean is very striking. Notice the stony surface in the trough of each 'wave'.

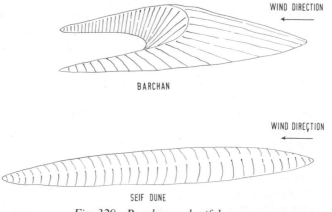

Fig. 329. Barchan and seif dunes

Whilst these long dune ridges, transverse to the wind direction, are each more or less straight, individual parts of the ridges are arcuate in form. When there is less movement of sand, such arcuate forms, as shown in Fig. 329, are known as *barchans*. They become arcuate because the tips of each dune contain less sand and thus can be moved more quickly than can the more massive central section. They overtake the latter and become *horns*.

If the wind is particularly powerful and the quantity of sand not too great, this tendency is strengthened and *longitudinal dunes* come into existence, with the long axis then in the same direction as the wind and not transverse to it (Fig. 329). *Seif* (Arabic for sword) is a name often applied to this type of dune.

LOESS

Loess is a much finer-grained deposit, and occurs in two types. The most famous area in which loess is extensively developed is in the basin of the Hwang Ho, China, and this may be termed *desert loess*.

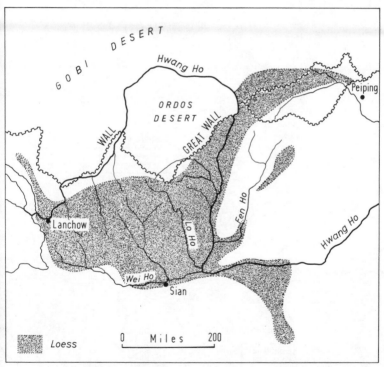

Fig. 330. The distribution of the Hwang-Ho loess

It results from the fact that the finer material is more easily and rapidly transported than is normal sand, and consequently it may be blown beyond the limits of the desert region that provided the source. Figure 330 shows the distribution of the Hwang Ho loess and its relationship to the Gobi and Ordos deserts.

Such loess is often more than 100 feet (30 metres) thick, and when trenched by streams it stands in vertical walls in spite of the soft nature of the deposit. It is held, virtually as a spongelike mass, by the presence of minute branching tubes which permeate it much as though they were the relics of now decayed rootlets of previous vegetation, which some have thought them to indicate. These tubes are lined by a thin cement of calcium carbonate and thus in a sense bind the dust grains together.

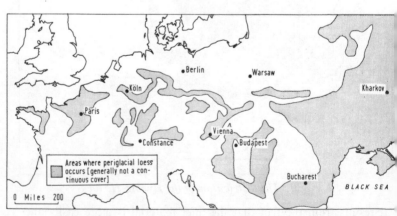

Fig. 331. *Principal areas where periglacial loess occurs in America and Europe*

The second type may be termed *periglacial loess*. This is to be found covering extensive areas in Europe and southwestern Asia, as well as parts of the United States. It is a dust which was blown from the morainic debris of the continental lowland ice sheets during the existence of which the dry conditions, caused by the below freezing temperatures, at times produced the effect of an arid climate and permitted great dust storms to develop. Figure 331 shows the location of some of the principal expanses of periglacial loess in both Europe and America.

CHAPTER THIRTY

Oceans and Ocean Floors

FROM coast to ocean bed is a natural step, and although apparently less important to man and but little known, it covers nearly three-quarters of the surface of the Earth and has a most complex form. It may roughly be divided into the continental shelf bordered by the continental slope and continental rise, and the ocean floor.

THE CONTINENTAL SHELF

Islands such as the British Isles, Newfoundland and others, which are adjacent to the main continental masses generally belong to the latter in a geological sense and are separated from them only by relatively shallow seas beneath which the rocks of the neighbouring land masses continue uninterrupted. The floor of these shallow areas is known as the *continental shelf*. Its depth varies from zero to about 650 feet (200 metres) in the case of the European shelf (Fig. 332), but in many instances it descends gently to greater depths than this before the gradient suddenly steepens to become the *continental slope*. The width of the shelf also varies very greatly, and in general it is wider when the neighbouring land is lowland, and narrower when it consists of high mountain ranges.

Even in those localities where the submarine relief seems to continue the land relief forms, when accurate surveys are made it is generally found that the sea floor is much smoother than the land surface and its character is very different from a subaerial one. Figure 333 is a profile across St George's Channel from the southern Wicklow Mountains to Wales just south of Aberystwyth. It is drawn accurately to scale excepting that in order to show the relief on the sea bed the vertical scale is about 80 times the horizontal one. This is a great exaggeration, much greater than is usually employed for profiles across land areas, and it makes the moderately hilly country of this part of the Wicklows, and the only slightly more mountainous part of Wales, seem to be lands of precipices and needlelike peaks.

The contrast between the relief of the subaerial and submarine portions of the profile is very obvious, and this leads to some doubt

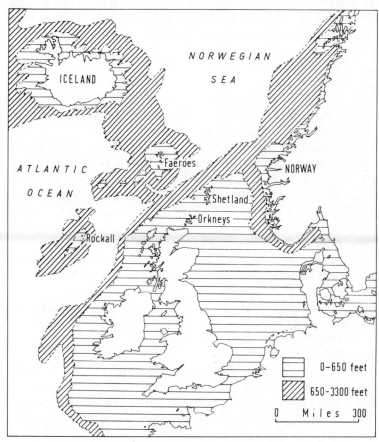

Fig. 332. *The European continental shelf*

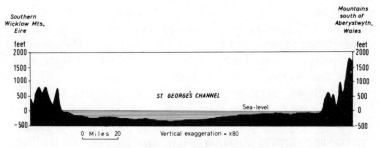

Fig. 333. *Profile from Ireland to Wales*

as to the origin of the surface features of the continental shelf, for if the area were merely drowned land, it would be expected to show subaerial features similar to the adjoining land although modified since submergence. This it does not do. It is natural to expect that any unconsolidated material, especially recent deposits, might be fairly evenly spread by currents, but there seems to have been insufficient time for so much infill in the few thousand years since the coldest parts of the Ice Ages, when much of the continental shelf around southern Britain was certainly land.

Whatever may be the origin of the surface forms of continental shelves, they are certainly geologically part of the mainland and of the neighbouring islands. It is for this reason that there are good possibilities of the presence of oil in the strata underlying parts of the North Sea, especially in those which are near an existing European oilfield, such as that of northeastern Netherlands and northwestern Western Germany.

Figure 332 shows that the limits of the continent of Europe in reality lie about 250 miles (400 km) west of Land's End, between 100 and 50 miles (160 and 80 km) west of the west coast of Ireland, and about 150 miles (240 km) off the mainland coast of Scotland. The whole of the North Sea, excepting for the narrow deep rounding the southwesterly coast of Norway (which is believed to be a rift valley), is part of the shelf. When the depth of the shelf reaches about 650 feet (200 metres) below sea-level, there is a relatively steep slope downwards to depths of more (sometimes much more) than 3,500 feet (1,000 metres) at an average gradient of about one in twenty. This and other similar continental slopes are some of the greatest slopes in world relief, both as regards length and the great difference in level between top and bottom.

Little is so far known concerning the origin of these shelves, but it appears to be fairly clear that they represent the seaward limits to which geologic sediments were deposited. Already there is considerable knowledge concerning the geology of the floor of the English Channel, and as more and more bore holes are put down in other areas, particularly in the North Sea, the geological link between Europe and Britain will become better understood.

The shelf was partially exposed during the low sea-levels of the Pleistocene and these parts must for those periods have been subject to subaerial weathering and erosion or to the presence of lowland ice sheets. The pattern of glaciated valleys extends far beyond the limits of the present coasts of Norway and Iceland (see Fig. 332).

Distinct from the general European continental shelf is the *Ice-land–Faeroe ridge*. This has depths not greater than 1,500 feet (460 metres) and it separates the great depths of the North Atlantic Ocean from the Norwegian Sea. It has great influence upon the circulation of water in the Norwegian Sea and more will be said concerning this in the next chapter.

At the foot of the continental slope there is generally the *continental rise*. This is at a gentler gradient (about one in five hundred) and forms a kind of apron or pediment around the foot of the slope, linking it with the great ocean depths. It varies greatly in width and occasionally is absent. In such localities the slope itself continues on at much the same steep gradient right down to the deepest parts.

Off the Atlantic coast of North America there are deep, narrow valleys known as *submarine canyons*. Some of these start at the edge of the continental shelf and are cut in the slope to very considerable depths. Others lie on the shelf itself, sometimes quite near to the present coast. Some are cut nearly 5,000 feet (1,500 metres) deep below the level of the adjacent shelf; they may be more than 100 miles (160 km) in length and often descend to as much as 10,000 feet (3,000 metres) below present sea-level.

In origin the canyons are probably partially subaerial, being cut during the low Pleistocene sea-level, and they may owe part of their present depth to recent subsidence, but it would appear to be necessary to ascribe at least the very deep portions to submarine erosion. Powerful currents can at times occur down the continental slope, and if these are concentrated by previously existing channels, however slight, and if they contain heavy loads of silt as is often the case, they form powerful erosive agents moving as fast as 50 miles an hour (80 km/h).

Sedimentation on the continental shelf is very complex. This is commonly known as the *neritic zone,* and most geologic sedimentary rocks have been deposited in such shallow water. The sediments brought down by rivers are commonly deposited in this area, and most limestone rocks were also formed in this zone. It should be remembered that calcium carbonate is formed as an organic deposit in the neritic zone either at the same time as inorganic deposits such as silt and sand, or in clear water. Limestone or chalk results when the organic deposition occurs without other deposits. It acts as a cement and greatly aids consolidation in the case of inorganic deposits.

Sediments on the continental slope are known as *bathyal,* and are largely the result of settling from suspension and of slumping and sliding.

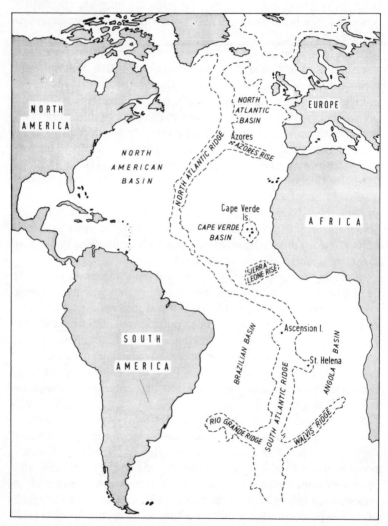

Fig. 334. Relief of the Atlantic Ocean floor

THE OCEAN FLOOR

The ocean floor descends to great depths and carries on it some of the greatest mountain ranges, which only occasionally reach the water surface. The best known of these are the *mid-oceanic ridges*, such as the Mid-Atlantic Ridge, which is 10,000 miles (16,000 km) in length up to 500 miles (800 km) in width and 10,000 feet (3,000 metres) in height above the ocean floor (Fig. 334). The Azores are an exceptionally high part of this ridge, and the group of islands emerge from the water at the point where an east–west ridge springs off from the Mid-Atlantic Ridge to reach as far as Cape St Vincent. This separates the North Atlantic Basin from the Cape Verde Basin at the southern edge of which the Mid-Atlantic Ridge spreads eastwards before it turns southwards again midway between South Africa and South America.

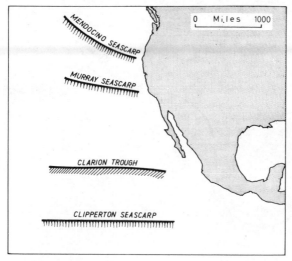

Fig. 335. Eastern Pacific seascarps and fracture zones

The pattern in the Pacific Ocean is more complex. There is some indication of a mid-oceanic north–south ridge, but it is by no means so well-developed as is the case in the Atlantic. For about half the width of the ocean there stretch westwards from the coasts of North and Central America several *seascarps* and *fracture zones*. These lie roughly parallel to one another and are fairly equally spaced. They are shown in Fig. 335 and are the Clipperton Seascarp, 3,300 miles (5,300 km) in length and 1,000 feet (300 metres) high; the Clarion Trough, which although quite narrow, averages 3,000 feet (900 metres) in depth and is 1,800 miles (2,900 km) long; the Murray Seascarp, 4,000 feet (1,200 metres) high and 1,600 miles (2,600 km) in length from near the central Hawaiian Islands to southern California; and the Mendocino Seascarp which is 5,000 feet (1,500 metres) high and 1,500 miles (2,400 km) long. It stretches eastwards from north of San Francisco almost exactly along latitude 40° N. These are all signs of comparatively recent tectonic stresses and movements in this part of the Pacific and no doubt are connected with the Alpine growth of the North American Cordillera, although structurally more or less at right-angles to it.

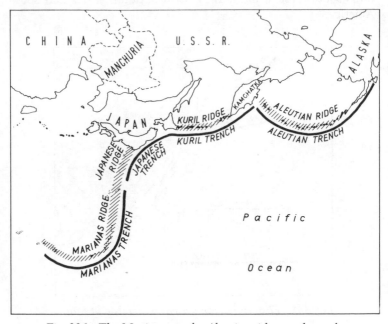

Fig. 336. The Marianas to the Aleutian ridges and trenches

The western half of the Pacific is much more complex and active. Here are the lowest places in the world. They occur in the bottoms of great narrow trenches which lie on the oceanic side of the Aleutian Islands, the Kuril, the Japanese and the Marianas Ridges. The trenches have the same names as the ridges and are shown on Fig. 336. The deepest known oceanic depth in the world occurs in the Marianas Trench and is at 36,200 feet (11,030 metres) below sea-level.

There are other ridges and trenches in the southwestern Pacific, and as with the northern ones, the summits of the ridges largely constitute the lines of islands or *island arcs* which are so characteristic of this area. The trenches are clearly relatively youthful features for they contain little or no sediment on their floors, and it is considered that they are the result of powerful tectonic forces, perhaps of thrust or perhaps of tension, which produced both the elongated hollows and the ridges.

The Indian Ocean is patterned on the Atlantic form with a mid-Indian Ocean–Chacos Ridge from the Laccadive and Maldive Islands to the Kerguelen Islands in the south. The Indo-Australian Basin falls below 20,000 feet (6,000 metres) and along the great island arc of Andaman–Nicobar–Sumatra–Java–Tanimbar there is the Sunda Trench. This is part of a complex system for it consists of outer and inner trenches. Some of the most active volcanoes are on the island arc, and the Sunda Platform is the centre of deep-seated earthquakes (Fig. 337).

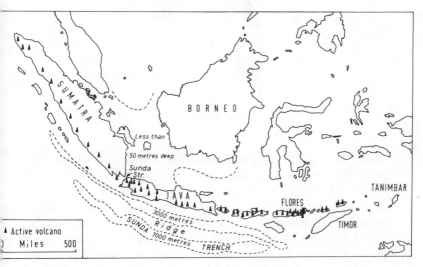

Fig. 337. *From Andaman to Tanimbar*

VOLCANIC ISLANDS, SEAMOUNTS AND GUYOTS

The recent and present tectonic activity in most parts of the Pacific Ocean basin has already been mentioned, and three relatively small features of the ocean support this. They are the presentday active *volcanic islands,* such as the Hawaii group, *seamounts* and *guyots.*

Figure 337 has already shown the number of active volcanoes, some of them forming isolated islands, and the Hawaii group also

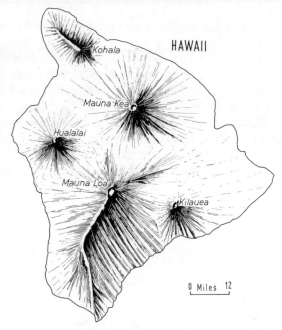

Fig. 338. Hawaii

largely consists of volcanic islands (Fig. 338). Hawaii itself comprises five volcanic mountains one of which is Mauna Kea, which rises to 13,800 feet (4,200 metres) above sea-level from an ocean depth of more than 17,000 feet (5,200 metres). It is thus the highest mountain in the world – nearly 31,000 feet (9,400 metres). Another one of the five is Mauna Loa, which is both the largest mountain in the world by volume and the greatest outpourer of lava. Kilauea, the most easterly of the five, has the largest crater and is the most continuously active of the group.

A very large number of *seamounts* and *guyots* have been discovered by more detailed surveys in recent years in different parts of the Pacific. The guyots are mostly between latitudes 10 and 30° N and in the western half of the ocean. They are flat-topped, eroded, past volcanoes, whilst the seamounts are cone-shaped to the summit which may be up to 12,000 feet (3,700 metres) high above the ocean floor although still of the order of 3,000 feet (900 metres) below the surface. Seamounts are of approximately similar dimensions, although their summits generally rise to within a few hundred feet of the surface.

Both are extinct volcanoes and the truncation of the guyots is taken to indicate that at one period they have protruded above water-level, and thus experienced erosion. Subsequent tectonic sinking has lowered them beneath the sea again.

Even in oceanic areas far away from land, there is still a little inorganic, fluvial material, but what has not settled in the littoral areas is of very fine calibre. It generally appears to be ferruginous and is known as *red clay*.

Organic deposits are the more important in such areas. They are termed *oozes*, and are derived from the 'skeletons' or 'shells' of minute plankton. They may be composed mainly of calcium carbonate (*calcareous ooze*) or of silica (*siliceous ooze*). The most important class of calcareous ooze is *Globigerina ooze,* which is formed by a particular group of foraminifera. The siliceous ooze is derived either from diatoms or radiolaria, two groups of planktonic animals.

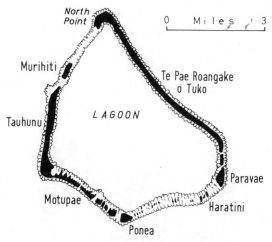

Fig. 339. Coral atoll, Manihiki

CORAL ATOLLS AND BARRIER REEFS

Coral atolls (Fig. 339) are related to both seamounts and guyots. Corals live only in clear water at a depth less than 150 feet (46

O

metres) and a temperature not less than 21°C (70°F). They are to be found capping many of the drowned volcanoes as a ring of coral which no doubt represents the rim of the old crater. They have a *lagoon* in the centre. Subsidence has occurred at much the same rate as the coral can build up its formation and so remain within the necessary shallow limit. In true atolls, no solid rock is visible and borings have been necessary to determine their nature.

Coral *barrier reefs* such as occur off the eastern coast of Australia are believed to have come into existence as the result of down-faulting of recent (Tertiary) date of a level plain to such a depth that coral could flourish upon it. Continued subsidence has kept pace with the coral growth and so led to the present appearance of the reefs. They do not consist entirely of living coral – there is also much dead coral as well as sand and other sea-wrack.

CHAPTER THIRTY-ONE

Sea Water

ALTHOUGH the Moon has a number of basins similar to the ocean basins of the Earth, nevertheless no water lies within them. Water is formed from the solidification of igneous rocks which contain more when molten than they do when solid. It is first freed in the gaseous state as steam or water vapour, and in the case of the Moon the force of its gravity is insufficient to hold molecules of gas as an envelope. The escape speed from the surface of the Moon is just under one and a half miles (2·4 km) per second, and many gas molecules at temperatures commonly reached there on the side facing the Sun have velocities in excess of this critical speed. They escape.

On the other hand, on the Earth, because it is more massive and thus has a more powerful gravitational field, the escape speed is 7 miles (11 km) per second, and even at boiling temperature the mean speed of the water-steam molecules is less than half a mile (0·8 km) a second, so that their chances of escaping from Earth are very slight indeed.

Although water is a substance which is liquid only within a small range of temperature, the temperature on most parts of the Earth's surface lies within this and most water is in the liquid condition. It is estimated that about 97 per cent of the total quantity is in the oceans. The remainder is in the atmosphere in the form of vapour, on land in the form of ice, rivers, lakes and soil water, or within living plants and animals. The total volume of the oceanic water is 329 million cubic miles (1,370 million cu km), the area is 139 million square miles (360 million sq km) and the average depth is nearly 12,500 feet (3,800 metres) or rather more than 2⅓ miles. These figures should be compared with the volume of the solid surface that is above sea-level, which is about 30 million cubic miles (125 million cu km) (less than 10 per cent the volume of the water) with an area of 58 million square miles (150 million sq km) and an average height above sea-level of 2,700 feet (800 metres).

SALINITY

Rivers bring a considerable amount of material down in solution as

411

well as in the solid state. Since evaporation from the ocean surface consists only of pure water, the material in solution is left behind, and through geologic time the amount in the oceans has progressively increased until now the total amount of dissolved salts is between 32 and 36 parts per thousand in most areas. (This can be written 32 to 36‰.) The figure varies for different areas. Those with high evaporation and few rivers flowing into them have a high salinity, such as the north end of the Red Sea, which has a salinity of 41 per thousand. The figure for the Atlantic in the latitude of Britain is about 35 per thousand. Some semi-enclosed seas have a very low salinity, such as the Baltic, which, in the Gulf of Bothnia, varies from about 2 to less than 1 per thousand according to the season of the year, being least in the spring when the melting snows supply great quantities of fresh water.

In inland lakes, the figure is often very high, and one of the saltiest natural waters in the world is the Dead Sea with a salinity of 238 per thousand, or more than a quarter the weight of the water.

Two salts account for nearly 90 per cent of the total quantity dissolved. These are sodium chloride (78 per cent) and magnesium chloride (11 per cent). The remainder is mainly magnesium, calcium and potassium sulphates, calcium carbonate and magnesium bromide. The proportions in which these are present is almost constant whatever may be the total amount, and it is for that reason that we may refer to the salinity as a whole, even when considerable precision is required.

TEMPERATURE

The temperature of sea water varies with the locality, the time of year and the depth. Naturally it follows to some degree the intensity of the sunlight that shines upon the surface, and is thus greater in the equatorial latitudes, but its response to variations in sunshine with the seasons of the year and with the weather of individual weeks or even days is much slower than is the response made by dry land.

This is partly due to the high specific heat of water, which requires approximately five times as much heat to raise its temperature as does the same weight of rock. Because of the heavier nature (greater density) of rock, a volume of water requires nearly twice the amount of heat to raise its temperature as does the same volume of rock. The principal reason for the sluggish response of water is, however, due to the fact that radiant heat from the Sun can penetrate farther into water because of its greater transparency and especially because the surface waters of the sea are constantly stirred by wind action and a surface layer several tens of feet in thickness is warmed compared with only a few inches in the case of rock. For example, although the surface temperature rises to 4°C (39°F) in Spitsbergen in summer, the ground is still frozen at 3-feet (1-metre) depth (the surface of the permafrost).

This results in the sea taking longer time to warm up in spring and summer than does the land, and it remains warm later into the autumn. The warmest month on land in East Anglia is July, whilst on the sea surface offshore it is August.

The fall of temperature with depth below the water surface is, because of mixing, generally very slight for the first hundred feet or so, the thickness depending on the surface wind strength. Then it falls rapidly to a depth of 4,000 feet (1,200 metres), by which time what was 13°C (55°F) at the surface will have fallen to about 3°C (38°F). Below this level it falls more slowly to about 2°C (35°F) in a second 4,000 feet, below which there is not much further decline.

DENSITY

Because of its salinity, sea water is a little heavier than fresh, but not by a great amount. The density is about $2\frac{1}{2}$ per cent greater than pure water, and so a cubic foot of sea water weighs very nearly 64 lb (about 1,025 kg per cu metre), or $1\frac{1}{2}$ lb (1·57 lb) heavier than fresh water. This is sufficient to make it easy for a human being to float in sea water. The buoyancy of a very salty water, such as the Dead Sea, is so great that it makes swimming quite difficult. It is almost impossible to get oneself sufficiently immersed!

The figures given in the last paragraph are averages, and the exact density varies with both variations in salinity and temperature. With the same salinity, the density increases from an average of 1·025 near the surface to 1·028 at depths of 8,000 feet (2,400 metres) and more, mainly because of fall of temperature.

Some of this increase in density is, however, also due to a very slight compression resulting from the great pressures in deep water due to the weight of the water above. On the surface the atmospheric pressure averages about 15 lb per sq inch (400 g per sq cm); at a mile depth pressure is just about one ton per sq inch (62 kg per sq cm), and in the ocean's greatest depth it is nearly $7\frac{1}{2}$ tons per sq inch (460 kg per sq cm).

The most important effect of variations in water density with temperature is perhaps the fact that it results in the denser of two water masses sinking beneath the lighter one when they are at different temperatures.

ICEBERGS, PACK-ICE AND ICEFLOES

Because of its salinity, sea water does not freeze until the temperature falls to $-1 \cdot 5°C$ ($28 \cdot 7°F$). The water may fall below this temperature in polar regions, and consequently the sea surface may

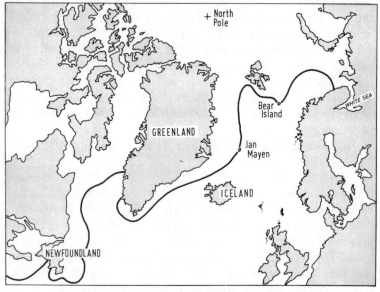

Fig. 340. Average southerly limit of pack ice in the North Atlantic

freeze. This results in the production of a fairly thin layer of ice known as *pack-ice*. It may reach a thickness of as much as 15 feet (5 metres) in one winter, but further growth is slow because of the low conductivity of the ice, which acts as a kind of blanket over the water below. Naturally it thickens on the surface by the accumulation of local snowfall.

Sea currents and wind may move the pack-ice and cause it to ruckle up into a hummocky surface, or contrariwise to break up into *icefloes,* which may later be rammed together to produce a very irregular sheet of ice. Ocean currents tend to drift considerable quantities of this ice away from polar regions and the normal limit reached by pack-ice in the Atlantic is shown in Fig. 340, although this in fact varies considerably from year to year.

Icebergs (see Fig. 180) differ from icefloes in being portions of much thicker ice which have calved off from glaciers whose snouts reach the sea. In the case of the Antarctic, the available land ice is mostly in the form of great lowland ice sheets, which move beyond the limits of land and become ice shelves, such as the Ross Ice Shelf (see Fig. 200). Ice shelf bergs are large in area compared with glacier bergs, and often measure 2 or 3 miles (3 to 5 km) in length with a thickness of the order of 200 or 300 feet (say, 50 to 100 metres). Glacier bergs, which are the normal type off Greenland, Spitsbergen and other North Polar islands, are much thicker, often reaching 1,000 feet (300 metres) or more, but at the same time they are of smaller area. Glacier bergs do occur in the Antarctic, as also do ice shelf bergs in the Arctic, but both of these are relatively rare owing to the configuration of the land masses of the two areas.

OCEAN CURRENTS

All atlases contain maps showing the pattern of the world's ocean currents, and only those of the Atlantic are shown in Fig. 341. They are primarily due to the play of wind on the surface water, but the direction in which the water moves is at an angle to the wind direction, for it is modified both by the configuration of the ocean and also by the rotation of the Earth. The latter produces the *Coriolis force,* which deflects the direction of movement clockwise in the northern hemisphere and anticlockwise in the southern in much the same way as does Buys Ballot's law in the case of atmospheric circulation (see p. 34). The actual direction taken by the moving water should be 45° off the direction of the wind, and in many instances this is the case, but naturally the extent to which the water is free to move is restricted by the limits of the ocean.

The North and South Equatorial Currents are in the region of the trade winds and result from their presence. These tend to pile up the water especially in the Caribbean, and this is one of the causes of the Gulf Stream. A similar effect, but of less magnitude because of the configuration of South America, occurs off Brazil and leads to the Brazil Current.

The Gulf Stream is a well-defined, fairly narrow current flowing at the fast rate of nearly 2½ miles (4 km) per hour about latitude 42° N and lying between two water masses, the warm water of the Sargasso Sea and the cool water immediately adjacent to the American coast. It succeeds in keeping these two separate, and thus prevents the lighter, warm water from flowing over the cooler. As the

Sea water

Gulf Stream passes farther across the Atlantic, it spreads laterally to a considerable extent and becomes slower moving. It divides in the latitude of northern Spain and part swings to the south to become the Canaries Current and so complete the circulation whilst the remain-

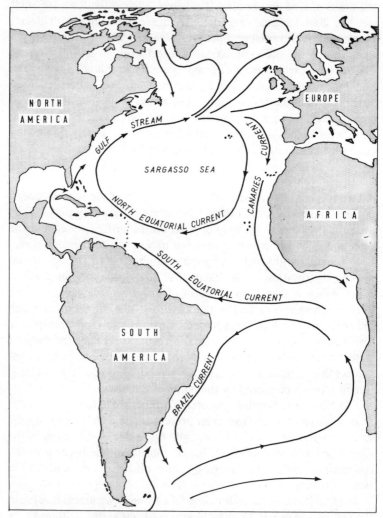

Fig. 341. Ocean currents of the Atlantic

der continues in the northeasterly direction to assist in warming the overlying air and give the British Isles and Scandinavia warmer winters than they might otherwise possess.

This description only concerns itself with the surface currents, and there are equally important ones in other directions beneath the surface. It is believed that the Gulf Stream, for example, does not extend to a depth of more than about 4,000 feet (1,200 metres), and the California Current in the eastern Pacific is not much deeper than 1,000 feet (300 metres). Beneath these there are deep currents some of which flow in the reverse directions to those on the surface above them. There is thought to be a current at about a third of a mile ($\frac{1}{2}$ km) an hour to a depth of 10,000 feet (3,000 metres) beneath the Brazil Current but in the northerly direction. Lack of direct observations makes information about these movements of water still very vague, and it is by no means possible as yet to give a complete picture of the circulatory systems of oceanic waters which takes into account both surface and depth currents.

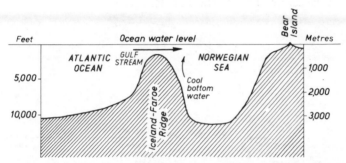

Fig. 342. Southwest to northeast section across the Norwegian Sea

The circulation into and within the Norwegian Sea is particularly important and fairly well known. The Iceland–Faeroe Ridge (see p. 403 and Fig. 332) lies between Scotland and Iceland and separates the Atlantic Ocean and Norwegian Sea basins, both reaching below 10,000 feet (3,000 metres), from one another by a shallow which is mostly no more than 1,000 feet (300 metres) deep.

The surface waters of the warm, salty Gulf Stream pass over this ridge northeastwards, but the cool bottom waters of the Norwegian Sea cannot escape southwards (Fig. 342). As the Gulf Stream enters, it draws up some of the cool water from the depths to mix with it, and produce conditions which are ideal for the growth of plankton to become fish food. The surface circulation within the Sea is anti-clockwise (see Fig. 341), and it is these special conditions which separate the hydrographic characteristics of the Norwegian Sea from those of the Atlantic and produce the fisheries.

TIDES

The twice daily change in sea-level, *tide*, is well known to all who
visit the seaside, and is a matter of great importance to all sailors
approaching a coast. An estuary which may be very safe to enter at
high water, may be dangerous at low because of the shallows produced by the fall in level. The *tidal range* varies along different coasts,
and while it may be almost zero in some places, as for example at
Stavanger, at others it may be as much as 28 feet or even more.

The tide is an astronomical phenomenon for it is produced by the
Moon and Sun acting jointly together. The part of the Earth which
at any moment is nearest to the Moon is attracted in that direction
with more than the average force of gravity for the whole world, just
because it is about 4,000 miles (6,400 km) nearer. The strength of the
pull towards the Moon at that point is about 3 per cent greater than
it is at the centre of the Earth (Fig. 343).

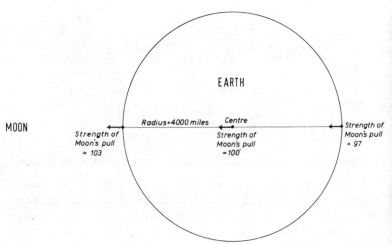

Fig. 343. Tide generating forces

In a similar way, the part of the Earth diametrically opposite to
the first point is the farthest from the Moon. It is 4,000 miles (6,400
km) more distant than is the centre of the Earth, and the pull towards
the Moon is about 3 per cent less than the mean for the whole Earth.
These are the *tide generating forces*.

These forces apply equally to the solid, liquid and gaseous parts
of the Earth. The last does not concern us at the moment, and the
solid finds response to the extra pull difficult, so it is the liquid part
of the envelope, the oceans and seas, which piles up in the part

beneath the Moon. This excess of water there produces a tide.

At the same time the part away from the Moon, with the 97 per cent pull, may be considered to tend to be left behind to some extent, so that there is high water there too. Two high tides on opposite sides of the Earth may thus be expected and there are corresponding low tides at the two intermediate places.

As the Earth rotates on its axis once a day, each part passes through the regions of high water twice, and thus experiences two tides.

The Sun produces tides in exactly the same way but in this case, although the total gravitational pull is considerably greater than with the Moon, the differences between the pull at the near, mean and far points are less than in the case of the Moon, and the solar tides are less than the lunar ones.

The two combine together, and when the Sun, Moon and Earth are in line, as is the case at full and no Moon, the tides add to produce large ones termed *spring tides*. When Sun, Earth, Moon form a right-angle, as at the first and last quarters, the two types of tide are out of phase. They subtract from one another and only small tides are produced. These are *neap tides*. Spring tides occur every fort-night, with neaps in the intervening weeks. The word 'spring' has no reference to the season.

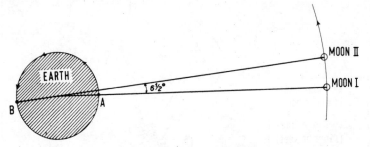

Fig. 344. The daily recession of tides

Because the Moon revolves round the Earth (actually round the centre of mass of the Earth–Moon system, which is about 1,000 miles (1,600 km) below the surface of the Earth on the line joining the centre of the Earth and the Moon) once a lunar month, that is in about 27 days 7¾ hours, successive lunar tides are about 12 hours 26 minutes apart, and not precisely 12 hours. Figure 344 makes this additional 26 minutes clear. From the time when a particular locality was at A, to the time when it reaches the position of the next high water at B, the Moon has moved from position I to position II. This is through an angle of about $6\frac{1}{2}°$, and it takes the Earth the 26 minutes to do this additional rotation.

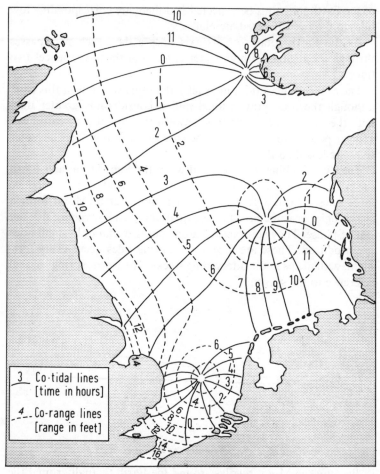

Fig. 345. North Sea tides

This *recession* in the time of tide makes high water about six hours later each week. It is often useful to know that, as a rough approximation, it will be high tide next week at the same time as it was low this week.

The above are some of the old ideas regarding tides, and although they are now proved to require some modifications, since they would require a continuous envelope of water uninterrupted by land masses, and also water much deeper than the oceans actually are, nevertheless they cannot be entirely discarded. It certainly is the Moon and the Sun which provide the generating forces described, and it is the relative positions of Moon, Earth and Sun which determine the occurrence of spring and neap tides, but the link between them and what has been found actually to happen is not so far known. Recent detailed surveys of actual tides at sea have revealed that they are in fact *rotational*.

The solid lines on Fig. 345 numbered 0 to 11 show the position of the *tidal wave* hour by hour as it rotates round the centre, which is known as an *amphidromic point*. Diametrically opposite to the high water radius is the low water radius, and these two sweep round and round the amphidromic point twice a day. As with waves at sea, one must remember that it is the sea surface contours which rotate, and only so much water moves as is necessary to produce the effect.

The broken circular lines numbered 4, 8, 12, etc. outwards from the centres, indicate the height of the tide in feet on a day midway between springs and neaps. It will be seen that there is no tide at all at the amphidromic points and that the tidal range increases as the locality is farther and farther away from them.

There are three tidal systems or *cells* in the North Sea, and Figs. 346 and 347 show the tides of the English Channel and of St George's Channel and the Irish Sea. In both these instances, it is to be noted that the amphidromic point is on land, and in such cases the movement is more complex. Land-bound amphidromic points are said to be *degenerate*. From these diagrams it is easy to see why there are very small tides on the southwest Norwegian coast and large ones between Dieppe and Boulogne, as well as on the east coast of the Irish Sea.

The spoke diagrams of Figs. 345, 346 and 347 have been marked as though the tide repeated every twelve hours. Since in fact it does so, as already explained, in about 12 hours 26 minutes, the twelve 'spokes' should correctly be labelled: 0 hr, 1 hr 2 min, 2 hr 4 min, 3 hr 6 min, and so on, with fractions of minutes also. They have been labelled 1, 2, 3, etc., to simplify the diagrams.

These maps make it quite clear that with the rotary movement there will be no accordance between the time of high water at a particular place and the passage of the Moon through that meridian. There is, however, a more or less constant difference between the two and this is known as the *tidal constant*. In the case of the British Isles,

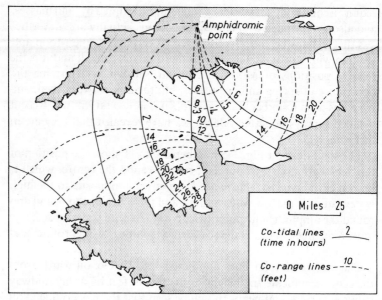

Fig. 346. English Channel tides

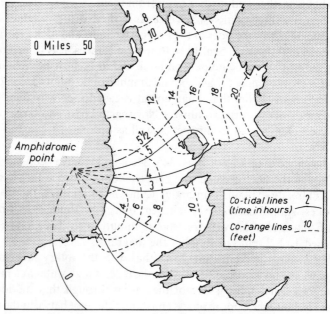

Fig. 347. Irish Sea tides

it is customary to print a tide table for a particular calendar period relating to the times of high water at Dover or some standard port. Lists of additions or subtractions are then supplied which must be used to obtain the time of high water at any other locality around the coast. For example, high water at Penzance is approximately 6 hours 25 minutes earlier than at Dover, and this is termed the tidal constant.

Another useful way to calculate the time of local high water dispenses entirely with printed tide tables. It is necessary to know at what time locally it is high water at full and no moon, or, as the seaman calls it, at *full and change*. Again taking Penzance, this time is 0430 hours. If therefore you wish to know the time of high water at Penzance in the morning three days after full Moon, it will be approximately 0430 hours + 52 × 3 minutes = 0706 hours. This will only be roughly correct, but it is sufficient for most usual purposes. For this method, it is only necessary to have a diary which gives the days of full moon and change.

Whilst discussing tide tables, it may be as well to point out that the *height* of the tide given in the table is the contour to which the water-level will reach, reckoned above a local (and not Ordnance) datum. This is known as the *bay* or *port datum* and is usually at about low water spring tide-level. It is different for different ports. The heights given for different harbours are therefore not comparable with one another until they have been adjusted for any difference there may be between their two datums.

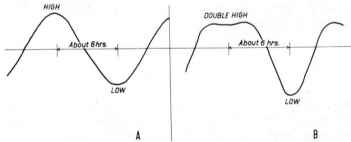

Fig. 348. a – A simple tidal form; b – The double high water at Southampton

TYPES OF TIDE

In open, straight coasts with regular increase of water depth seawards, the pattern of the rise and fall of water-level as time passes may well be a simple sine curve as is shown in Fig. 348A. There are, however, all kinds of shapes of curve for different localities. In some, the level rises quickly and ebbs slowly. In others the first part of the rise may be more rapid than the later part, and it may even be, as in the case of Southampton (Fig. 348B), that the high water begins to ebb, then reverses and flows again to a second high, before it finally falls to a single low.

At one time it was thought that this was connected with the idea that one tidal wave approached Southampton up the Solent and another, coming later, used the Spithead route. The fact that at Weymouth, where there is no isolated island to make this kind of pattern possible, there is a single high peak and a double low, discounted the Southampton explanation. In all such examples, the modifications of the simple curve are the result of the configuration of the local sea floor and of the adjoining coasts, both of which have their effects on the tidal flow.

Funnel-shaped estuaries concentrate the approaching tidal waters in narrowing channels, with the result that the height of the tide is considerably increased. This is the cause of the very great tidal range in the Bristol Channel and some other similarly shaped estuaries. In many of these, too, retardation on the sea bottom causes a steepening of the tidal wave, at least during some part of the flow, and this sudden change of level as the tide progresses up-estuary is known as a *bore*. It is also influenced by the fact that the in-flowing tide meets the out-flowing river.

Tidal currents of considerable power are set up in narrow straits and some other coastal patterns, and examples of these have been described in Chapter 25.

STORM SURGES

Particular weather conditions may have a considerable effect upon the sea-level. Strong onshore winds tend to pile up the water near the coast. A low barometric height over one part of a sea coincident with high pressure over another part may also produce a difference in sea-level. Such abnormal increases in sea-level are known as *storm surges,* and the precise circumstances required to cause them depend upon the peculiarities of the neighbourhood, and each area has to be studied individually.

Storm surges from 3 to 6 feet (1 to 2 metres) in height are fairly common, but they pass unnoticed, excepting by those directly concerned with shipping, unless they happen to coincide with high water of a particularly high tide. Then, the additional few feet in level, accompanied as it generally is by powerful waves, results in very considerable erosion and flooding of low-lying coastal land. Whether or not the surge comes at the same time as high water is almost pure chance, but it was this coincidence which resulted in the great damage along the east coast of England and the south coast of the North Sea in February 1953. On that occasion, the sea embankments of the Netherlands were breached in numerous places and 600 sq miles (1,500 sq km) of land were temporarily flooded. In southeastern England, the sea flooded marshland in the Foulness district for as far as 10 miles (16 km) inland, and caused great damage to many miles of coastal cliffs and property.

TSUNAMIS

Submarine earthquakes or volcanic eruptions may produce surface waves in the ocean which, although only 3 feet (1 metre) or so in height when over deep water, travel with great speeds, varying from 100 to 700 miles (150 to 1,100 km) per hour according to the water depth. When they pass into shallow water, they greatly increase in height, so that on reaching the coast they may cause a momentary rise of as much as 100 feet (30 metres) in sea-level in bays and estuaries. This naturally results in great damage, and the very sudden nature of their arrival often gives no time for the inhabitants to flee to higher ground. Many deaths from drowning occur in such circumstances.

The waves are termed *tsunamis,* and the description *tidal wave,* which is sometimes given to them, should be avoided, since they have no connection with tides. They may travel for more than 1,000 miles (1,600 km) across the ocean from the earthquake that produced them without losing much of their height.

Part Six

Volcanoes and Vulcanism

CHAPTER THIRTY-TWO

Vulcanic Landforms

IF the Earth were devoid of atmosphere, and consequently almost certainly without oceans or seas, most of the effects described in the preceding chapters (12 to 31) would be non-existent, and the only landforms would be tectonic and extrusive vulcanic ones. The former, such as fault scarps, anticlinal ridges and synclinal valleys, are generally so modified by fluvial or other processes that several of the simpler types have been described already in Chapter 17.

Vulcanic or *igneous landforms* result from heated materials or *magma* moving in the Earth's crust, most often in a liquid or even a gaseous state. Internal pressure may be sufficient to make them reach the surface before solidification and so produce *volcanic* or *extrusive vulcanic forms,* or they may move more slowly and have time to solidify whilst still covered by other rocks and become *plutonic* or *intrusive vulcanic features.* Note that the word *vulcanic* applies both to *volcanic* (= surface cooled) and *plutonic* (= sub-surface cooled) rocks.

Vulcanism has been active throughout geologic time, but especially so in periods of major tectonic activity such as during the Caledonian orogeny. Extrusive rocks of such periods have been so modified by weathering and erosion that they now reveal but little of their vulcanic origin so far as relief features are concerned, excepting that they may have proved to be more resistant to erosion than their neighbours and so are now upstanding areas, such as the Borrowdale Volcanic Series of the central, higher part of the English Lake District. On the other hand, and this particularly applies to plutonic rocks which have become exposed, they may turn out to be easily eroded and weathered and thus lead to low ground.

Intrusive rocks, being beneath ground, naturally do not produce landforms, unless they deform the surface due to the additional subterranean volume, or until the pre-existing rocks which lay above them have been removed by erosion, so that the intrusive rocks become surface ones. Then they will produce landforms in much the same way as do extrusive rocks, and some of the various types will be described.

429

Nevertheless, the relicts of ancient vulcanic forms have usually so acquired the general characteristics of other rocks of similar age that their forms display the result of weathering and erosion, rather than of their special origin, and as such they have already been described in the preceding chapters.

This chapter is mostly concerned with the constructional forms of younger vulcanic rocks, and it pays but little attention to the sub-terranean forces and conditions which have led to their formation – that is a subject which belongs more to geology.

Fig. 349. The areas covered by flood lavas in the Columbia and Snake river basins

PLATEAU OR FLOOD LAVAS

The most obvious extrusive vulcanic form is the *volcano* itself, where rock has been extruded from the interior through a more or less circular *vent*. When the eruption occurs along a *fissure* of considerable length, large areas may be covered by widespread sheets of lava without building up an actual cone. In all these cases, the lava was poured out as a liquid probably at a temperature of about 1,100°C (2,000°F), and being quite fluid it spread over large areas before solidification brought it to rest.

These *plateau* or *flood lavas* form very extensive areas of gently rolling topography not always of very great altitude. The north-western Deccan is the largest, and covers nearly three-quarters of a million sq miles (approaching 2 million sq km); the Columbia and

Snake river areas of U.S.A. cover 300,000 sq miles (nearly 800,000 sq km) (Fig. 349); and the Parana basin is another area of flood basalts, extending to nearly a quarter of a million sq miles (more than half a million sq km). As compared with these the largest area of such basalts in Britain, the Antrim Plateau, covers a mere 800 sq miles (2,000 sq km), although one must remember that this is only a remnant of a much more widespread flow whose relics are now to be found in western Scotland, Iceland and Greenland.

The various plateaux listed are composite in form, comprising a large number of sheets of lava of slightly different date one above the other. This is illustrated in Fig. 307, where layers of lateritic weathered basalt separate the individual flows. The age of this particular extrusion is Tertiary, but the others which have been named vary from Precambrian to Miocene or even later, the Deccan being of Eocene age.

VOLCANOES

When basaltic lava issues from a more or less circular hole or *vent,* the successive flows gradually build up a volcanic cone, which is, however, of very gentle slope. It is often termed a *lava shield* from the shape of the round military shields of historic time.

This basalt is a basic lava, and Mauna Loa, Hawaii (Fig. 338), is an example of a lava shield. As already stated (p. 408), Mauna Loa is the world's highest mountain in the sense that its summit is 31,000 feet (9,400 metres) above the level of its base on the ocean floor. The diameter of this base is more than 300 miles (nearly 500 km), giving the gentle mean gradient for its slope of approximately one in thirty – clearly indicative of the originally highly fluid nature of the lava of which it is composed.

VOLCANIC CONES

Cinder or *ash cones* are a rather commoner type of volcano. These result from the material being ejected from the vent with considerable vigour and thrown high into the air. As it falls back around the vent it gradually builds up the typical volcanic cone.

The general name given to pieces of solid material thrown into the air during an eruption is *pyroclast,* and a mass of such material still unconsolidated and not containing what might be termed second-hand rocks from the break-up of rocks from previous eruptions or from the countryside rock is termed *tephra.*

Tephric material is given various names according to the size of the fragments. The finest particles are *dust*, the next are *ash*, small stones up to a little more than an inch in diameter are *lapilli,* and larger ones are *blocks*. If they were ejected from the vent in a molten condition, they probably partly solidified whilst in the air and are more or less rounded. These are *bombs*.

When a previously dormant volcano erupts, the sequence of events is often as follows, although there are many variants. First there are rumbling noises underground with some slight earthquake effects. Then, as the plug of cooled and shrunken lava which has been filling the old vent within the crater is gradually melted off from below, and as internal pressure builds up, cracks may appear from which gases may pour forth. Soon the plug is blown out in a shattered but solid form, and this is generally the source of the dust, ash, lapilli and blocks. It is after this stage that the molten lava appears. This pours over the rim of the crater, and, flowing down the slopes of the cone that has been produced by previous eruptions, converts the solids, which have already fallen, into solid rock. Whilst the temperature remains sufficiently high, a mixture of molten lava and the solid fragments may slowly move down the side of the cone as *block lava* or *aa* (Fig. 350).

Fig. 350. Block lava around Vesuvius

Fig. 351. Ropy lava on the flanks of Vesuvius

When volcanic dust and ash are thus consolidated, the resulting rock is *tuff*; lapilli and bombs form *agglomerate*; and blocks form *breccia*. When the material is vesicular, it is variously known as *cinders, pumice* or *scoria*.

Lava without blocks is known as *ropy lava* or *pahoehoe* (Fig. 351), whilst if it solidifies quickly by being cooled beneath water, it becomes *pillow lava*.

Due to the succession of events repeated for each of the many eruptions that have built a single cone with lava alternating with ash, lapilli, bombs and blocks, most cones form *composite volcanoes*.

Two cone-shaped volcanoes are shown in Figs. 352 and 353. The former, Fuego Volcano of Guatemala, rises to 12,600 feet (3,840 metres) in a single steep-sided cone consisting largely of ash, lapilli and bombs. The steep gradient of about 40°, or 1 in $1\frac{1}{4}$, is the angle of rest of this material (contrast this with Mauna Loa). The crater has been ruptured on the near side and lava appears to have flowed over the lip. This volcano is similar in form to the extinct Mount Demavend of Iran (Fig. 353). This reaches a height of 18,600 feet (5,670 metres), and is situated in the Elburz Mountains whose general summit level is considerably less. Being extinct, Demavend has experienced some gullying and other forms of erosion, largely due to

Fig. 352. The shattered cone of Fuego Volcano, Guatemala

the fact that at this latitude and height the temperature is sufficiently cool to permit snow to lie on the mountain. There are even two or three small glaciers. This is thus a good example of the first effects of erosion on an originally smooth-sloped conical mound. Its general slope is 25°, or about 1 in $2\frac{1}{4}$.

Both these volcanoes have simple cones, and this type only occurs when successive eruptions break through at the same vent and thus produce a single crater. It very often happens that it is easier for the internal pressure to be relieved by way of a fissure or hole through the side of the existing cone. In this case, a subsidiary cone is built up and such volcanoes are *compound.*

Another type is the *caldera,* which is a ruin of a volcano after an explosive eruption has shattered and largely blown away the pre-existing cone. Within this ruin, new cones are built up, which in their turn may be partially destroyed by later explosions, so that the whole mountain becomes a complex mass of remnants within which the presentday cone is often a seemingly small affair. The most famous of this type is Vesuvius, which blew up in A.D. 79, leaving only a fraction of the old cone, now known as Monte Somma. Numerous eruptions have since built a new cone within the old remains, as is seen in Fig. 354.

Fig. 353. *The snow and ice-clad, and partly weathered, cone of Demavend Volcano, Iran*

Fig. 354. *Vesuvius – the newer cone within the older*

DISTRIBUTION OF VOLCANOES

Vulcanic rocks are to be found in most parts of the world. Their formation is associated particularly with mountain-building and in the past there has been much activity of this kind even in areas now completely free from vulcanism.

There are perhaps 600 volcanoes which either are still *active* or have been dormant for insufficient time to merit classification as *extinct*. There are about 180 on the Asiatic side of the Pacific Ocean and 130 on the American side. There are nearly 100 on the Indonesian arc stretching from New Zealand to the Banda Sea. There has been a scatter of submarine eruptions along the central ridge of the Atlantic Ocean and in Europe they are mainly confined to the Italian examples.

During the last few years several entirely new volcanoes have come into existence. Paricutin began as an open crack in a field which was actually being ploughed at the time in February 1943. Within eighteen hours it reached a height of 120 feet (37 metres). The eruption continued more or less without interruption for nine years by which time the cone had reached 1,300 feet (400 metres) above the original ground level and an area of about 3 miles diameter (5 km) had been covered by lava.

Barcena Volcano on San Benedicto island, Mexico, came into existence in August 1952, reached 1,000 feet (300 metres) within a fortnight, and continued to be active for seven months.

In November 1963, a new island appeared off the south coast of Iceland. This has since been named Surtsey and what at first was a narrow ridge became a 500-foot (150-metre) high cone within a month. This was composed of pyroclastic ashes, cinders and bombs, but six months after its first appearance above water fluid lava began to flow and produce a lava shield of the Mauna Loa type.

VOLCANIC NECKS

When a volcano becomes extinct or at least quiescent, it is subject to the usual agents of weathering and erosion. If the cone is mainly composed of ash and cinder, its porous nature causes rain to be absorbed within the mass, and there is little or no surface run-off. This greatly delays the development of erosional features, but some have already been seen in Fig. 353.

Because of the essential difference of the central core of the volcano from the bulk of the cone itself, it very often happens that eventually the whole, or almost the whole, of the cone may be re-

Fig. 355. The gently rounded Puy du Dôme area

moved by erosion, leaving only the *neck* or *plug,* the old crater infill, upstanding as a steep-sided circular pinnacle. Part of the Massif Central of France is a particularly interesting area from the vulcanic point of view. There are the crystalline granites and other rocks of Livradois and Forez, much of which forms a fairly level top surface at about 3,000 feet (900 metres), although occasionally it rises to 5,000 feet (1,500 metres); the volcanic area of Les Puys forms a second district of extinct, but geologically recent, lava and ash cones which are now severely eroded. Some of these were originally as large as Vesuvius and Etna (Mounts Dore and Cantal, which still rise to 6,188 feet (1,886 metres) and 6,096 feet (1,858 metres)), and the gently rounded Puy de Dôme, 4,806 feet (1,465 metres) (Fig. 355), composed of viscous trachyte lava. Finally there is the remarkable group of small rock pinnacles which rise a few hundred feet above the general ground level and are almost certainly the resistant plugs of small volcanoes, whose cones have been removed by erosion. One of these at Le Puy en Velay, Haute Loire, is shown in Fig. 356.

Edinburgh and Stirling Castles are on somewhat similar volcanic plugs, and when they occur at the coastline, it often happens that they form small promontories such as the succession which mark the eastern terminations of the series of shingle and sand beaches of the north coast of Cardigan Bay (Fig. 357).

INTRUSIVE FEATURES – DYKES AND SILLS

Intrusive vulcanic features include dykes and sills. Both of these are relatively thin formations as compared with their lateral extent.

A *dyke* may be vertical or it may slope upwards at a fairly steep angle. Since it transgresses the strata of the rock through which it passes, it is a discordant feature. On the other hand, a *sill* is often more or less horizontal, and always lies between individual strata of the bedrock, although still it transgresses occasionally from one bed to another. A sill is thus mostly a concordant feature.

Dykes may feed volcanoes with lava, or they may supply molten rock to the intrusive masses which are described below. Dykes also frequently radiate from volcanoes, since it may be easier for the magma to move through the surrounding rock and find an alternative route to the surface instead of forcing its way through the old vent. The well-known dyke swarm which radiates out from the islands of Skye and Rhum falls into this category.

Fig. 356. La Roche de l'Aiguilhe at Le Puy

Dykes may branch or join. They often die without ever having broken through to the surface. Their thickness may vary from a few inches to several tens of feet.

When they are exposed by erosion of the rock above them, dykes sometimes form upstanding features and sometimes trenches. This variation is not always a measure of the relative resistance to erosion

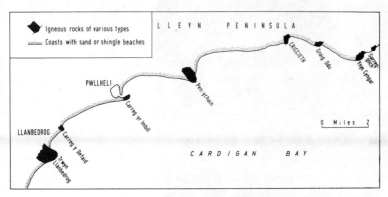

Fig. 357. Headlands resulting from resistant igneous intrusions on the Lleyn Peninsula, north Wales

offered by the dyke and the bedrock, but is often the result of contact metamorphism by baking the layer of bedrock on either side of the dyke when the magma was intruded. This metamorphosed rock is thus cracked or otherwise made readily susceptible to erosion. When it has been removed, the dyke, being flanked by two thin gaps, is attacked from both sides and may be destroyed so as to form a trench. Figure 358 shows a vertical dyke about 3 feet thick on the Northumberland coast at Howick. In the foreground it forms a trench, but farther away it is a wall about 5 feet in height.

A *sill* may extend laterally for many miles, and may vary very greatly in thickness. It is formed when the molten rock, forcing its way upwards, finds that it is easier to lift the weight of the sedimentary rocks which lie above than the column of its own material. The magma then forces its way between two strata and so a sill is formed.

One of the best known is the Whin Sill of Northern England. This now outcrops along much of the coast between Holy Island and Alnwick, Northumberland, and then swings westwards in two discontinuous lines right across the Pennines. It outcrops in the escarpment to the west of Cross Fell, and then passes eastwards again just south of Durham. In places it is two sills, one above the other. It has

Fig. 358.
Dyke forming both trench and
wall on beach at Howick,
Northumberland

Fig. 359. An outcrop of Whin sill surmounted by Hadrian's Wall

formed several caprock waterfalls, such as High Force, at Middle-
ton-in-Teesdale. Figure 359 shows part of the east–west outcrop,
which forms an escarpmentlike feature facing north, and was utilised
by the Romans when they were building their defence wall.

LACCOLITHS AND LOPOLITHS

The occurrence of a sill with so large an area as compared with its
thickness implies that the material was in a very fluid state when it
was intruded, and thus shows its basic nature. This is confirmed by
its usual dark colour. When the magma is rich in silica and thus
more viscous, it is easier for the intrusion to dome up the strata
which overlie it, than to spread very far laterally. Such conditions
lead to the formation of laccoliths and lopoliths (Fig. 360).

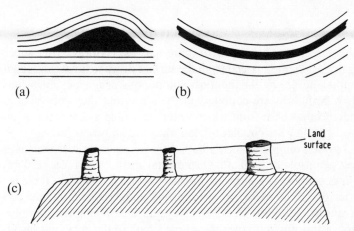

*Fig. 360. Diagrammatic representations of (a) laccolith, (b) lopolith
and (c) batholith*

A *laccolith* arches up the overlying rock and thus immediately
produces a domelike feature long before later erosion has been able
to expose the igneous intrusion itself. Very often the presence of a
laccolith may only be inferred when it remains covered with sedimentary rocks, and even when its upper surface is exposed, a laccolith is still very difficult to identify with certainty. It is thought that
most of these intrusions were supplied with their material from one
side rather than from directly beneath, for they often occur in groups
more or less encircling a batholith (see below). The only closely
studied laccoliths occur in the Colorado Plateau, where they vary
from 1 to 5 miles in diameter.

P

Lopoliths must occur in places where the crust is more critically balanced, or they must be of greater mass than laccoliths, for they have the effect of producing a saucer-shaped depression in the strata amongst which they lie. Figure 360 shows diagrammatically the difference between the two types of intrusion.

When erosion has partially removed the rock from above a lopolith, the first effect is for a circular outcrop of the intruded material to appear. This is not usually simple, and is known as a *ring-complex*. It is thought that most lopoliths are multiple, comprising a kind of nest of lopoliths, one above the other with layers of the bedrock between each. The best known are near Duluth, extending for 120 miles (190 km) from the southwestern limb of Lake Superior. The largest is the bushveld complex of the Transvaal.

BATHOLITHS

Batholiths (also spelt *bathyliths*) are massive features. After superficial erosion, they extend from the surface down to great (unknown) depths and are by far the most voluminous of igneous intrusions. Most batholiths are complex, in the sense that they consist of an underground base from which columns, called *stocks*, stretch upwards. If they are circular in plan, they are known as *bosses*.

As one example of such a batholith, we may consider the southwest peninsula of England. Over a total span of 136 miles (220 km) in a general west–southwest to east–northeast direction, there is a series of seven stocks rising from one immense, continuous, subterranean batholith. Gravity surveys have demonstrated the presence of this intrusion over the whole length of the area, and each of the stocks which reaches the surface rises with almost vertical sides from the base to outcrop as an oval or circular high area, generally moorland, of granite rock. The seven stocks in order from west to east are detailed in Fig. 361. Note the general way in which both the maximum height and the dimensions increase eastwards.

Not all batholiths are multiple in this way, but whether they outcrop as a single large area, or as a series of stocks, the rock is either a granite or of a granitic type. This, coupled with the fact that they usually form ground which is higher than the surroundings, impermeable and of irregular contour, produces ill-drained moorland with typical vegetation and economic poverty. The Isles of Scilly, famous for their cultivation, are exceptional in this way on account of their low elevation and special climate.

	Maximum height		Dimensions		(Separation) (centre to centre)	
	Feet	Metres	Miles	Kms	Miles	Kms
Isles of Scilly	136	41	5 × 11	8 × 18		
					38	61
St Just, Land's End nearly to St Ives	780	238	5 × 15	8 × 24		
					11	18
Tregonning, between Marazion and Helston	635	194	2 × 3½	3 × 6		
					8	13
Carnmenellis, west of Falmouth	819	250	6 × 8	10 × 13		
					24	39
Hensbarrow, north of St Austell	1026	312	4 × 10	6 × 16		
					16	26
Bodmin Moor	1375	419	8 × 12	13 × 19		
					29	47
Dartmoor	2039	621	14 × 20	23 × 32		

Fig. 361. Granite stocks of southwest England

HOT SPRINGS AND GEYSERS

Hot springs and geysers are not entirely unrelated to vulcanism, for again the heat comes from the interior. *Hot springs* chiefly occur in areas where there is presentday volcanic activity. The most famous areas are New Zealand, Iceland and Yellowstone Park, Wyoming. In all these, the water appears to be mostly what has fallen as rain or snow (= *meteoric water*) and soaked into the ground to a considerable depth. There it has come into contact with heated rock and so been warmed before reappearing as a spring. Water may also be produced from deep-seated igneous rocks. This is known as *juvenile water* and may be added to the meteoric water. Juvenile water is normally at a high temperature, and thus may supply part of the heat.

The temperature of the water issuing from a hot spring varies greatly in the different cases, and may be anything from nearly boiling to, for example, the 48°C (120°F) water which issues from the hot springs at Bath, England. The latter is an illustration of the fact that hot springs may occur in localities which are not at present volcanic. At Bath the water is used for therapeutic purposes, and in many of the other instances it is piped to local towns for central heating, warmed swimming baths and so on. Generally the water from hot springs is rich in dissolved minerals, especially calcium bicarbonate, which is deposited as calcium carbonate or *travertine* around the mouth. This material in solution renders such waters

Fig. 362.
Old Faithful geyser
in ejection

unsuitable for domestic water-supply. In New Zealand the water from a spring at Wairakei is used in an electricity power station.

Geysers are hot springs which have an explosive, intermittent flow. The old theory, that the water was suddenly driven out of the more or less vertical supply pipe by the formation of superheated steam below, has now been replaced by one which suggests that the cause is more a reduction of pressure near the top of the column by the replacement of some of the water by large bubbles formed from the dissolved gases in the water. These become saturated with water vapour and, because of their high temperature, remove considerable quantities of water. This overflows as a mass of bubbles at the top of the pipe, the pressure at depth is thus reduced, which causes the water there to 'flash' into steam and so expel the remainder of the column. The fount may be high, often of the order of 200 feet (60 metres).

The time taken for the repetition of this process is often fairly constant for a particular geyser, and Old Faithful, Yellowstone National Park, for example, ejects its water roughly once an hour for a duration of about five minutes each time (Fig. 362).

Part Seven

Soils and Natural Vegetation

CHAPTER THIRTY-THREE

Soil and Soils

SOIL is the result of continued further development of the regolith. It differs from the latter in any of several different ways, as will be described, and is distinguished from it by forming a distinct layer above it. This layer of soil may be a single one, or may be divisible into up to four separate subdivisions, each known as a *soil horizon*. The soil forms the basis upon which all vegetation finds its abode.

GENETIC TYPES OF REGOLITH

There are at least seven major, genetically different types of regolith. The broken up bedrock may be of volcanic origin, the result of weathering, or it may be an alluvial, lacustrine, marine, aeolian or glacial deposit. Each of these types of residue has been described in some detail in the preceding chapters and only a few brief comments are necessary here, before passing on to their further development into soil.

Regolith directly of *volcanic* origin is primarily volcanic ash (see p. 432), for this is the only volcanic deposit which is likely to be initially in a fragmented state. Lava and other volcanic deposits are in general in large solid masses, and when broken into regolith this occurs by the normal processes of weathering, and thus belongs to this latter type. It so happens that volcanic ash deposits are often particularly fertile, with the result that the flanks of many volcanoes are cultivated and occupied, with great danger to the inhabitants if the volcano is a still active one. On numerous occasions in history there has been great loss of life when such a volcano has burst into life so quickly that those living on its lower slopes have not had time to flee. Pompeii is the best known example of this. It is estimated that several thousand perished in this eruption of Vesuvius in A.D. 79.

The products of *weathering,* whether physical or chemical, have already been described in Chapter 12. They may be of very varied size from several feet across (see Fig. 63) to much smaller pieces as are seen in Fig. 71, where disintegration has proceeded much further.

DIAMETER RANGE

	British	Metric
Boulders	greater than 10 inches	greater than 25 cm
Cobbles	10 to 3 inches	25 to 7·5 cm
Gravel	3 to 1/12th inches	75 to 2 millimetres
Sand	1/12th to 1/1000th inch	2 to 0·02 mm
Silt	1/1000th to 1/10,000th inch	0·02 to 0·002 mm
Clay	less than 1/10,000th inch	less than 0·002 mm

Fig. 363. Limiting sizes of different types of particles

The remaining types of regolith are all characterised by the general description of *deposit,* and this implies that they have been transported by some means or other from their place of origin to the site where they now lie. The nature of the transporter is indicated by the five adjectives which are used to distinguish them. These again have all been fully described in their appropriate chapters, and there may often be great variations within each type.

Alluvial and marine deposits may consist of particles of a wide range of size. *Alluvial deposits* generally contain few or no particles in the silt and clay range – they are mainly sand and gravel, generally well sorted and stratified. *Lacustrine deposits,* whilst containing particles of larger size, often include a very high proportion of the finer calibre material. *Marine deposits* may be sand, shingle or mud; *aeolian* are almost exclusively sand; and *glacial deposits* are very variable, but, unless they belong to the intermediate type of fluvioglacial deposits, normally contain a considerable proportion of clay. They are unsorted and boulders within them may be of any size, and may be scattered quite irregularly through the thickness.

Besides differences in calibre, the varying modes of deposition lead to differences in compaction, orientation of individual particles, degree of mixing of the various sizes and so on. These all have a most important effect on the physical characteristics of the resulting regolith.

PHYSICAL NATURE OF THE REGOLITH

The size of the particles of which the regolith is composed is of the first importance in connection with plant growth. The texture determines to a great extent the ease with which rainwater may drain through, and also the ease with which plant roots may penetrate. Apart from gravelly material, *sand* produces a regolith which drains well and thus rarely becomes waterlogged. On the other hand, it does not hold much moisture and quickly becomes very dry in times of drought. Plants growing on sand suffer from great changes in the day to day moisture condition of their soil, and very often therefore must be of drought-resisting species, even in an area of considerable rainfall.

On the other hand, *clay* is composed of such small particles that rainwater has the greatest difficulty in passing through. It therefore often becomes a very wet, sticky mass, whose moisture incidentally is so firmly held by the individual particles that plants often have difficulty in securing it for themselves. It contains little air and thus cannot provide these requirements for the plant roots. If it does dry out it becomes a very hard mass which often strangulates the plant roots within it. It also at the same time opens up in a number of cracks at the surface (see Fig. 68), which permit the entry of many undesirable elements.

Silt lies between sand and clay as regards size (Fig. 363), and consequently produces a regolith which has intermediate qualities between the two. It combines many of the advantages of both.

Loam is the ideal type of regolith from the point of view of vegetational growth. It consists of a mixture of sand, silt and clay, so that the clay holds moisture and the sand prevents undue clogging. This forms a permeable, easily worked mixture and is the type of regolith which a farmer desires to possess. By definition, it comprises not more than 50 per cent sand, not more than 30 per cent clay and between 25 and 50 per cent silt.

These individual particles have a tendency to build themselves up into groups of particles more or less firmly held together and so produce a *structure*. It is a well-known fact that when digging soil, an individual clod, when tossed to the ground, will break up into smaller pieces which are characteristic of the particular soil. When these are irregular with fairly sharp corners, the soil is said to have *block structure*. If the pieces are more or less rounded, and generally fairly small, it is said to be *granular* or to have a *crumb structure*. This is the structure most favoured by the farmer. Other shapes belong to *platy, prismatic* and *columnar structure*. All these affect the water-holding powers of the material and its ease of working.

P 2

CHEMICAL NATURE OF THE REGOLITH

The *chemical nature* of the solid rock from which the regolith was derived is of less importance than would be expected, for there is a strong tendency for its development to equalise any differences which may have originally existed. Any soluble minerals in the bed-rock are very soon removed in solution by ground-water slowly making its way through the mass. More will be said of this process in the section on soil profile, but it is this fact that results in the final state of the fully developed regolith being much more dependent upon climatic conditions than upon the chemical constitution of the rock from which it was formed. This is not to say, of course, that bedrock and lithology are of no significance, but they dominate to a much less degree than might have been anticipated.

Some minerals in rocks are in the form of oxides or carbonates (the latter constituting limestones and chalk), but by far the majority are complex aluminium or iron silicates of calcium, magnesium, potassium or sodium. There are a large number of varieties of these, but most will react chemically with water by the processes known as *hydrolysis* and *carbonation* (see p. 108), to form soluble substances such as hydroxides, carbonates and bicarbonates. This is important since the soil-water may then easily remove them (see below).

Not only do these reactions alter the chemical constitution of the regolith and thus make its components available or not available to plants which may be living upon it, they also alter the degree of acidity, and this is of first importance to plant health.

Acidity is increased by the replacement of some of the metallic parts of the compounds by hydrogen derived from the carbonic acid which is contained in rainwater. It is measured by the *hydrogen-ion concentration,* which is expressed by a logarithmic scale with the prefix *p*H. A value *p*H 7 indicates a neutral soil – neither acid nor basic. A smaller number than 7 indicates that the soil is acid, whilst a larger number signifies alkalinity. A soil of *p*H 5 is strongly acid, and different species of plant flourish best in soils of differing degrees of acidity. Some require an alkali soil.

When a soil becomes almost waterlogged and there is thus a shortage of air within it, oxidation is impeded and the iron compounds are deposited in the ferrous (instead of ferric) condition, with the result that the soil acquires a bluish-grey colour. This is called a *gley soil,* and is common in poorly drained parts of Britain, such as low-lying meadows and bogs.

The presence of organic matter within the soil naturally affects its chemical nature, and this forms the subject of the next section.

ORGANIC MATTER WITHIN THE SOIL

The regolith reaches its first stage in becoming a soil when humus is added to it. Plants die and fall to the ground. Decay is normally rapid. This is accomplished by a variety of soil organisms which include bacteria, actinomycetes, fungi, algae and protozoa. This list names them roughly in order of size, and all are able to make use of the dead vegetation and convert it into soluble organic compounds of various kinds. Little is understood concerning the chemistry of these organic materials, but their presence is one of the essential factors for flourishing plant growth.

Nitrogen also is of fundamental importance, and it may be obtained directly from the air (and converted into soluble nitrogen compounds that are available to plants) by certain bacteria, especially those which live within the nodules that are developed on the roots of the leguminous (pea) family.

Besides the obvious importance of the chemical processes they carry out, these various micro-organisms are of great value in producing a sort of network of filaments which envelop the various particles of soil and hold them together in aggregates to produce the crumb and other structures which have already been described (see p. 449).

The decayed organic material is termed *humus,* and it is this which gives the common dark colour to many soils, it is this which maintains the productivity of a soil, and it is this which the farmer is most anxious to preserve. Fully decayed leaf humus is termed *mull.* This provides conditions favourable to plant nourishment and because it is generally inhabited by a large worm population, it is kept in a broken-up, aerated condition, which also increases its advantageous properties.

When the ground is wetter, becoming almost waterlogged, bacterial and other similar actions are slowed down so that much less decay occurs and an acid soil is produced, consisting of a surface layer which is almost entirely partly-decayed humus. This is known as *mor.*

In the extreme case when little or no decay occurs and there is a high moisture content, *peat* may be formed. There are two particular types. One is *fen peat,* which is black, amorphous, rich in proteins but with no cellulose, and is alkaline. The other is *bog peat,* which is very dark-brown colour. These differences are largely due to the differing water conditions which existed at the time of the peat formation, leading to the growth of different groups of plants. The fen peat consists mainly of grasses, sedges and rushes, whilst the bog peat contains large quantities of moss (often sphagnum moss).

WATER AND AIR IN THE SOIL

The effects of water within the soil may be regarded for convenience under two headings: water which is moving either downwards or upwards through the soil, and those properties of water which are dissociated from whatever movement it may have. It is the former which eventually produce the soil profile, the subject of the next section; and here we are concerned only with the results of the fact that water is or is not present.

From the vegetational point of view, the *water content* is most important, since plants can only absorb nutrients when they are in a dissolved condition. In other words, plants drink, but do not eat. The presence of water as a food carrier is therefore of vital importance. It is also important that it shall be present in good quantity, for the strength of the soil-water solution must be weaker than that of the fluid within the plants themselves, or the soil-water cannot enter. It does this by *osmosis,* the process by which fluids pass through semipermeable membranes, in this case the cell walls of the plant, at rates which are dependent upon the strength of the solutions (for a fuller account of this process, refer to textbooks of botany or of physical chemistry).

The amount of water within the soil is determined by the rate of supply and the rate at which the surplus can get away. There is also water which is adherent to the surface of each grain of soil like a skin. It is microscopically thin and very difficult to remove. The smaller the individual grains the larger the total surface they have, and thus the larger the amount of this type of soil-water. It is its presence which is largely responsible for the way in which clay soils cling to one another and may be moulded. It is this which makes clays heavy soils. The word *heavy* in this connotation more refers to the fact that it is not easy to dig or plough them (= 'heavy work'). They are sticky. It is difficult to part them with the blade of the working tool, and they cling to the tool when this has been done. These soils are also often actually heavier in weight compared with an equal volume of a *light soil,* such as sand.

Wet soils are more difficult to warm under the sun's rays in spring, for not only is there the additional water to heat up, but also more evaporation takes place on the surface than occurs with a dry soil, and this also leads to considerable cooling. Wet (clay) soils are thus *cold soils,* and this delays germination and slows growth, so that crops grown on such soils are generally later than others.

The pore spaces within the soil that are not occupied by water are filled with *air*. This is an important contributor to the wellbeing of the plants growing on the soil. The amount of air within the soil decreases with increased wetness, and especially with decrease in size of soil particle, which results in a much larger proportion of the spaces between these particles being filled with water. The air within the soil tends to become richer in carbon dioxide than atmospheric air, and *aeration,* that is the circulation of the air within the soil, is promoted by movement of soil-water, changes of temperature, and, to a lesser extent, by barometric changes. When the soil is saturated, there is naturally no remaining air, and conditions are then said to be *anaerobic*. This is very detrimental to plant health.

THE SOIL PROFILE

The vertical movement of water within the soil may be downwards or upwards. The former is the movement associated with normal drainage, and Chapter 15 has described the movement of underground water through the rocks themselves. The downward movement results in the partial or complete removal of the soluble constituents from the upper layer of soil. This is known as the *A horizon* (Fig. 364), and the process of this removal is known as *leaching*. An A horizon from which most of the soluble components have been so removed is said to be *leached*. There is a tendency for many of the chemicals removed from the top layer to be reprecipitated in the second layer, known as the *B horizon,* and this therefore is of considerable assistance to deep-rooted plants which can penetrate to it and so obtain nutriments which those with shallower roots cannot do.

This layer is followed by the C and D horizons. The *C horizon* is the zone of weathered parent rock with little or no additions from above. It therefore is purely mineral in content and provides the opportunity for further deepening of the A and B horizons as the soil develops. It is the regolith. The *D horizon* is the unbroken solid rock base.

Together these layers constitute the *soil profile* (Fig. 364). It is not necessary for all four horizons to be present. In more detailed work it is customary to subdivide at least the A horizon, and often the B horizon also.

The chemical deposition in the B horizon sometimes leads to the formation of a compact, usually impermeable, *pan layer,* often too hard for plant roots to penetrate. A high concentration of clay leads to a *clay-pan*; the presence of certain oxides, silica or calcium carbonate often leads to cementation which is known as *hard-pan*. If the hard-pan is principally due to cementation by calcium carbonate, it is often termed a *caliche*.

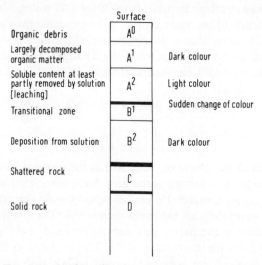

	Surface	
Organic debris	A⁰	
Largely decomposed organic matter	A¹	Dark colour
Soluble content at least partly removed by solution [leaching]	A²	Light colour
Transitional zone	B¹	Sudden change of colour
Deposition from solution	B²	Dark colour
Shattered rock	C	
Solid rock	D	

Fig. 364. Soil profile showing horizons A to D

These features result from downward movement of soil-water. When an area has a distinct dry season, especially when this is also the hot season, there is considerable upward movement of water due to capillarity resulting from evaporation of the surface moisture. The upward movement produces reverse effects to the downward, and evaporation of the water at the top surface especially results in complete precipitation of whatever soluble materials may be in it. Consequently a type of pan layer is formed on the surface. It is rich in soluble material, but is usually hard, and this influences plant growth considerably. Another name for this surface hard-pan is *duricrust,* and for it to occur the area must be almost perfectly flat, so that surface drainage cannot remove the soluble deposits. For the same reason, there must only be sufficient rainfall in the wet season to enable it to soak into the soil at that time, and put material into solution so that it may be returned to the surface during the subsequent drought when there is upward water movement.

Soils produced in this way are termed *latersols* or *laterites,* although the second has been employed in the past with a whole range of meanings and has fallen into some disrepute in consequence.

SOIL CLASSIFICATION

The nature of a soil is thus very complex and the various factors which tend to produce different types are very numerous. It is clear, however, that the nature of the underlying rock is only of importance by the ways in which it leads to different types of grain structure and in certain cases where the chemical composition is of a type to influence the final result. The nature of the humus which is formed on the upper surface is of more importance, coupled with the amount and constancy of the water supply which distributes the humus through the depth of the soil and to a large extent determines the amount of leaching that occurs.

This in turn is controlled by the free nature of the drainage, which is a factor both of the physical structure of the soil and the ability of the water to get away. In exceptional cases, as has been seen, it is possible, with a high water-table and high surface temperatures associated with low rainfall, for the direction of soil-water movement to be reversed and to become upward, so that leaching is prevented and a duricrust is formed.

There are many and varied systems of classifying soils, much of this variation resulting from the degree of detail that is required. The table given below is a very generalised classification, and within many of the classes there are in fact a number of varieties of soil. As with climates – with so many variables and so fine a grading from one to the other, a separation into neat compartments is very difficult. A major division into two great groups which is often used, classes all soils either as pedalfers or pedocals.

The word *pedalfer* is made up of the three units, *ped* meaning soil, and *al* and *fer* symbolising aluminium and iron. These soils contain good supplies of these metallic elements, and this is the result of the removal of calcium and other soluble metals in the form of salts. These therefore are leached soils and occur in humid regions.

Pedocals are soils rich in *cal*cium carbonate or lime. These are necessarily fairly dry areas, and the soils are unleached or only lightly so.

Soil Class	Associated climatic type
PEDALFERS (Humid; leached) *Hot*	
LATERSOLS	
1 Savanna duricrust soils	Tropical wet-and-dry
2 Tropical soils	Often monsoon
3 Terra rosa soils	Mediterranean
PODSOLIC SOILS	
1 Red-yellow soils	Humid subtropical
2 Grey-brown soils	Southern temperates*
PODSOLS	
Not subdivided	Northern temperates* and subarctic
TUNDRA SOILS	
Not subdivided *Cold*	Arctic
PEDOCALS (Dry; unleached or lightly leached)	
DESERT SOILS	
1 Red soils	Hot desert climates
2 Grey (serozëm) soils	Hot desert climates
CHESTNUT SOILS	
1 Tropical	Tropical grassland
2 Temperate	Part of temperate grassland
CHERNOZEMS	
Not subdivided	Part of temperate grassland
MARGALITIC SOILS	
Not subdivided	Equatorial
INTERMEDIATE (between pedalfers and pedocals)	
PRAIRIE SOILS	
Not subdivided	Part of temperate grassland

* 'Southern' and 'northern' are here applicable to the northern hemisphere.

Fig. 365. Generalised broad soil classification and associated climatic types

Within these two major divisions, subdivision chiefly takes the form of distinguishing those soils which belong to areas of differing degrees of humidity and temperature. This leads to the production of differing degrees of oxidation and other chemical changes, and, amongst other things, alters the colour of the soil. From hot to cold, four subdivisions are often recognised, namely the *laterites* (or better, *latersols*), *podsolic soils, podsols* and *tundra soils.* The colours of these change progressively from the red of the latersols through browns to the grey of the tundra soils.

In the table, the type of climate chiefly associated with these soils is named in brackets, but it should clearly be realised that the soil areas only have approximately the same boundaries as the climatic regions. Nevertheless, the fact that it is possible, in a general way, to associate one soil type with a particular climate, does emphasise the dominant effect that climate has on soil development over and above the effect produced by type of rock.

The pedocals are subdivided into four major types, these being *desert soils, chestnut soils, chernozems* and *margalitic soils.* The chestnut refers to the colour of the soil. The chernozems are black when typically developed.

Falling into an intermediate class between leached and unleached, humid and dry, are the *prairie soils,* which occupy part of the temperate grassland climatic zone. These various types of soil will each be discussed in turn in conjunction with the vegetation that grows upon them.

These are only the major world types and apply fully only to the *zonal soils,* that is, those which are well developed and more or less mature. In addition, there are *intrazonal soils,* which do not fall into any of these classes satisfactorily either because they are not yet fully developed or because excessive or deficient drainage or some other factor modifies their characteristics. *Azonal soils* are those which do not have their profiles at all well developed. These include new soils such as, for example, recent blown sands within which horizons have not yet had time to develop.

The fourteen categories into which the zonal soils were divided in the above table are naturally insufficient for detailed studies, and so each of these is subdivided again into smaller *groups* (there are about forty of these in the United States), and these are again split into *families, series* and *types.*

The Soil Survey of Great Britain divides the soils it maps into *major soil groups,* such as Raw soils, Calcareous soils, Brown earths,

Podsolised soils, Gley soils, Organic soils, Warp soils and so on. These then are subdivided into *soil series,* which are soil profiles each of a characteristic type and of which there are often as many as thirty or more in an area of some 15 miles square (say, 25 km square). Most of these series are of fairly local distribution, and clearly this is a detailed analysis of the soil types. There are in fact so many that it becomes difficult to absorb the pattern, but if such a survey is to be of any use at all to a farmer or planner, it must necessarily be as detailed as this.

The broad worldwide *major classes* are only a very generalised first attempt at a breakdown into the different kinds.

A MULTIPLE SOIL-REGOLITH

The extent to which regolith and soil may be developed is illustrated by two very different examples from Lancashire.

If a boring is taken through the coastal dune belt of southwest Lancashire, the following sequence is found:

Top

a – *Recent blown sand* of the presentday sand dunes

b – *Peat* formed in a pre-existing bog about 5,000 years ago

c – Remains of oak and birch trees from a *forest* which preceded the bog

d – *Silt* (mud) of a beach which was associated with the Hillhouse coastline during a period of higher sea-level about 6,000 years ago

e – *Till* deposited by the ice sheet which covered the whole plain and filled the Irish Sea basin until about 27,000 years ago

f – Solid *Triassic rock* formed about 225 million years ago.

There are thus five distinct layers of regolith, each formed during a separate phase in the glacial and post-glacial history of the area. The total thickness of these five layers may be of the order of 100 feet (30 metres).

Again, in a low-lying area to the east of Liverpool, there are no post-glacial deposits and from below the presentday soil, there is a continuous deposit of till until the solid rock is reached as low as 351 feet (107 metres) below the present surface. This is an exceptionally thick layer of till, but serves to demonstrate how important it may be in the future development of an area.

CHAPTER THIRTY-FOUR

World Vegetation

As the regolith is an indication of the effect of climate on rock, so *natural vegetation* is at first the image of the sum of climate and regolith, and later of the sum of climate and soil. The vegetation that may be found in a particular locality is the combined product of these factors; it averages out the day-to-day variations in weather; it sums up the total properties of the regolith or soil upon which it grows, and, changing as the soil changes, shows a development which tends ultimately to a static, balanced assemblage of plants which is known as the *climax vegetation* for the particular region.

Given a particular soil and climate, the ultimate vegetation will not develop at once. Climate is a permissive factor in the sense that under a particular type nature may successfully grow a considerable range of species not all of which may be compatible with one another. For example, conditions may be favourable both for the growing of grasses, certain types of herbaceous plants and a selection of trees. It is probable that grass and herbaceous plants may develop the more quickly, for trees are slow growers. There will be a considerable period at least while the trees are fairly small, but eventually they will overtop the remainder of plant growth, and if the trees are sufficiently close together they may well produce so much shade and prevent so much of the rain from reaching lower levels that the grasses and other lower plants perish.

Thus the group of plants which occupy the area slowly changes, until eventually it reaches the optimum selection for mutual occupance of the area. Henceforth, providing external conditions, such as climate, do not change, the same group of plants will continue to occupy the area indefinitely. This is what is meant by the phrase *climax vegetation.*

This is truly *natural vegetation,* but it is not known how long is required for this stage to be reached, although it is probable that there has been sufficient time in most areas which are outside human interference. Further, the vegetation has not yet been able generally to reach its climax in the more recently deglaciated regions.

Because of the way in which the climax vegetation reflects the combined effects of variable weather, it serves as a good indication of the true climate of a locality. This is why so many classifications of climate have been based on vegetation, and also why it has been possible in this book to use the same boundaries for both climate and vegetation regions.

Again as in the case of climates, there is no sharp transition from one type of vegetation zone to another, and the lines marked on the maps as bounding the different regions are quite unwarrantably thin and definite. In fact, there is always a gradual transition zone where, say, forests become gradually less and less dense until there are only a few scattered trees, and where the herbaceous vegetation, which perhaps is replacing it laterally, gradually increases in the proportion of ground it covers.

This is the primary reason why vegetation maps drawn by different geographers often show somewhat different distinctive areas. The general pattern is always the same, but the emphasis on certain characteristics varies with each cartographer, and the precise posi-

Climatic type	Natural vegetation type
TROPICAL VEGETATION	
1 Equatorial	Tropical rain forest
2 Tropical wet-and-dry	Tropical savanna
3 Monsoon	Monsoon forest
4 Humid subtropical	Subtropical woodland
5 Tropical grassland	Short-grass savanna
6 Hot desert	None
TEMPERATE VEGETATION	
7 Mediterranean	Mediterranean evergreens
8 Marine temperate	Deciduous woodland
9 Continental temperate	Mixed woodland
10 Temperate grassland	Prairie and steppe
ARCTIC VEGETATION	
11 Subarctic	Taïga
12 Arctic	Tundra
13 Polar	None

Fig. 366. Correlations between climatic and natural vegetation types

tion where the bounding line is placed within the transitional zone varies.

The maps contained in the following chapters are thus quite generalised. Small areas of other type of vegetation are omitted; little or no notice is taken of the influence of altitude; and the actual lines themselves are smoothed into swinging curves. The purpose of these chapters is to give a *general* idea of the distribution of the various major different types of vegetational assemblages over the whole world, and for that reason they have been kept quite simple.

It thus becomes possible to take each of the climatic regions described in Chapters 6 to 10, and to allocate to them a type of vegetation which is typical of that climate. Further comment in the text shows some of the major variations within each area, and also draws attention to the fact that a forest may well go by one name in two continents (such as 'temperate deciduous forest') and yet often may consist of entirely different species of trees. Figure 366 summarises the vegetation types and correlates them with their climates.

CHAPTER THIRTY-FIVE

Tropical Vegetation

TROPICAL RAIN FOREST

Tropical rain forests occupy the climatic zone described as Equatorial. The two largest areas are the Amazon, where they are called *selvas,* and the Congo basin (Fig. 367). To these may be added parts of the north coast of Australia, parts of the coasts and islands of southeastern Asia, and most of Central America.

Early descriptions of these areas were made by travellers who only saw them from the rivers, the first natural highways, and at these points the vegetation is very different from what it is farther within the depths of the forest. There the trees grow high, usually over 100 feet (30 metres). They consist of a great variety of species although there is a tendency for most of the leaves to be of much the same shape – somewhat like a laurel leaf. The leaves are leathery and thus able to withstand the high temperatures of the midday sun without too much transpiration. Besides these tall trees, there are also others that are much shorter with leaves adapted to dealing with lower intensity sunshine, so that much of the height from the top down to about 30 feet (say, 10 metres) above ground-level is occupied by leafy branches. There is very little light at the actual ground and consequently little or no undergrowth.

It is in this respect that photographs and descriptions from the river give misleading impressions, for at that point sunshine may enter the base of the forest laterally and there is a dense undergrowth which extends a hundred yards or so in from the river bank. The phrase 'impenetrable jungle' is, however, often quite apt. Apart from the initial problem of getting through the first hundred yards, the going is still very difficult within the forest proper, for the ground is often miry and there may be a very soft surface from the accumulation of fallen leaves.

The trees are almost entirely evergreens, most of which shed a few leaves continuously and at the same time continuously develop fresh ones, so that there is no time when growth stops. In the intense competiton of the continuously favourable weather conditions, no tree could survive if it had a resting period, as do deciduous trees.

In spite of the luxuriant growth which these areas display, it has been found that, when the natural vegetation is cleared, the soil is

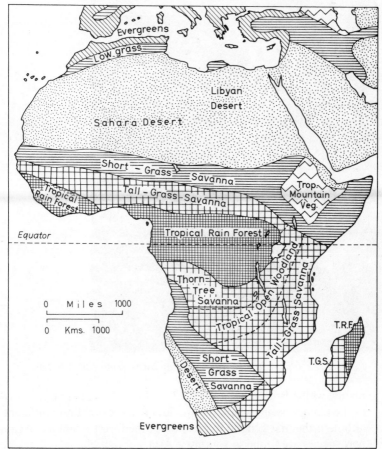

Fig. 367. Generalised natural vegetation zones of Africa

often by no means fertile. It is deeply leached by the continuous downward movement of the contained water, and only plants such as deep-rooted trees are able to penetrate sufficiently to make use of the nutrients to be found in the lower layers.

One of the notable features is the number of varieties of plants which are to be found in these forests. It has been estimated that there are as many as 2,500 species of forest tree in the Amazon basin alone (Fig. 368), and between 20,000 and 50,000 species of other

Fig. 368. A jungle track leading away from the Amazon

plants, whilst Britain has a mere 2,000. Few of these are duplicated in the Congo basin, where the species are almost entirely different, although the first general impression of the forest is similar. Again new species are found in southeast Asia.

The tropical rain forest is limited by the fact that it requires more or less continuous rain throughout the year and cannot withstand a dry season. This is usually divided into two on the east of Brazil, one part being a narrow coastal strip of humid, tropical, coastal forest, and the other tropical forest of the more usual type. The latter spreads beyond the climatic boundary towards São Paulo and into northern Parana.

A distinctive type of tree of these areas which should be mentioned is the *mangrove* (see Fig. 299), which is particularly to be found in the coastal regions. This curious tree sends down aerial roots from overhanging branches, which, when they strike the ground, penetrate it, become true roots and start off a new tree. It is thus possible for a 'single' tree to cover several acres. They grow with their roots directly in salt water, and reach between 15 and 50 feet ($4\frac{1}{2}$ and 15 metres) in height according to the species. The trees naturally spread very rapidly to the exclusion of all other species, and the great tangle of roots leads to rather rapid marine accumulation and the formation of *mangrove swamps*.

The soils of these forests are very varied and little is known concerning their nature and origin. There is often a fairly free downward drainage of soil-water, but leaching has not occurred to any very great extent. They are mostly black or very dark brown in colour, calcareous, and heavy to work. They appear to be distinct from other types, and are generally given the name *margalitic soils*.

THE CAATINGA

The *caatinga* or light forest region of eastern Brazil is distinct from the neighbouring selvas and cerrado largely on account of the fact that its soils are highly permeable, mostly on a base of granites and gneisses, and the rainfall is low – 20 to 30 inches (50 to 75 cm) per annum, unequally distributed through the year so that there are dry periods of considerable irregularity.

The vegation takes the form of short thorny shrubs, so that the area is very often known as *thorn forest,* the plants being adapted to periodic drought. Most species lose their leaves during the dry spells, and many have special features such as the unique Brazilian *bottle-tree,* which possesses a great swollen trunk within which water is stored as a protection against the drought. Tall cacti are also to be found.

MONSOON FOREST

Although this is distinguished from tropical forest on the natural vegetation map (Fig. 369), there is little to distinguish it in fact. If the word jungle should be employed at all (it has been used so variously that it is in some scientific disrepute), it might well be that the monsoon forest of Burma and adjacent areas most deserves this description. Figure 370 shows monsoon forest in Thailand. Its density and impenetrability can easily be imagined even though the small river fights its way through by numerous meanders.

In the Indian subcontinent there is considerable difficulty in determining precisely what is the natural vegetation. It has been so altered

by man that little of the original remains. This particularly applies,
for example, to the Deccan, which is distinguished on the map (Fig.
369) as tall-grass savanna within the monsoon region. The present
uncultivated vegetation of this area is of this type (see below), but
there is considerable doubt as to whether or not this is the climax
vegetation for the area.

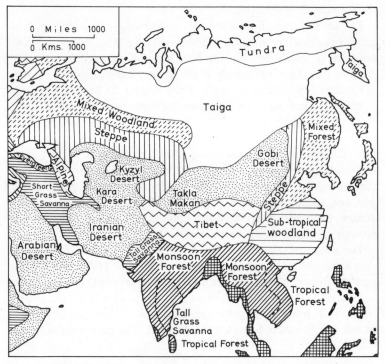

Fig. 369. Generalised natural vegetation zones of Asia

The black *cotton soils* of the Deccan have been derived from
basalt. They are sometimes known as *regur soils,* and because of the
seasonal distribution of rainfall they are calcareous latersols.

TROPICAL SAVANNA

Much of the tropical wet-and-dry climatic areas is occupied by the
variety of savanna generally known as the *tall-grass* or *tropical
savanna*. This grass grows in the wet season, and it appears to be
essential for it to experience a dry period each year. The tall-grass
savanna stretches across Africa to the north of the tropical rain

Fig. 370. Monsoon forest in Thailand

forest, but in the much wider belt occupied by the wet-and-dry climate to the east and south there is *thorn-tree savanna, tropical open
woodland* and *tall-grass savanna* in three broad belts.

This last is the most vigorous type of savanna and is only to be
found to any extent in Africa. It consists of grasses which reach
maximum heights of as much as 12 or even more feet ($3\frac{1}{2}$ metres)
with trees reaching average heights of 40 feet (13 metres) or so. Most
often the trees are scattered, but occasionally they are found in
groups in which cases they may reach a somewhat greater height.

Often the outer edges of the areas marked 'tall-grass savanna' on
the Africa vegetation map (Fig. 367) are subdivided to provide a
narrow belt of transitional savanna between the tall and short grass
types. This is still 'tall-grass', although the maximum height has
decreased to about 8 feet ($2\frac{1}{2}$ metres), and the trees have become

smaller, often being acacia. This is the type of savanna found in South America in the llanos plains of the northern part of the continent and in the cerrado region of the Matto Grosso, although in both these instances there are fewer trees than in Africa.

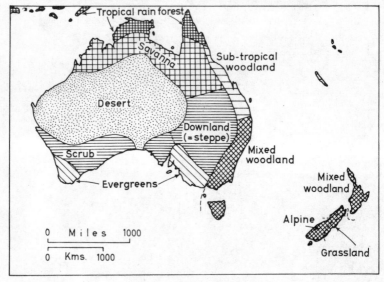

Fig. 371. Generalised natural vegetation zones of Australia and New Zealand

The *tropical open woodland* area of South Africa encloses the southern tall-grass savanna on its south and eastern sides and is an area that is sometimes known as *dry forest* or *tree steppe*. It is a land of scattered deciduous trees, with grass 3 feet (1 metre) or so in height between, and with some bushes. It is occasionally described as *savanna woodland*, and the density of the trees, which generally cuts visibility down to about a quarter of a mile (400 metres), makes it perhaps more accurate to describe it as *grassy woodland,* rather than wooded grassland. The difficulty regarding the correct description of the tropical open woodland is emphasised by the fact that the acacia tree, tall-grass savanna is found between the woodland and the east African coast.

In Australia there is a broad belt of savanna bordering the north and northeastern parts of the central desert area. This savanna is one

Fig. 372. Short-grass savanna with acacia trees in Kenya

of few trees, excepting in localities where there is a slightly heavier rainfall, when acacia occurs. In the northwestern part of the area marked *savanna* in Fig. 371, trees become more prominent. Eucalyptus is common and the area is often distinguished from the general savanna by the term *savanna woodland.* There is again considerable doubt concerning nomenclature, some considering that this should be termed *open woodland* whilst others prefer *tree savanna.*

Savanna soils experience downward movement of soil-water during the wet season, which encourages leaching, but a strong upward movement due to capillarity during the dry season. Evaporation of this at the surface causes the deposition of the dissolved salts and the formation of a hard *duricrust,* often inadvisedly called a *laterite.* According to the metals present in the duricrust, various names are given, such as *bauxite* (rich in aluminium), *calcrete* (generally calcium carbonate), *ferricrete* (rich in iron), and *silicrete* (largely silica). *Terra rosa* is a form of bauxite resulting from the weathering of a sandy limestone and *laterite* itself, although often used as an all-embracing term, may well be restricted to those duricrusts which contain much aluminium and little iron. The word *latersol* is favoured for the comprehensive term.

SHORT-GRASS SAVANNA

More than one kind of savanna has already been described, and in
Africa another type, the *short-grass savanna,* bordering both the
Sahara and the Kalahari and Namib Deserts, consists of a scatter of
acacia trees with a grass which grows something like a foot (say, $\frac{1}{2}$
metre) in height and often provides fairly good grazing. It stretches
eastwards into Kenya where it is shown in Fig. 372. Its quality is
naturally very variable. The density of growth falls off progressively
as the desert itself is approached. A considerable part of what is
commonly called the Kalahari Desert is in fact covered with a scatter
of this grass. The same occurs in South America between the pampas
and the neighbouring desert, whilst the Australian savanna equally
merges into the desert in the same way.

In all the savanna types, the characteristic of the vegetation is the
ability to withstand the dry period which often extends through
three or four months. During this period the grasses shrivel up, but
quickly grow again with the return of the rains, whilst the trees are
all of the type which have leaves suitable for restraining transpiration and thus are able to withstand the drought.

THE HOT DESERTS

Deserts in general are by no means so devoid of vegetation as is
generally believed. Certainly there are extensive areas entirely barren
of all life, but there are also equally other areas which have some type
of vegetation. This, however, generally consists of individual plants
rather than of groups or areas with continuous cover (Fig. 373). In
these circumstances each plant is an independent individual in every
sense of that word and is in no way modified by its neighbours, as is
usual in normal plant communities.

Two types survive. One is an annual. It germinates, grows, flowers
and produces seed in an extremely short time – often in the length of
time during which it can obtain moisture from one rainstorm. Its
seeds are covered with an almost impermeable coat which enables
them to survive long periods of complete drought without death.
The other is perennial and owes its ability to exist to its long
roots. When travelling across many parts of the Sahara, it is very
striking to note that a few plants are growing in almost every hollow
place in the sand. In these small depressions they are that much
nearer to the water-table and so can survive. In other places, plants
may send down roots sufficiently far to reach this water-table and so
obtain a supply.

Fig. 373. Flowers in bloom along low-lying sand in the desert in Egypt

Oases are in general enclosed hollows into which very large quantities of water may drain after a local thunderstorm. This concentration and the fact that it so rapidly soaks beneath the surface of the sand and thus reduces evaporation losses, enables a permanent cover of vegetation to persist in such localities. Inhabited oases have, of course, long ago lost their natural vegetation. There is some doubt as to what should be the climax vegetation in such circumstances, for the plants are existing on the subterranean water and not upon the surface conditions.

Desert soils are naturally *pedocals* and vary in colour. Red soils are found in the hot tropical deserts such as the Sahara. These are drier than the deserts of the western United States, which on the whole have grey soils of a type known as *serozëms* (sometimes spelt *sierozëms*). These have a little humus amongst the sand and are less oxidised than are the red soils. The reddish colour is the result of the presence of relatively small amounts of iron compounds.

SUBTROPICAL WOODLAND

On the eastern side of the continental masses, often in a similar latitude to the savannas, is the important vegetation zone of the *subtropical woodland*. In North America most of the States south from

Fig. 374. Cypress swamp in southern Alabama

the latitude of North Carolina, and from the Atlantic seaboard westwards to the Ozark Plateau, come into this type. The dominant characteristic is that most of the trees have needle-shaped or narrow, wax-surfaced leaves to reduce the amount of transpiration in this hot summer – mild winter climate which averages 50 to 60 inches (125 to 150 cm) of precipitation each year for most of the area.

Several varieties of pine, usually intermingled with oak, are by far the most common types of trees. Mixed pine areas merge along the northern fringe of the region with the broadleaf deciduous forest of northeastern United States. Along valley bottoms (including the Mississippi) and in Florida, bald cypress and gum are common.

Soils in much of Florida and the coastal plain are sandy, and despite the fairly heavy precipitation, they do not hold moisture. Some such areas are consequently known locally as 'pine barrens'. This has given rise to the development of vegetation types which can tolerate high temperatures and periods of drought. Pine trees do well in these circumstances, for their deep tap root system enables them to reach more remote water. In Florida other characteristic species include: palmetto (a type of dwarf palm), 'scrub oak' (a small and very hardy variety) and several types of cactus.

In South America, the single area of the humid subtropical climate (see Fig. 35) has considerable variations over the one zone. Around the mouth of the river Plate, the annual rainfall is about 60 inches

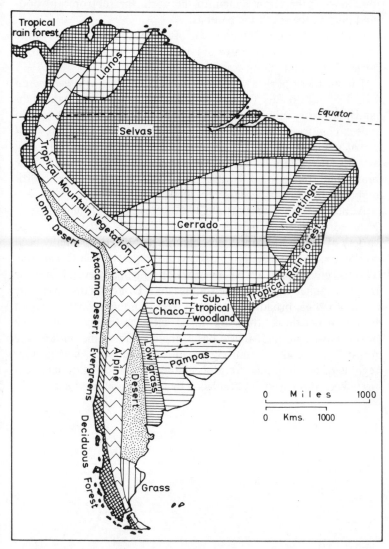

Fig. 375. Generalised natural vegetation zones of South America

(150 cm), whilst on the northeastern coastal borders of the area it rises as high as 80 or 90 inches (200 or 230 cm) a year. This makes it necessary to subdivide the region from the vegetational point of view, and in fact the northeastern part has already been included with the tropical rain forest (Fig. 375). To the northwest of the

Q

remainder is the Gran Chaco, to the north the subtropical woodland, and to the south the pampas.

In places, the Gran Chaco is one of the most difficult parts of the
world to traverse. It is an area of low rainfall with scrub thorn trees,
dwarf shrubs and giant cacti.

The northern part of this area (marked *subtropical woodland* on
Fig. 375) is in reality the southernmost tip of the Brazilian Highlands, with broadleaf trees both of the deciduous and evergreen
types. This forest has a less hot climate than the rain forests of
Brazil and is notable for the presence of the araucaria pine. The area
extends into eastern Paraguay. The pampas are closely related to the
prairie and steppe so far as vegetation is concerned, and are accordingly described in that section (p. 484).

Although the greater part of China east of the plateau of Tibet is
grouped under the same climatic type, this is a rather specialised
variety of the humid subtropical climate and has occasionally been
considered to be virtually unique, with the description *China type*.
This has given rise to a type of vegetation which, however, is in some
respects similar to that of the southeastern United States. Near the
coast of China, broadleaf evergreen trees dominate; farther inland,
broadleaf deciduous trees are mixed with the former; and to the
north, mostly in the Yangtse basin, the evergreens die out and the
forests become almost entirely broadleaf deciduous. As with other
regions of dense population, this climax vegetation has almost entirely been destroyed, and replaced by agricultural products.

CHAPTER THIRTY-SIX

Temperate Vegetation

MEDITERRANEAN EVERGREENS

THE most important characteristic of the Mediterranean region, and
of other areas with a similar climate, is the fact that there is a very
real summer drought. This distinguishes it from the other climatic
type which has unequal rainfall distribution – for the savanna lands
have 'winter' drought. Amongst world climates this is unusual and
the vegetation associated with it is equally specialised. Everything
must be able to withstand the dry period which is likely to last for
several months during what would otherwise be a fast-growing
season. Consequently thick-skinned or waxed leaves are general to
restrain transpiration. Some plants survive the dry summer because
they are deep rooted, and this naturally especially applies to the
trees.

Amongst many variants and intermediates, there are two main
types of vegetation. One consists of scattered trees, especially certain
types of oak (including cork oak) and olive. This is *Mediterranean
woodland* (Fig. 376).

The other comprises a much closer growth of bushes and dwarf
trees, including myrtle and oleander associated with creeping vines.
This is the *maquis* of southern France, and very often is almost
impenetrable. It corresponds to the *chaparral* to be found in California, and much of the Adelaide Mediterranean area of Australia
has this type of vegetation, whilst the Perth Mediterranean is more
of the dry woodland type. The former is there known as *mallee scrub*
(Fig. 377). Much of the actual Mediterranean area is mountainous
and thus considerable modifications in vegetation occur. The
Mediterranean pine, especially the Corsican, is to be found, together
with horse chestnut and the tall, stately cypress. Several kinds of
cypress also occur in California, as well as the wonderful redwoods.

In both the European and American examples of this type of
vegetation, man has worked the ground for several thousand years
and so modified the natural cover that it is today almost entirely

475

Fig. 376. Mediterranean open woodland, modified by cultivation, on the east coast of Sardinia

Fig. 377. Mallee scrub in South Australia

artificial. It is thus difficult to imagine the climax vegetation as being a forest cover.

So far as soils are concerned, these are both complex and localised, but there is a tendency towards laterisation due to the summer drought, with *terra rossa* as a red-coloured residual soil. It compares with the *rendzina* of temperate chalklands, such as those of Britain.

DECIDUOUS WOODLAND

Although deciduous woodlands are to be found in a variety of climatic types, they are developed to the true climax especially in marine temperate climates. Deciduous woodland is the climax vegetation in the major part of Britain and of western Europe away from the Mediterranean. It also is the type in southern Sweden and the

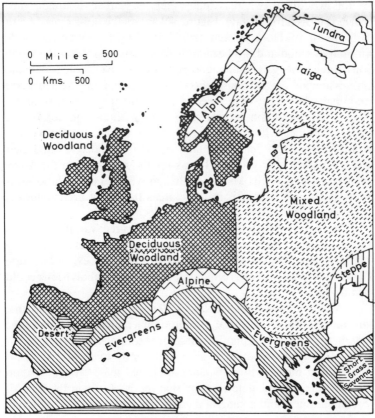

Fig. 378. Generalised natural vegetation zones of Europe

coastal regions of south and middle Norway. As a rather mixed woodland, it occupies in Australia the eastern coast belt south of Brisbane, and covers much of New Zealand.

These are all areas long occupied by man where the winter climate is quite cool, and where consequently vast quantities of the forest have been cut during a considerable number of centuries (excepting of course in Australia and New Zealand) to provide heating fuel. This timber consumption was in addition to the amount used for constructional and other purposes. Consequently these woodlands now exist in their original, fully developed form only in a few small localities. In others, they have long been cleared, and the land used for cultivation. It is only with considerable difficulty that we may picture these regions as they were.

Only two thousand years ago great areas of Britain were covered by this woodland, whereas today there is scarcely a square yard which is in its natural state. Figure 379 shows the dip-slope of Leith Hill, south of Dorking and the North Downs. A considerable amount of woodland has been allowed to remain here on the sandy soils of the lower Greensand, and perhaps this gives some superficial impression of the original vegetation, although the clearings are man-made and many of the species of tree are also man-introduced.

Even the mountain tops have their vegetation modified by the presence of sheep. It was very largely because the valley floors were so wooded and wet that the Roman legionaries tended to build their roads on the higher ground. It was for the same reason that early man occupied the chalklands of Britain where the vegetation was more open, and thus it is in these areas that most archaeological finds are to be made.

As in all other vegetation regions, there are great variations within the one area. In the British Isles it is generally considered that there were five separate types of climax vegetation which existed because of the different types of ground, but many more subdivisions could be made.

1. Most of the ground below 1,500 feet (450 metres) became covered with *deciduous forest*. A minimum length and warmth of the summer period is required for these trees to regenerate (that is, for their seeds to germinate and grow sufficiently to survive the next winter), but most of those which established themselves in Britain survived the climatic deterioration that set in, chiefly in the form of cooler summers and a general increase in rainfall, at the beginning of the Sub-Atlantic about 2500 B.P.

Fig. 379. Woodland on the dip-slope of Leith Hill, Surrey

2. The *conifers* which also established themselves in Scotland after the end of the Ice Ages constitute the second type of vegetation, and these survived the Sub-Atlantic deterioration only in Scotland, although previously they probably existed in considerable numbers on certain slopes in England and especially in Wales.

3. The same climatic deterioration killed off the deciduous forest on the open uplands of the Pennines, Dartmoor and other similar areas and also in much lower areas in Ireland. These plant communities were replaced by *bog*, which led to peat formation. The soil had become impoverished by its exposure to the excessive rains and was badly leached, so that it possessed but little nutriment. Most of these peat bogs continue in existence to the present day. Many are now being weathered and eroded (Fig. 380), and it is almost certain that no peat is being formed in Britain today. At the foot of many peat cuttings in these areas, the remains of the previous tree cover may be found.

4. Steep slopes of westerly aspect between the 1,500-foot (400-metre) level and about 3,000 feet (900 metres) were too well drained to permit the formation of bog and too windy to allow trees to sur-

Fig. 380. Peat on Dartmoor undergoing dissection

vive. In such areas the climax vegetation was herbaceous plants and dwarf shrubs, producing a heathlike community.

5. The fifth area lay above about 3,000 feet (900 metres). Here conditions were too severe for the vegetation so far described, and thus *alpine* and *subarctic* plants were able to take over.

This account serves to illustrate the complexity of the vegetative cover over a comparatively small area, and when a detailed study of the vegetation is undertaken it is further subdivided into many more types and subtypes. Such complexity is not peculiar to the British Isles and every one of the vegetation regions so far described, and to be described, can be subdivided in the same way.

A further point occurs in this and most of the regions remaining to be dealt with. They have been glaciated. The other regions so far described have been covered with vegetation without interruption for a very long time and thus have had a long period in which to develop their climax communities to the full, even though they too experienced some modification of climate during the Ice Ages. On the other hand, glaciated areas experienced a more or less complete removal of all vegetation and on average have had little more than 10,000 to 30,000 years (according to locality) in which to develop their present coverage. Thus in many instances in such areas it is doubtful whether or not the present natural vegetation is the climax.

It is considered that at the presentday the climax vegetation for Britain, if undisturbed by man, would be roughly as follows. The chalklands of the south would have a cover dominated by mixed beech and oak forest. The areas round the Wash would be fenland. There is the probability that Dartmoor, Exmoor, the mountains of Wales, the Pennines, Lake District and southern Scotland would be covered by active blanket bog, except in the higher areas, although this is not certain. There would be some heath on the steeper slopes. The remainder of England and Wales, the lowlands of Scotland, including the eastern plain, would be oak forest. The Highlands of Scotland would be a complex of pine forest and heathland with some patches of blanket bog, and with alpine–subarctic vegetation on the higher summits.

The difference between this and the vegetation actually found is very obvious and demonstrates the extent to which man has interfered with nature.

Similar conditions prevail in the parts of continental Europe covered by the same maritime temperate climate. The climax vegetation is essentially a mixed deciduous forest, but now, after more than two thousand years of continuous cultivation, only small fragments of the forestland remain. The typical trees on the lowlands were oak, beech, elm, sycamore and hornbeam. These are all deciduous trees, for the winters are sufficiently cold to encourage the annual seasonal shed of leaves with new growth each spring. The colour changes in the vegetation corresponding to the change of seasons; the change from the bare trees of winter to the bursting of bud in spring; the full growth of green foliage in the summer; and finally the wonderful browns, reds and golds of the autumn fading, produce a sequence which contrasts remarkably with the monotony of the evergreen of the tropics. The natural vegetation only now survives in Europe in a few places where agriculture cannot profitably be carried on, and besides the forest type already described there are the heathlands of the poorer quality gravelly soils, the moors of the uplands and the bogs of the poorly drained areas.

It is difficult to say much about the soils of these areas of deciduous woodland, since, like the vegetation itself, they have been so altered by man that there is scarcely a natural soil to be found. All are podsols, chiefly grey-brown in the lowlands with a tendency towards lithosols in the uplands where the ground-rock becomes more important.

Q 2

MIXED WOODLAND

The European deciduous woodland merges gradually and with much interdigitation into the *mixed woodland* of eastern Europe. This is not unlike the mixed woodland areas of northeastern United States, Manchuria, Korea and Japan. These are all areas of continental temperate climate with the coldest month below freezing temperature and the warmest month above 10°C (50°F).

In the States, the climax vegetation is rather similar to the European with perhaps less heathland (Fig. 381). In Maine, the woodland is mainly spruce and fir. This becomes birch, pine, hemlock and maple south of Lake Superior and between Lakes Michigan and Huron, whilst hemlock, maple and beech are the commonest varieties in the northern Appalachians and in New Hampshire. These gradually mix with more broadleaved trees to the south. Around Lakes Erie and Ontario there are beech and maple, whilst oak is important in the southeast of the area, with oak and ash in the southwest.

A traverse from the mountain summits in north central Sweden to the Baltic coast near Härnösand shows the effects of altitude in this vegetation zone. At the highest, about 150 miles (240 km) from the coast, there is ice and snow for the greater part of the year with a little subarctic flora. Below that, at about 4,500 feet (1,400 metres) and down to about 3,000 feet (900 metres) there is an alpine flora of herbaceous plants capable of surviving the cold winters and quite cool summers.

Below 3,000 feet (900 metres), which is the tree line in this part of Sweden, there is a forest consisting entirely of silver birch with an undergrowth of subarctic plants. The trees are quite short under these conditions and grow only to a height of about 20 feet (6 metres). This comes down to a height of about 2,000 feet (600 metres) above sea-level, and then gradually gives way to a pine and spruce forest with some birch. Here the pine and spruce account for about 85 per cent of all the trees, the remainder being the birch.

Finally, below about 2,000 feet (600 metres) the forest becomes pine on the drier gravelly and sandy soils associated with the river or glacial outwash deposits, with spruce on the slopes and more level hill-tops.

In U.S.S.R., the mixed woodland zone is one of oak, lime and elm with a considerable intermixture of spruce and pine, although, like the United States, much of it has long ago been modified by cultivation by man. It has four months or so with the mean temperature below freezing, but the summers are quite warm (above 20°C: 68°F). Because much of this area is of very low altitude in spite of its distance from the sea, drainage is often very poor so that bog is very

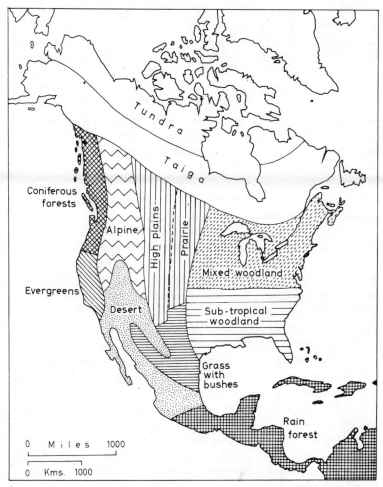

Fig. 381. Generalised natural vegetation zones of North America

common. Amongst these are the famous Pripet Marshes now to some extent artificially drained. The soils of the mixed woodland zone as a whole are mainly transitional in type between the true podsols of the coniferous forests to the north and the black earth chernozem soils of the south.

In Japan the natural forest varies considerably from north to south for there are more than 15 degrees of latitudinal range, which means nearly 1,000 miles (1,500 km). It is central Honshu which chiefly possesses the mixed forests of birch, beech, ash and maple together with cypress and Japanese cedar. To the south, it becomes virtually subtropical, and to the north trees of cooler climates dominate. As in other areas, Japan's natural vegetation has long since been greatly modified by this agriculturally-minded and garden-loving people.

PRAIRIE AND STEPPE

In the great continental masses of North America and Eurasia, the areas of podsolisation, where leaching has removed the major part of the natural soil nutriment, give way in the very hearts óf the land to areas where there is a much smaller rainfall, although conditions are still sufficiently moist for considerable vegetative growth. These are the areas of the *chernozem soils,* often known as the *black earths,* and other fertile grey, tan or brown soils.

The largest of this type forms the *steppeland* of U.S.S.R. both in Europe and in Asia. It extends from the northern shores of the Black Sea far eastwards to about longitude 85° E. It lies between the mixed woodland just described and the hot deserts to the south. One of the most important characteristics of these chernozems is the large amount of humus which they contain together with calcium carbonate, which is normally leached out of other soils.

The hot summer almost completely dries out the soil during that season, but during the winter the area is largely covered with snow, and in the spring when it thaws the meltwater encourages a luxuriant growth of grass – hence the general name for this type of vegetation is *temperate grassland.* The subsequent drought stops the grass growth, causes the almost total absence of trees, and often leads to wind erosion of the soil. This is less serious under natural conditions where the dead grass covers the ground with a veritable thatch. Under cultivation this does not occur, and wind erosion becomes a major problem.

The *prairies* and *high plains* of the States are very similar, especially in their natural state, where grasses up to 10 feet (3 metres) in height on the east gradually become shorter and shorter westwards with increasing drought, and eventually on the western border of the zone, where the high plains are merging into the Rockies, they are only a few inches in height and generally in isolated clumps. As with the steppes, cultivation by man has completely altered the natural environment.

The *pampas* of South America fall into the humid subtropical climatic zone, but its southern part is tall grassland whose characteristics bring it midway between the savannas of the tropics and the steppes of temperate regions. The name in fact refers to the plain across central Argentina, and its eastern part is the land of prairie grass that has become the economic heart of Argentina. In Uruguay, this vegetation type is generally known as the *campos*. The western part of the Pampas Plain becomes more and more arid, so that the prairie grass gives place to low grass and then to desert.

CHAPTER THIRTY-SEVEN

Arctic and Mountain Vegetation

TAÏGA

MUCH of Canada and Alaska and the greater part of Siberia fall within the climatic type known as subarctic. These are the regions where the vegetation is often described by the Russian word *taïga,* and it is here that the *coniferous forest* finds its greatest development. These trees with their needle-shaped leaves are able to withstand the cold winters, collect little snow upon themselves, and require a fairly small supply of water, since the small area of leaf reduces transpiration. They grow slowly as compared with tropical or even temperate trees, their timber is technically known as *soft*, although with certain types of conifer it may in fact be harder than some of the so-called *hard-woods*. The dominant tree is the pine (several species), but fir, spruce and larch (not evergreen) are also common. One of the few broadleaved trees to be found in these areas is the silver birch, which often has the ability to survive in conditions which are too rigorous to permit the growth of conifers.

These forests are some of the great wood providers for world trade and consequently are of the greatest commercial importance. Nevertheless, although man may have harvested timber from them for some time, they are still mostly very near to their natural condition (Fig. 382). They occupy land which was entirely covered with ice during the Pleistocene glaciations and consequently have not been back in occupation for any long duration of time. During the cold periods they were to be found considerably farther from the Poles than they are now.

Like all evergreens, the trees do lose their leaves and the pine needles generally form a continuous mat over the ground beneath the trees several inches in depth. The needles decay very slowly and this retards the evaporation of soil moisture from the ground. The rain and meltwater which pass through this layer of needles pick up considerable organic acids and thus are very efficient leachers of the soil beneath, which becomes a podsol that is most often grey but may have become almost white. This is the A horizon, and beneath

Fig. 382. In the pine forests of Scandinavia

it the B horizon traps most of the minerals washed out of the layer above. It consequently becomes brown in colour.

The taïga is of little use agriculturally both because of the low temperatures of the climate and also because of this great leaching of the surface soil, which renders the A horizon almost sterile.

TUNDRA

Finally, in northern Canada, Siberia and the Arctic islands there is the *tundra*. This is the region of permafrost where the ground is frozen for several months of the year and the top yard or two only thaws out in the summer. Drainage is consequently poor, for the frozen ground is impermeable and the water content of the surface is thus often very high. The winter is very cold, the summers are short, but have the advantage of permanent daylight often for several months and consequently growth is much more rapid than the low temperature would seem to indicate likely. There are no trees at all, no earthworms and consequently no mixing of soil layers. There is very little leaching, the subsoil is almost entirely the result of weathering of the rock and the surface soil is almost entirely humus.

The range of low, quick-growing herbaceous plants is considerable. Ice has but recently vacated the ground and much of it is in fact
still covered by glaciers and ice sheets. Deep snow still covers the
ground for several months of the year.

Various types of sedge (*carex*) are very common, cotton grass,
various saxifrages, and a considerable range of mosses and lichens are
also to be found. The vegetation is almost entirely uninfluenced by
the presence of man (agriculture of any kind is quite impossible),
although it may not have reached its climax, since individual areas
have been occupied by vegetation only for a relatively few years.

MOUNTAIN VEGETATION

But little has been said about *mountain vegetation* and perhaps it is
unnecessary to go into details here. Clearly several of the climatic
factors on mountain slopes and summits are different from those
which prevail in the same locality at low levels. The slopes often
inhibit the retention of soil and sometimes this results in bare rock
surfaces. Where, however, there is soil, aspect becomes of great importance with regard to the amount of insolation the area receives,
and this commonly varies not only on different sides of the mountain
but also from point to point. Drainage is in general very good on the
slopes, but may be poor indeed on the summits, so that the climber
soon becomes accustomed to the fact that mountain tops are often
bog. Finally, the greater height results in lower temperatures.

All this produces a rapid passage through a whole succession of
vegetational zones as one ascends a mountain of any considerable
height, and it has much the same effect as moving rapidly to areas of
high latitude. The sequence is not the same, since the climatic
changes are different, and also the close juxtaposition of differing
types of vegetation results in their interacting upon one another.

Taking the extreme cases of high mountains situated in tropical
regions, the general sequence from low level upwards is first the local
tropical rain forest. This may clothe the mountainsides up to a
height of 4,000 to 5,000 feet (1,200 to 1,500 metres). Above this,
after a transition belt generally extending through the next thousand
feet (300 metres), one reaches a zone known as *montane forest* consisting of somewhat stunted trees. Above about 10,000 feet (3,000
metres) this gives way first to heathers and allied plants, then to
scrub and grassland, and eventually to vegetation closely allied to
the tundra type.

Fig. 383. The snow-clad summit of Kibo, Kilimanjaro, near the equator

If the mountain rises to sufficient height (about 17,000 feet (5,200 metres) at the equator), the permanent snowline is passed and one has the curiosity of finding a snow-capped mountain even at the equator. The higher peak, Kibo, of Kilimanjaro, 3° south of the equator, is seen from the air in Fig. 383. How high you consider it to be depends upon whether or not one includes the thickness of the ice. The rock summit is generally stated to be about 19,340 feet (5,890 metres) above sea-level, and the ice is about 250 feet (80 metres) thick.

Index

All references are to page numbers. Individual items often receive further mention on consecutive following pages without these being noted in the index. Chapter headings are given in CAPITALS. Place names, excepting for those very well known, are followed by country or continent of location.

Abbreviations

Af. = Africa, Am. = America, Aus. = Australia, Bri. = Britain, Can. = Canada, Den. = Denmark, E.L.D. = English Lake District, Eng. = England, Eu. = Europe, Fra. = France, Ger. = Germany, Ind. = India, Ire. = Ireland, Nor. = Norway, N.Z. = New Zealand, Scot. = Scotland, Swe. = Sweden, Swi. = Switzerland, U.S.A. = United States of America.

aa, 432
ablation, glacial, 233
abrasion bench, 365
accordant summit levels, 213
adiabatic cooling, 18;
— lapse rate, dry, 18;
— — saturated, 19
Adriatic sea, wave fetch, 328
AEOLIAN DEPOSITION, 389
aeolian deposits, 448
AEOLIAN EROSION, 389
Africa, climatic regions, 54
Agassiz lake, Can., 319
agglomerate, 433
Agropyrum junceum, 392
Aiguilhe, Le Rocher de l', Fra., 438
Ailsa Craig, Scot., 251
AIR CURRENTS, 34
AIR MASSES, 34
air masses, types of, 42
air, stable, 22
Albuen spit, Den., 384
Aletsch glacier, Swi., 232, 386
Aleutian islands, n. Am., 406
Algonquin dome, n. Am., 203
Alice springs, Aus., 69
Allegheny escarpment, n. Am., 204
Alleröd phase, 294
alluvial deposits, 448
alluviation, 156
alluvium, pushed, 285
Alpine orogeny, 194, 203

altocumulus cloud, 26
altostratus cloud, 26
Alum bay, Isle of Wight, s. Eng., 118
Alum pot. n. Eng., 132

Alyn riv., n. Wales, 266
Amazon vegetation, 462
Ambleside, E.L.D., rainfall, 31
Ammophila arenaria, 392
amphidromic point, 421
—, degenerate, 421
Ancyclus fluviatilis, 274
Ancyclus lake, 274
—, beaches, 377
Andes, uplift, 212
Andreeland, Spitsbergen, 130
anemometer, cup, 38
—, pressure-tube type, 38
antarctic glaciation, 289
— ice cap, movement of, 234
antecedence, fluvial, 212
anticlines and synclines, alternating, 198
anticyclone, cold, 81
—, warm, 81
Antrim plateau, n. Ire., 431
anvil cloud, 26
Appledore, sw. Eng., 348
Aqaba desert, Asia, 395
aquifer, 141, 144
ARCTIC CLIMATES, 89
Arctic climatic regions, 92
— glaciation, 289
Armorican orogeny, 194
Arnafjord, Nor., 307
artesian well, 145
Arun river, Asia, 213
Asia, climatic regions, 83
aspect, thermal effect of, 15
Atlantic City, U.S.A., 352
Atlas mts., uplift, 212
atmosphere, 5, 36
—, transparency of, 14

491

ATMOSPHERIC STABILITY, 14
atoll, 409
attrition, 152, 155
avalanche, 116
Avon (Bristol), river, s. Eng., 208
— (Salisbury), river, s. Eng., 202
axis, anticlinal, 202
Azores, 405

back (of wind), 39
backshore, 335
— of tideless beach, 343
backwash, 329
badland, 128
Baghdad, Asia, climate, 69
Bakewell, Eng., terracettes, 114

— ice lake, 273
— sea, salinity, 412
Bantry bay, sw. Ire., 384
bar, backshore, 344
—, barrier, 351
—, foreshore, 344
—, offshore, 342, 344
Barcena volcano, Mexico, 436
barchan dune, 396
barometer, 6
barrier reef, coral, 410
base level, 165
—, change of, 209
basin, river, 194
batholith, 442
bathyal sediments, 403
bauxite, 469
BEACH, 340
beach balance sheet, 337
—, barrier, 351
—, bayhead, 332, 342
—, down-combing of, 340
— movement and man, 353
— profile, 340
—, raised, 356, 379
— ridges, 363
—, tidal, 341
—, tideless, 343
—, upbuilding of, 341
beaded valleys, 306
bed, bottom-set, 358
—, fore-set, 358
—, top-set, 358
bench, raised, 379
Bengal, bay of, winds, 61
Ben Wyvis, Scot., 179
Bergen, Nor., climate, 84
Berwyn mts., Wales, 269
Birchington cliff, se. Eng., 371
biscuit-board topography, 314
Bismarck rock, lake Victoria, e. Af., 110
Blaaisen glacier, Nor., 245, 248
black earth, 484
Black hills, s. Dakota, 109

Blakeney point, re-orientation, e. Eng., 363
Blea cirque, E.L.D., 313
block production, 99
bluffline, 167
Bodmin moor, sw. Eng., batholith, 442
bog, 479
—, blanket, 481
bomb, volcanic, 432
Bombay, climate, 59
Boreal phase, 294
Borrowdale Volcanic Series, E.L.D., 429
Borth, Wales, cliffs, 366
—, coast, 336
boss, batholithic, 442
bottle-tree, Brazilian, 465
boulder clay, 249
—, *see* moraine, till
boulder train, 251
Bow, riv., Can., 164
Boya glacier snout, Nor., 235
— river, 155
— valley, 100
Boyle's law, 7
Braunton Burrows, sw. Eng., 330, 393
Brazilian highland, vegetation, 474
breccia, 433
Bride hills, Isle of Man, moraine, 270, 283
Brimham rocks, n. Eng., 391
Brixdal glacier, Nor., 118, 235
Bryce canyon, Utah, 128
Bristol Avon, riv., s. Eng., 208
— Channel, tide, 424
Bulawayo, s. Af., climate, 67
Bulken gorge, Nor., 182, 186
Buys Ballot's law, 34

caatinga, 465
Cader Idris, Wales, solifluction, 115
calcrete, 469
caldera, 434
Caledonian orogeny, 194
caliche, 454
Callow hill, central Eng., 139
campos, 485
Canterbury plains, N.Z., 207
canyon, 157
—, submarine, 403
capacity, of a river, 152
Cape Cod spits, Mass., 351
Cape Verde basin, 405
captive, 211
captor, 211
capture, consecutive, 181
—, elbow of, 211
—, fluvial, 176, 211
—, single, 176
Carex, 488
carbon 14, 289
carbonation, 108, 450

Carlingford moraine, Ire., 283
Caspian sea, 166, 173
catastrophic movements, 112
Caucasus, uplift, 212
Causey Pike, E.L.D., 126
cavern, 134
—, collapsed, 144
cavitation, 152, 155
cerrado region, 468
channel, one-sided, 263
—, overflow, 259, 266
chapada, 56
chaparral, 475
Charnian orogeny, 194
Cheddar gorge, sw. Eng., 142
chernozem, 457, 484
Chesapeake bay, U.S.A., 352
Chesil beach, s. Eng., 351
Chiltern hills, Eng., 190
China type vegetation, 474
chinook wind, 19–20
chronology, varve, 249
Churchill, Can., climate, 84
cinders, volcanic, 433
cirque, 313, 232, 284
—, hanging, 233
—, tributary glacier, 232
cirriform cloud, 28–9
cirrocumulus, 25, 28
cirrostratus, 25, 28
cirrus, 25, 26, 28
Clarion trough, Pacific, 405
classification, causal, 47
—, climatic, 49
—, empirical, 47
—, genetic, 47
—, systematic, 47
clay, 448–9
clay-pan, 454
Cleveland lakes, ne. Eng., 269
cliff, 365
—, bevelled, 370
—, collapsed, 369
—, crenulated, 371
— plan, 372
— profile, 369
—, rotational slope collapse, 367
—, slope-and-step, 370
—, stepped, 370
—, straight, 372
—, undercut, 367
—, vertical, 369
climate, 48
—, antarctic, 51
—, arctic, 51, 89–90
—, China type, 64
—, continental temperate, 82
—, cool temperate oceanic, 74
—, dry, 49
—, equatorial, 51, 53, 62
—, hot desert, 68
—, humid subtropical, 64

—, marine temperate, 74
—, Mediterranean, 72
—, monsoon, 59
—, polar, 49, 91
—, snow, 49
—, subarctic, 89
—, temperate grassland, 85
—, tropical, 49, 51, 70
—, tropical grassland, 67
—, tropical wet-and-dry, 56
—, warm temperate, 49
CLIMATES, CHANGING, 93
—, EQUATORIAL, 53
—, temperate, 51, 72
—, WORLD'S, 206
climatic change, 206
— future, 296
— optimum, 95, 294
— —, Gresswell, 51
— types, Köppen, 49, 52
— —, Thornthwaite, 50
climax vegetation of Britain, 481
clints, 107
Clipperton seascarp, Pacific, 405
cloud, 19
CLOUDS, 25
clouds, formation of, 29
—, instability, 23
Clwyd, Vale of, n. Wales, 266
coasts, classification, 387
—, emergent, 378
—, mangrove, 362
—, marsh, 359
—, prograding, 354
—, re-orientation of, 363
—, retrograding, 354
—, submergent, 383
coastal accretion, 336
— terms, 334
COASTLINES, 354
col, 178
Colombo, Ceylon, climate, 55
Colorado laccolith, U.S.A., 441
Columbia river, U.S.A., lava, 430
combe rock, 116
competence of a river, 152
cone, ash, 431
—, cinder, 431
—, compound, 434
—, simple, 434
confluence, fluvial, 161
congeliturbate, 116
Congo vegetation, 462
conifers, 479
Coniston, E.L.D., drumlins, 244
—, glacier, 247, 284, 316
—, cirques, 318
continental rise, 403
— shelf, 400
— slope, 400
— temperate climate, 87
contrail, 29

convectional up-current, 29.
convergence, 43
cooling, adiabatic, 19
coombe rock, 116
coral atoll, 409
Coriolis effect, 34, 415
corrasion, 152

corrosion, 152
— by wave action, 367
cosmic dust, 278
cove, 372
cotton grass, 488
cracks, desiccation, 104
craggy ground, 128
Crater lake, Oregon, 322
Creag Ghorm, Scot., 313
creep, 112
crestline, lowering of, 192
crevasse, 222, 225
Cromer, e. Eng., cliff, 367, 372
— forest bed, 281
Cromerian warm period, 281
crust compaction, synclinal, 198
— lengthening, anticlinal, 198
Cuiaba, Brazil, 58
cumiliform cloud, 28
cumulonimbus, 26, 28
cumulus, 26, 28
current, Brazil, 415
—, California, 417
—, Canaries, 416
—, Gulf Stream, 415
—, inshore, 337
—, longshore, 337
—, onshore surface, 341
—, tidal, 337
CURRENTS, 327
currents, ocean, 415
cut-off, 167
cwm, *see* cirque
cycle, 205
cypress, 475

Dal river, Swe., 274
dale, 142
Danau glaciation, 281
Daniglacial, 247, 286
Danube-Rhine water switch, 137
Dart ria, sw. Eng., 384
Dartmoor, sw. Eng., 109, 110
— batholith, 442
dating, by pollen analysis, 291
—, radioactive, 289
—, by sedimentation rate, 295
—, by varve counts, 290
datum, port, 423
daylight, length of, 18
Dead Sea, 197
—, salinity, 412
Death valley, Calif., 395
Deccan, Ind., lava, 431

—, vegetation, 466
Dee, Eng., estuary, 238–9
— siltation, 356
deflation hollow, 390
DEGLACIATION, 261
Delaware river, U.S.A., 352
delta, 172, 355
—, estuary-head, 355
—, incipient, 355
Demavend mt., Iran, 433
dendritic drainage pattern, 194
Denmark, glacial deposits, 286
density, fluvial, 149
—, sea water, 413
Denver, Colorado, climate, 86
deposits, grading of fluvial, 152
depression, 29, 75, 77
—, occluded, 79
Derwent valley, ne. Eng., 127
desert, cold, 69
—, hot, 68, 394, 470
dew, 32
Dingle bay, sw. Eire, ria, 384
dip slope, 139, 141
disintegration, granular, 102
distributary, 171
divergence, 43
divide, migration of, 178
doldrums, 53
dolina, 133
dome and basin topography, 203
Dowel dale, central Eng., 132
drainage, extra-ice, 265
—, subglacial, 263
—, superimposed, 208
—, superposed, 140, 208
dreikanter, 392
drizzle, 30
drumlin, 241
— envelope, 250
—, partially drowned, 243
—, twin, 243
Dryas octopetala, 294
Dryas zone, 294
dune, 396
Dunedin, N.Z., climate, 75
Dunmail Raise, E.L.D., 301
duricrust, 454, 469
dyke, 438

Eagle, Alaska, climate, 89
earthquake, 407
Easedale, E.L.D., glacier, 301
East Anglia, e. Eng., storm surge, 425
Eastern General glacial, Ire., 284
ebb, 334
Edale, central Eng., 121, 179
Edinburgh, volcanic plug, 437
eddy, turbulent, 153
Egmont, sw. Eng., cliff, 367
Elbe, river, 192

Ellesmere-Wem moraine, central Eng., 269
Elymus arenarius, 392
energy, fluvial, 149
— output, of Sun, 14

English Lake District, glaciation, 237
environment lapse rate, 20
equinoxes, 17
erg, 394
erosion, 99
EROSION, AEOLIAN, 389
erosion, by attrition, 152, 155
—, by cavitation, 152, 155
—, by corrasion, 152
—, by corrosion, 152
—, fluvial, 152
—, fluvial and glacial contrasted, 162
—, hydraulic, 152
—, sheet, 157
erratic, 251
—, indicator, 252
escarpment, 124, 138, 190
—, inward-facing, 200
—, *see also* scarp
Escrick moraine, ne. Eng., 146, 246, 252, 283
esker, 252, 315
—, beaded, 256
—, Bow, Can., 164
— kame, 256
—, Scottish, 255
—, Strangford lough, ne. Ire., 255
—, pseudo-, 256
estuarine banks, 354
estuary, 354
—, drowned, 384
—, funnel, 383, 424
Europe, climatic regions, 73
eustatic change of sea level, 376, 386
EVAPORATION, 5
evaporites, 106
evapotranspiration, potential, 50
evergreens, Mediterranean, 475
exfoliation, 105
extrusive vulcanic landforms, 429

face, buried rock, 124
—, free, 122, 124
fan, alluvial, 171
—, outwash, 251
Fannaråki, Nor., 232
fault scarp, in ice, 227
felsenmeer, 101
fenland, 481
Fenno-Scandian ice cap, 221
ferricrete, 469
fetch, length of, 327
Finnafjord, Nor., 307
Finse, Nor., micro-terracettes, 113
firn, 219
— limit, 234

fissure, volcanic, 430
Fjaerland, Nor., fore-set beds, 358
Fjaerlandsfjord, Nor., 307
fjard, 311
fjeld, 216
fjord, 309
—, Danish, 311
—, hanging confluences, 307
Flandrian transgression, 95, 274
flood, 164
—, catastrophic, 165
— plain, 167
Florida, U.S.A. vegetation, 472
flow, laminar, 146
—, mud, 117
—, tidal, 334
—, turbulent, 146
fluting in river bed, 155
fluvial cycle, 205
— distributaries, 354
— diversion, 266
FLUVIAL FLOW, CHANNELLED,
fluvial flow, in curved river, 159
— — in straight river, 146
— pattern, dendritic, 194
— — trellis, 196
— sequence, 205
— topography, single-cycle, 191
—, *see also* river
foehn wind, 19
fog, advection, 32
—, radiation, 32, 81
Folkestone Warren, se. Eng., 121
fore-set beds, in kame, 256, 257
foreshore, 334
forest, coniferous, 486
—, deciduous, 478
—, dry, 468
—, montane, 488
—, natural in Japan, 484
Forth estuary, Scot., 380
Foulness, se. Eng., storm surge, 425
fracture zones, in Pacific, 405
Franz Josef glacier, N.Z., 226
free face, 117, 122, 124
frequency of wave, 329
friction in water flow, 147
front, cold, 78
—, warm, 78
frost, 33, 82
— action, 102
— -heaving, 102
— hollow, 36
freeze-thaw, 99
Fuego volcano, Guatemala, 433
Fulking, se. Eng., 139
full, on beach, 341

Ganges-Brahmaputra delta, Ind., 356
Gaping gill, n. Eng., 132
Garry river, Scot., 305
Gävle, Swe., glacial deposits, 255

Geirangerfjord, Nor., 311
geyser, 443
Giant's Causeway, n. Ire., cliffs, 370
Gipping glacial, 282
Glacial, Cirque, 284
—, Danau, 279
—, East General, Ire., 284
—, Gipping, 282
—, Günz, 279
—, Kirkham, nw. Eng., 283
—, Lowestoft, 282
—, Main Irish Sea, 283
—, Midland General, Ire., 284
—, Mindel, 279
—, Newer, 283
—, North British, 283
—, Riss, 279
—, Saale, 285
—, Valley, 283
—, Würm, 279
glacial ablation, 233, 297
— accumulation, 233
GLACIAL CHRONOLOGY, 276
glacial conditions, onset of, 276
— convergence, 306
— deflation, 233
GLACIAL DEPOSITION, 241
glacial deposits, 448
— equilibrium 233
— erosion, 297
— finger lake, 305
GLACIAL LANDFORMS, 297
glacial over-deepening, 303
— pavement, 225
— plucking, 297
— shoulder, 298
— trough, 297
GLACIATED LANDSCAPES, 297
— valley on continental shelf, 402
GLACIATION, 219
glaciation, multiple, 315
— in North America, 288
— in polar regions, 289
— recent maxima, 386
— in U.S.S.R., 287
glacier balance sheet, 233
—, cirque, 313
—, dead, 261
—, living, 261
— moraines, 229
—, Nigard, Nor., 276
—, piedmont, 237, 242
—, shrinkage, 94
— snout, 235, 244
— systems, 229
—, tidal, 239
—, upper Severn, Brit., 269
— volume, 234
GLACIERS, 219
Glass, river, n. Scot., 169
Glen More, Scot., 305
Glenridding beck, E.L.D., 155

gley soil, 450
Gobi desert, 398
gorge, Ironbridge, Eng., 269
—, Kirkham, ne. Eng., 270
grade, modification of, 155
—, stream, 146
Grahamsland, 222, 227
Grampian mts., Scot., 276
Gran Chaco, s. Am., 474
Grand Canyon, U.S.A., 157
granite, ribeckite, 251
—, Shap, 251
—, weathering of, 108
Grasmere, E.L.D., rock barrier, 303
grassland, temperate, 484
grassy woodland, 468
Great Lakes, n. Am., 203
Greenland ice cap, 221
grikes, 107
ground, patterned, 103
groyne, 337, 353
Gudvangen, Nor., 156
Gulf of winter warmth, 84
Gulf Stream drift, 84, 415
Günz glaciation, 279
guyot, 407

Hadrian's wall, n. Eng., 440
hail, 30
hamada, 394
Hardangerfjord, Nor., rock barrier, 304
Hardangerjokul, Nor., 65
Hardangervidda, Nor., 188, 189, 216
hard-pan, 454
Hardraw falls, n. Eng., 187
hard-woods, 486
Hatteras, cape, U.S.A., 353
Hawaiian islands, 406
Haweswater, E.L.D., 314
haze, 32
head, 115
heat, black, 263
—, latent, 10
—, radiant, 13
—, solar, 8
heathland, 481
Heiligenhafen, W. Ger., shingle complex, 350
High Force, n. Eng., waterfall, 439
Highland re-advance, 283
Hillhouse stage, 95
Himalayas, uplift, 213
Holderness, e. Eng., 283
hollow, deflation, 390
Holyhead, n. Wales, wind, 40
Hope Dale, central Eng., 139, 140
Hornindal lake, Nor., 305
horse chestnut, 475
Hoxnian interglacial, 282
Humber estuary, e. Eng., 345
—, siltation, 356
humidity, relative, 10

humus, 451
Hunstanton till, 283
Hwang Ho loess, 397
hydration, 108
hydrogen-ion concentration, 450
hydrological cycle, 205
hydrolysis, 108, 450
hydrosphere, 5

Ice age, cause, 277
— —, Permo-Carboniferous, 278
— area in Swi., 94
—, blue, 219
— cap, 220
— cap, movement of Antarctic, 234
— cap, Fenno-Scandian, 221
— cap, Greenland, 221
— cap, Jostedal, Nor., 235
— cap, melting, 261
— cap terrain, 206, 314
—, dead, 250, 255
—, decrease in world volume, 387
— erosion, 236
— flow, 222
—, formation of glacial, 219
— partition, 261
— protection theory, 236
— recession, 235
— sheet, lowland, 237
—, shelf, 239–40, 415
— tunnel, 235
—, white, 219
iceberg, 221, 240
—, glacial, 415
—, shelf, 415
icefall, 226, 227
iceflow, 414
iceshed, 262
Iceland, sandar, 258
— -Faeroe ridge, 403, 417
iceway, 238, 239
igneous landforms, 429
IJsselmeer, 285
impermeable material, 131
India, winds, 61
Indian ocean, relief, 407
Indo-Australian basin, 407
Ingleborough, n. Eng., 132
inselberg, 395
instability, absolute, 21
—, conditional, 22
integration, fluvial, 178
interglacial, 281
—, Hoxnian, 282'
—, Ipswichian, 283
intrusive vulcanic landforms, 429
ionosphere, 36
Ipswichian interglacial, 283
Irish Sea ice, 238
—, during the ice ages, 376
—, tides, 421
Ironbridge gorge, central Eng., 269

Irrawaddy delta, 171, 356
irrigation, 164
island arcs, 407
—, volcanic, 407
Isle of Man, Brit., central valley, 270
isobar, 34
isostatic changes of level, 377
— rise in Britain, 378
— tilt, 383
isothermal layer, 24
isotopes, 290

Japanese ridge, 406
jet stream, circumpolar, 37
—, subtropical, 37
joints, development of, 106
—, widening, 100
Jölster lake, Nor., 299
Jordan, river, 196
— valley, 167
Jöstedal ice cap, Nor., 220, 235
Jotunheim, Nor., 276, 277, 321
junction, accordant, 162
—, discordant, 162
jungle, 462, 465

Kalahari desert, vegetation, 470
kame, 256, 315
—, crevasse, 256
—, delta, 256
—, esker, 256
—, lateral lake, 258
Kano, Nigeria, climate, 58
Kells moraine, Ire., 283
Kenmare river, sw. Ire., ria, 384
Kennet, river, s. Eng., 194
Keswick ice, E.L.D., 301–2
kettle-hole, 231, 250
kettle moraine, 250
Kilauea, Hawaii, 408
Kilimanjaro, e. Af., 275, 489
Kirkham (Lancs.), nw. Eng., glacial, 283,
    318
— (Yorks.), ne. Eng., gorge, 270
Kjösnesfjord, Nor., 298
Köppen, Wladimir, 49
Kuh-i-Bisyair, Iran, 199
Kuh-i-Pabda, Iran, 200
Kuril ridge, Pacific, 406

laccolith, 441
lacustrine deposits, 448
lagoon, coastal, 358
—, coral, 410
—, tidal, 352
lake, basin, 321
—, crater, 322
—, deglaciation, 266
Lake District, English, glaciation, 242
lake, finger, 305
—, ice-contact meltwater, 258
—, ice lateral, 258

—, ice marginal, 258
—, oxbow, 167
—, rift valley, 321
—, temporary, 266
LAKES, 321
lakes, Cleveland, ne. Eng., 269
—, impermanence, 323
—, Swedish, 323
laminar flow, 146
Lampeter, s. Wales, 181
Lancashire Plain, nw. Eng., ice sheet, 238
land breeze, 29
Langdale, E.L.D., valley flat, 323
— — glacier, 300
— — rocks, 128
Langenhoe marsh, se. Eng., 359
lapilli, 432
lapse rate, adiabatic, dry, 18
— —, —, saturated, 19
— —, environment, 20
Lapworth, lake, central Eng., 267
Larne, n. Ire., raised bench, 380
laterite, 455, 469
latersol, 455, 469
latitude, thermal effect of, 16
Laurentian plateau, ice centre, 288
— shield, n. Am., 203
lava, 430
leaching, 453
Leith hill, s. Eng., vegetation, 478
Les Puys, Fra., 437
level, present-day changes, 386
—, tectonic changes of, 386
Leven, loch, Scot., 312
lightning, 31
Limfjord, Den., 311
Limnea phase, 274
lichen, 488
limestone pavement, 107
—, weathering of, 107
Linnhe, loch, Scot., 305
links sand, 393
lithosphere, 5
Littorina littorea, 274
Littorina sea, 274
— —, beaches, 377
Llandovery, s. Wales, 181
llanos plains, 468
Lleyn coast, n. Wales, 342
load, bed, 149
—, calibre, 151
—, push, 150
— release, 106
—, solution, 149
—, suspended, 149
loam, 449
Lochy, loch, Scot., 305
Loen, lake, Nor., flood, 165
loess, desert, 397
—, periglacial, 399
Lolland, Den., spits, 348
Long island, U.S.A., 351

Longmynd, Brit., 269
lopolith, 442
low, beach, 341
Lowestoft glacial, 282

Måbödal, Nor., 188, 228
mackerel sky, 25
magma, 429
Maine, U.S.A., woodland, 482
Main Irish Sea glacial, 283
Malham cove pavement, n. Eng., 107
— tarn, n. Eng., sink, 134
mallee scrub, 475
mangrove coasts, 362
— swamp, 464
maquis, 475
Maree, loch, Scot., 305
margalitic soil, 465
Marianas ridge, Pacific, 406
— trench, Pacific, 406
marine climate, transition into continen-
    tal, 76
— deposits, 448
— limit, upper, in Nor., 382
— temperate climates, 87
— terraces of Nor., 381
marram grass, 392
Marseilles, mistral, 36
marsh, salt, 359
MASS MOVEMENT, 112
Massif Central, Fra., 437
Matterhorn type of peak, 314
Matto Grosso, s. Am., 468
maturity, fluvial, 192
Mauna Kea, Hawaii, 408
— Loa, Hawaii, 408, 431, 433
meander, 160, 166
— belt, 167
—, incised, 211
— swing, 180
—, wavelength, 169
Mediterranean climates, 87
— evergreens, 475
meltwater, 262
— deposit, 252
— stream, 257
Menai straits, n. Wales, 337
Mendip hills, sw. Eng., 142
Mendocino seascarp, Pacific, 406
Mersea island, se. Eng., 359
Mersey basin, nw. Eng., 339
— estuary, 238
— siltation, 356
mesopause, 36
mesosphere, 36
metamorphism, contact, 439
meteorites, 278
Michigan basin, n. Am., 203
Middlesbrough, ne. Eng., 252
Midland General glacial, Ire., 284
millibar, 8
Mindel glaciation, 279

Minneapolis, climate, 84
Mississippi delta, 356
— river, 194
mist, advection, 32
—, radiation, 32
mistral, 35
Mjolfjell, Nor., exfoliation, 105
Mole, river, se. Eng., 135
Mön, Den., cliff, 369
monsoon forest, 465
Monte Rosa, Swi., 228
— Somma, Italy, 434
Montevideo, climate, 66
mor, 451
moraine, 241
—, ablation, 230, 249
—, annual, 247
—, Bride hills, Isle of Man, 283
—, Carlingford, Ire., 283
—, Coniston, E.L.D., 284
— -covered lowlands, 318
—, Ellesmere-Wem, central Eng., 269
—, end, 241, 244, 257
—, englacial, 229
—, Escrick, n. Eng., 283
—, ground, 229, 241, 249
—, hummocky, 250, 302
—, Kells, Ire., 283
—, lateral, 229
—, medial, 229
—, push, 247
—, shear-plane, 229
—, subglacial, 253
—, submerged lateral, 229
—, supraglacial, 229
—, terminal, 244
—, washboard, 249
—, Wexford, 283
—, Windermere, 284
—, York, 283
Morar loch, Scot., 305
Morecambe bay, nw. Eng., ice, 238
— marshes, 360
—, rainfall, 31
— siltation, 356
Morfa Dyffryn, w. Wales, coast, 363
— Harlech, w. Wales, coast, 363
Moscow, climate, 84
movement, castrophic, 112, 116
mud flats, 337
mull, 451
Murray seascarp, Pacific, 405
Mya phase, 274
myrtle, 475

Naeröydal, Nor., 298, 309
— scree, 123
Naeröyfjord, Nor., 310
Neagh, loch, n. Ire., 320
Needles, Isle of Wight, s. Eng., 373
neritic zone, 403
Ness, loch, Scot., 306

Netherlands, storm surge, 424
névé, 219
— limit, 234
New Jersey coast, U.S.A., 352–3
Newer glaciation, 283
Newton Dale, ne. Eng., 270
Niagara escarpment, n. Am., 204
Nibthwaite morane, E.L.D., 318
nick-point, 210
Nigard glacier, Nor., 276
Niger delta, w. Af., 172, 356, 359
Nile, n. Af., 207
— delta, 356
— flood, 164
nimbostratus, 26, 28
Nordfjord, Nor., 305, 311–2
North America, climatic regions, 65
— British glacial, 283
— Carolina, U.S.A. coast, 352–3
— Downs, s. Eng., gaps, 200
— Sea, ice ages and, 376
— —, oil, 402
— —, tides, 421–2
Norwegian sea, currents, 417
Nyköping, Swe., glacial deposits, 255

oak, cork, 475
— forest, 481
—, scrub, 472
oasis, 394, 471
Oban, w. Scot., fossil cliff, 380
OCEAN FLOORS, 400
ocean-level during Great Interglacial, 376
ocean, *see also* water
OCEANS, 400
oceans, salt in, 149
Odessa, U.S.S.R., climate, 86
offshore, 335
— zone, 337
Oich, loch, Scot., 305
oil in North Sea, 402
Old Faithful geyser, U.S.A., 444
— Man of Hoy, Orkneys, 373
oleander, 475
olive, 475
Onondago escarpment, n. Am., 204
ooze, calcareous, 409
—, *Globigerina*, 409
—, siliceous, 409
Ordos desert, Asia, 398
orogenic cloud, 29
orogenies, major, 194
orogeny, Alpine, 213
—, Caledonian, tectonic activity, 429
Oslo, Nor., frost-heaved road, 102
—, raised beach, 382
osmosis, 452
outwash fan, 257
overflow channel, 259
Oviksfjällen, Swe., ester, 253
oxbow, lake, 167

oxidation, 108
oxygen 18, 295
ozonosphere, 36

pack-ice, 414
pahoehoe, 433
palmetto, 472
pampas, 474, 485
pan layer, 454
Parana, s. Am., lava, 431
Paricutin volcano, Mexico, 436
Paris, climate, 75
patterned ground, 103
pavement, glacial, 223
peat, bog, 451
—, fen, 451
— formation, 479
pedalfer, 455
pediment, 125
pedimentation, 124
pediplain, 194
pedocal, 455
—, in hot desert, 471
Penck glacier, Spitsbergen, 226, 247
peneplain, 194
periglacial conditions, 261
perimeter (of stream), 147
permeability, primary, 132
—, secondary, 132
permafrost, 91, 487
—, in Spitsbergen, 413
Perth, Aus., climate, 74
Pewsey, Vale of, s. Eng., 202
physical geography, 1
Pickering, vale of, ne. Eng., 270
piedmont glacier, 237
pillars, 128
Piz Palu, Swi., 228
pine, araucaria, 474
— barren, U.S.A., 472
Pine Bluff, Ark., climate, 66
pine, Mediterranean, 475
plains, 128
—, coastal, 352
—, flood, 167
—, till, 250
—, upland, 213, 484
plants, alpine, 480
—, subarctic, 480
platforms, 213
Playfair, John, 161
Pleistocene chronology, 279
— sea-level, 376
— tectonic activity, 212
Pliocene tectonic activity, 212
plutonic landforms, 429
podsol, 456
polje, 133
pollen analysis, 291
— zones, 293
Pompeii, Italy, 447
porosity, 131

porous material, 131
port datum, 423
Porthcurno bay, sw. Eng., 333
Portland island, s. Eng., 351
pothole, 133, 152
powder-snow, 219
prairie, 85, 484
Pre-Boreal phase, 294
PRECIPITATION, 25
pressure, atmospheric, 6, 34
—, gaseous, 6
Pripet marshes, U.S.S.R., 483
processes, geomorphological, 5
Psamma arenaria, 392
pumice, 433
Pyrenees, uplift, 212
pyroclast, 431

Qattara depression, n. Af., 391

rain, 30
— -shadow, 31
raised beach, 373
Ramsey, Isle of Man, Brit., 270
Rangoon, climate, 59
Red Rock canyon, Utah, 124
— Sea, salinity, 412
redwood, 475
reg, 394
regelation, 223
regime, fluvial, 162
regolith, 111
—, types of, 447
regur soil, 466
rejuvenation, 209
relief, absolute, 175, 192
—, relative, 192
rendzina, 477
reservoir, 320
residual forms, 128
Rheidol river, w. Wales, 212
Rhine, river, outlet, 285
Rhone valley, mistral, 35
Rhum, w. Scot., dyke swarm, 438
ria, contrasted with fjard, 311
—, fluvial, 384
—, structural, 384
Ribble, river, nw. Eng., 152, 160
ribeckite granite, 251
ridge, Iceland-Faroe, 403, 417
—, mid-Atlantic, 405
—, synclinal, 202
Rigg Beck, E.L.D., 158
ring-complex, 442
rise, continental, 403
Riss glaciation, 279
river, beheaded, 180
—, consequent, 175
—, fully-laden, 152
—, life of, 174
—, misfit, 180
—, on new land, 174

—, obsequent, 176
—, overfit, 180
—, secondary consequent, 176
—, simple, 165
—, subsequent, 175

— —, POLYCYCLIC, 205
— —, SINGLE-CYCLE, 174
river terraces, 190
—, underfit, 180
—, *see also* fluvial
roche moutonnée, 223, 242
rock barrier, 303
— hollow, 303
—, impermeable, 131
—, permeable, 131
— step, 303
rollel̇, Atlantic, 328
Rome, climate, 74
Ross ice shelf, 240, 415

Saale glacial, 285
saddle, 178
Sahara desert, 394, 470
—, deflation, 390
—, drainage, 163
—, dust, 390
St. George's channel during Ice Ages, 376
—, profile, 400
St. Lawrence valley, 204
salt marsh, crenulation, 375
—, oceanic, 149
— pans, 360
saltation, 150, 389
Salzach river, Austria, 213
sand, 448
—, abrasion by, 391
— dunes, coastal, 390, 392
sand, links, 393
— sea, 395
—, transportation of, by wind, 389
sandar, 257
Sandwich coast, se. Eng., 363
Sargasso Sea, 415
saturated zone, 140
savanna, 466–70
saxifrage, 488
Scandinavian ice, 273
scarp, fault, in ice, 227
scarps, twin, 139
Scolt Head island, e. Eng., 363
Scoria, 433
Scottish re-advance, 283
scree, 122, 124
—, alluvial, 124
— collapse, 117
— cone, 122, 130
—, deglaciation, 120–1, 297
screes, lining gorge, 189
sea breeze, 29
— couch grass, 392

— -floor sediments, 295
SEA-LEVEL AND LAND LEVEL, 376
sea-level, rise in, 387
— lyme, 392
SEA WATER, 411
seamount, 407
sea scarps, 405
seasons, 17
sector, 78
sedge, 488
sedimentation, 151
sediments, bathyal, 403
—, compaction of, 378
—, decompaction of, 378
seepage line, 138
seif, 397
Seine river, 192
—, funnel estuary, 383
—, glacial course, 285
selva, 462
serac, 226
serozëm, 471
Severn, upper, Brit., glacier, 269
Sevier desert, Utah, 396
Shanghai, climate, 65
sheet flood, 114
— wash, 113
shelf, continental, 400
— ice, 239–40
Shiel, loch, Scot., 305
shooting stars, 278
shore, 335
shrinkage, aridity, 104
sierozëm, 471
silcrete, 469
Silkeborg, Den., tunnel valley, 259
sill, 438–9
silt, 448–9
siltation, estuarine, 354
—, tidal slack, 360
Skye, w. Scot., dyke swarm, 438
slacks, 390
sleet, 30
slide, rock, 119
slip, 112, 116
—, types of, 117
SLOPE, 122
slope collapse, 157
— —, rotational shear, 120
— —, straight shear, 119
slope, continental, 400
—, debris, 122
SLOPE DEVELOPMENT, 122
slope, straight, 122
—, of stream, 146
—, waxing, 125
Snake river, U.S.A., lava, 431
snow, 30, 82
— -line, 234
— -melt, 279
—, powder-, 219
— slips, 116

Snowdon, Wales, 206, 314–5
Sognfjord, Nor., deglaciation screes, 121
—, deepest, 310
—, marine terraces, 381
SOIL, 447
soil creep, 112
— groups, 457
— -water, 131
SOILS, 447
solifluction, 113, 115
solution benching, 369
South America, climates, 57
Southampton, s. Eng., tide, 424
South Downs, s. Eng., 138, 200
— Stack, n. Wales, 373
spit, 344–50
Spitsbergen, climate, 91
—, coal, 91
—, glaciers, 123, 130, 226–7, 248
—, polygons, 103
—, rotted granite, 108
—, weathering, 130
spring, fault, 145
—, hot, 443
— line, 138, 141
spur, truncated, 130
Spurn Head, e. Eng., 345
stack, 373
stalactite, 134
stalagmite, 134
Stalheim, Nor., 106
Stanleyville, climate, 55
Stardal glacier, Nor., 222
Stavanger, Nor., tide, 418
steppe, 85, 484
stillstand in glacier retreat, 258
Stirling, Scot., 437
stock, 442
Stockholm, Swe., esker, 255
storm surge, 424
strandflat, 385
Strangford lough, n. Ire., 243, 256
stratoform cloud, 28
stratocumulus, 26, 28
stratopause, 36, 37
stratosphere, 36
stratus, 26, 28
stream density, 178
streams, meltwater, 257
—, strike, 200
— *see also* rivers
striation, 223, 225
Subarctic climates, 92
Sub-Boreal phase, 294
subsoil weathering, 107
Sugar Loaf mountain, s. Am., 106
summit levels, accordant, 213
Sunda platform, se. Asia, 407
— trench, — 407
superimposition, 208
Surf City, U.S.A., 352
Surtsey volcano, Iceland, 436

Sutton Bank, ne., Eng., 121
Svaerafjord, Nor., 307
swallow-hole, 132
swan's neck, 167
swash, 329
Sweden, vegetation traverse, 482
swell, 328

taïga, 486
tall-grass savanna, 466
Tapes decussatus, 274
Tapes stage, 95, 274
tectonic changes of level, 386
TEMPERATE CLIMATES, 72
TEMPERATURE, 14
temperature, gaseous, 7
— inversion, 21, 24
—, past, 94, 295
—, Pliocene, 94
—, sea water, 412
tephra, 431
terrace, river, 190
—, paired river, 210
—, single-cycle, 191
terracettes, 113
terra rosa, 469, 477
Thames, s. Eng., basin, 194
—, funnel estuary, 383
—, glacial course, 285
—, mudflats, 361
—, river, 160
—, siltation, 356
thermal fluctuations, 104
thermometer, wet-and-dry bulb, 11
thixotropy, 117
thorn forest, 465
Thornthwaite, climatic classification, 50
Thornton force, n. Eng., 188
threshold, shallow, 310
thunderstorm, 31
tidal bore, 424
— cell, 421
— constant, 421
— currents, 424
— glacier, 239
— range, 334, 418
— recession, 420
— system, 421
— wave, 421, 425
— zone, 334
tide, 334, 418
—, full and change, 423
— generating forces, 418
—, height, 423
—, neap, 419
—, pseudo-, 334
—, rotational, 421
—, spring, 419
—, types of, 423
till, 249, 458
—, Hunstanton, 283
— plain, 250

tombolo, 351
tongue, rock slide, 119
topography, composite, 206
—, polycyclic, 209
tors, 109
trade wind, 53, 65
transportation, fluvial, 149
travertine, 443
tree savanna, 469
— steppe, 468
trench, fluvial, 324
TROPICAL CLIMATES, 64
tropical rain forest, 462
— savanna vegetation, 466
tropopause, 36
troposphere, 36
trough, counter, 301
—, diffluent, 300
— end, 303
—, ice cap, 299
—, over-deepened, 301
—, transfluence, 301
—, valley-head, 300
tsunamis, 425
Tudweiliog, n. Wales, bayhead beach, 342
tuff, 433
tundra, 487
tunnel, subglacial, 252
— valley, 259, 312
turbulent flow, 146

UNDERGROUND WATER, 131
undertow, 341
up-current, convectional, 29
—, orogenic, 29
uplift, tectonic, rate, 192
Uppsala, Swe., plain, 249
—, varves, 290
U-shaped valley, 297

uvala, 133

valley, anticlinal, 198, 202
—, beaded, 306
— discordance, 307
—, dry, 140, 142
— flat, 323
— form, 182
Valley glacial, 283–4
valley, hanging, 307
— head, 228
—, hidden hanging, 307
—, karst, 142
— profile, transverse, 157
—, subsequent, 200
—, tunnel, 312
valley, U-shaped, 297
— -within-a-valley, 210
valleyside form, 187
Väner, lake, Swe., 274
Vangsvatn, Nor., 182–5

vapour, saturated, 9
—, trail, 29
—, water, *see* water vapour
Variscan orogeny, 194
varve chronology, 249
— counting, 290
veer, 39
VEGETATION, ARCTIC, 486
vegetation, climax, 459, 481
—, heath, Jutland, Den., 286
VEGETATION, MOUNTAIN, 486
vegetation, natural, 459
VEGETATION, TEMPERATE, 475
—, TROPICAL, 462
—, WORLD, 459
velocity head, 264
—, terminal, 150
—, water, 149
vent, volcanic, 430
ventifact, 392
Vesuvius, Ita., 432–5, 447
Vetlefjord, Nor., 307
Victoria falls, Rhodesia, 189–90
— lake, e. Af., 320
vidda, 216
virga, 30
viscosity, fluvial, 149
VOLCANO, 429
volcano, composite, 433
volcanoes, distribution, 436
Volga, U.S.S.R., delta, 173
Vöringfoss, Nor., 188–9
Vosso, river, Nor., 182
volcanic ash, 432
— blocks, 432
— bomb, 432
— cone, 431
— dust, 432
— islands, 407
— land forms, 429
— lapilli, 432
— neck, 436
— plug, 432, 437
VULCANIC LANDFORMS, 429

wadi, 163, 394
Wairakei, N.Z., power station, 444
Wales, peneplains, 213
Walney island, ne. Eng., marsh, 375
water cycle, 205
— density, 413
— droplets, 30
—, formation of, 411
—, ground, 131
—, juvenile, 443
—, meteoric, 443
—, salinity, 411
—, soil-, 131
— supply, 50
— table, 140
— temperature, 412
WATER, UNDERGROUND, 131

— VAPOUR, 5
water velocity, 149
— volume, 411
waterfall, 162, 187
WAVE, 327
wave approach, dominant, 341, 363
—, tidal 421
Weald, se. Eng., 200
weather, duplex, in Europe, 77–79, 81
— —, in U.S.A., 84
—, simplex, 81
WEATHERING, 99
well, 145
Wenlock Edge, mid. Eng., 139, 269
West Bay, sw. Eng., 337
Westward Ho!, sw. Eng., 348, 361
Wexford moraine, e. Ire., 283
Weybourne crag, e. Eng., 281
Weymouth, s. Eng., tide, 424
Wharfe, river, n. Eng., 153
Whin sill, n. Eng., 439
wind, capacity, 390
—, chinook, 19
—, competency, 390
— erosion, 389
—, foehn, 19
— frequencies, 39
—, geostrophic, 34
—, katabatic, 36
—, monsoonal, 61
— -rose, 40–41
—, trade, 65
—, upper air, 37
— velocities, 38
Windermere, E.L.D., basin, 197

— moraine, 284
— rock barrier, 304
windgap, 178
Winnipeg, lake, Can., 319
Winnipegosis, lake, Can., 319
Wisconsin dome, n. Am., 203
Woo dale, mid. Eng., 142
woodland, deciduous, 477
—, grassy, 468
—, Mediterranean, 475
—, mixed, 482
—, open, 469
—, savanna, 469
—, subtropical, 471
—, tropical open, 467
WORLD VEGETATION, 459
Wrexham, mid. Eng., meltwater deposits, 267
Wrightsville, N. Carolina, delta, 354
Würm glaciation, 279
Wye dale, mid. Eng., 142

Yakutsk, climate, 89
Yangtse basin, vegetation, 474
Yellowstone park, U.S.A., geysers, 443
Yoldia arctica, 273
Yoldia sea, 249, 273
— —, beaches, 377
York, n. Eng., moraine, 246–7, 252, 283
—, vale, 246, 252, 269
Yorkshire moors, n. Eng., 269
— rainshadow, 31
Ystwyth valley, Wales, 213

zeugen, 392